AQA BIOLOGY 1

A-Level Year 1/AS **Student Workbook**

AQA BIOLOGY 1
A-Level Year 1/AS **Student Workbook**

Meet the Writing Team

Tracey Greenwood
I have been writing resources for students since 1993. I have a Ph.D in biology, specialising in lake ecology and I have taught both graduate and undergraduate biology.

Tracey
Senior Author

Lissa Bainbridge-Smith
I worked in industry in a research and development capacity for 8 years before joining BIOZONE in 2006. I have an M.Sc from Waikato University.

Lissa
Author

Kent Pryor
I have a BSc from Massey University majoring in zoology and ecology and taught secondary school biology and chemistry for 9 years before joining BIOZONE as an author in 2009.

Kent
Author

Richard Allan
I have had 11 years experience teaching senior secondary school biology. I have a Masters degree in biology and founded BIOZONE in the 1980s after developing resources for my own students.

Richard
Founder & CEO

Thanks to:

The staff at BIOZONE, including Gemma Conn and Julie Fairless for design and graphics support, Paolo Curray for IT support, Debbie Antoniadis and Tim Lind for office handling and logistics, and the BIOZONE sales team.

First edition 2015
Second printing

ISBN 978-1-927309-19-3

Printed by REPLIKA PRESS PVT LTD using paper produced from renewable and waste materials

Purchases of this workbook may be made direct from the publisher:

BIOZONE Learning Media (UK) Ltd.

Telephone local:	01283 530 366
Telephone international:	+44 1283 530 366
Fax local:	01283 831 900
Fax international:	+44 1283 831 900
Email:	sales@biozone.co.uk

www.**BIOZONE**.co.uk

Cover Photograph

The American white pelican (*Pelecanus erythrorhynchos*) is a large aquatic bird native to North America. During the breeding season both sexes develop a breeding horn on the upper bill. The function of the breeding horn is not fully understood, but may be involved in courtship as it is often pecked by other birds during pair selection. The horn is shed after the birds have mated and the eggs have been laid.

PHOTO: BOB CROSLIN / OFF SET

Contents

Activity is marked: • to be done;   ☑ when completed

Contents

Activity is marked: ☐ to be done; ☑ when completed

Using This Workbook

This first edition of AQA Biology 1 has been specifically written to meet the content and skills requirements of AS/A Level AQA Biology. Learning outcomes in the introduction to each chapter provide you with a concise guide to the knowledge and skills requirements for each section of work. Each learning outcome is matched to the activity or activities addressing it. The six required practicals are identified in the chapter introductions by a code (*PR-#*) and supported by activities designed to provide background and familiarity with apparatus, techniques, experimental design, and interpretation of results. A range of activities will help you to build on what you already know, explore new topics, work collaboratively, and practise your skills in data handling and interpretation. We hope that you find the workbook valuable and that you make full use of its features.

▶ The outline of the chapter structure below will help you to navigate through the material in each chapter.

Introduction
- A check list of the knowledge and skills requirements for the chapter.
- A list of key terms.

Activities
- The KEY IDEA provides your focus for the activity.
- Annotated diagrams help you understand the content.
- Questions review the content of the page.

Review
- Create your own summary for review.
- Hints help you to focus on what is important.
- Your summary will consolidate your understanding of the content in the chapter.

Literacy
- Activities are based on, but not restricted to, the introductory key terms list.
- Several types of activities test your understanding of the concepts and biological terms in the chapter.

Linkages are made between ideas in separate activities

Structure of a chapter

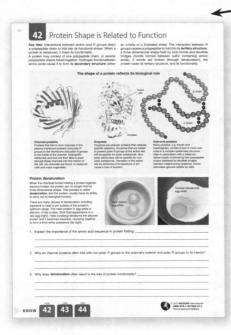

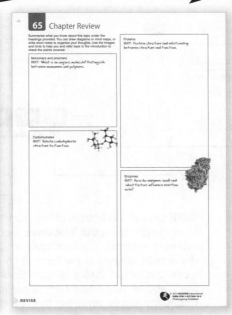

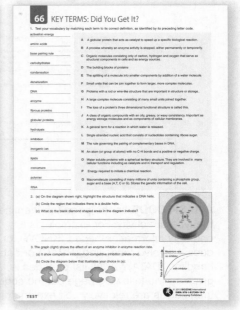

► Understanding the activity coding system and making use of the online material identified will enable you to get the most out of this resource. The chapter content is structured to build knowledge and skills but this structure does not necessarily represent a strict order of treatment. Be guided by your teacher, who will assign activities as part of a wider programme of independent and group-based work.

Look out for these features and know how to use them:

The **chapter introduction** provides you with a summary of the knowledge and skills requirements for the topic, phrased as a set of learning outcomes. Use the check boxes to identify and mark off the points as you complete them. The chapter introduction also provides you with a list of key terms for the chapter, from which you can construct your own glossary as you work through the activities.

The **activities** form most of this workbook. They are numbered sequentially and each has a task code identifying the skill emphasised. Each activity has a short introduction with a key idea identifying the main message of the page. Most of the information is associated with pictures and diagrams, and your understanding of the content is reviewed through the questions. Some of the activities involve modelling and group work.

Free response questions allow you to use the information provided to answer questions about the content of the activity, either directly or by applying the same principles to a new situation. In some cases, an activity will assume understanding of prior content.

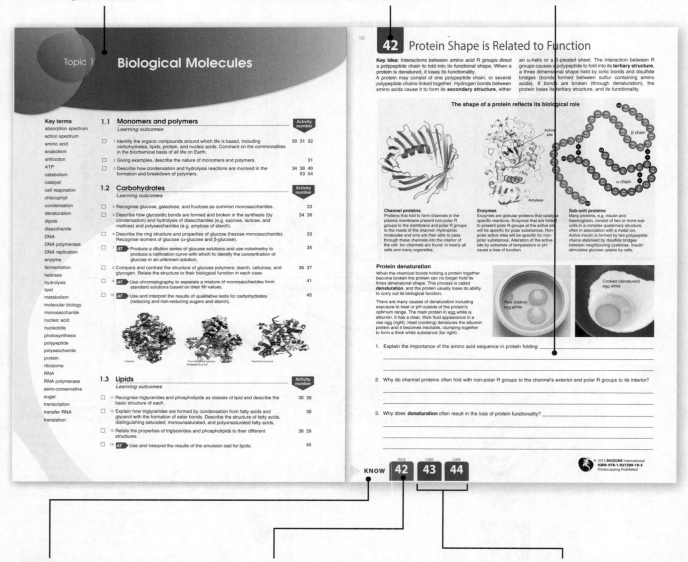

A **TASK CODE** on the page tab identifies the type of activity. For example, is it primarily information-based (KNOW), or does it involve modelling (PRAC) or data handling (DATA)? A full list of codes is given on the following page but the codes themselves are relatively self explanatory.

WEB tabs at the bottom of the activity page alert the reader to the **Weblinks** resource, which provides external, online support material for the activity, usually in the form of an animation, video clip, photo library, or quiz. Bookmark the Weblinks page (see next page) and visit it frequently as you progress through the workbook.

LINK tabs at the bottom of the activity page identify activities that are related in that they build on content or apply the same principles to a new situation.

Using the Tab System

The tab system is a useful system for quickly identifying related content and online support. Links generally refer to activities that build on the information in the activity in depth or extent. In the example below, the weblink 42 provides a short movie on the nature of proteins. Activities 43 and 44 cover protein folding and the structure of globular and fibrous proteins respectively, each examining the topic in more detail. Sometimes, a link will reflect on material that has been covered earlier as a reminder for important terms that have already been defined or for a formula that may be required to answer a question. The weblinks code is always the same as the activity number on which it is cited. On visiting the weblink page (below), find the number and it will correspond to one or more external websites providing a video or animation of some aspect of the activity's content. Occasionally, the weblink may access a reference paper of provide a bank of photographs where images are provided in colour, e.g. for plant and animal histology.

Activities are coded

COMP = comprehension of text
DATA = data handling and interpretation
KNOW = content you need to know
PRAC = a paper practical or a practical focus
REFER = reference - use this for information
REVISE = review the material in the section
TEST = test your understanding

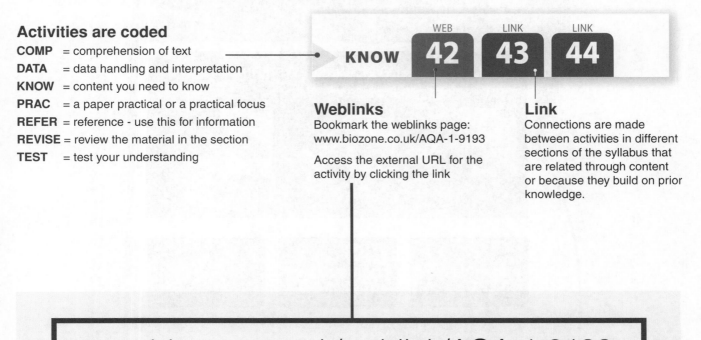

Weblinks
Bookmark the weblinks page:
www.biozone.co.uk/AQA-1-9193

Access the external URL for the activity by clicking the link

Link
Connections are made between activities in different sections of the syllabus that are related through content or because they build on prior knowledge.

www.biozone.co.uk/weblink/AQA-1-9193

This WEBLINKS page provides links to **external web sites** with supporting information for the activities. These sites are separate to those provided in the BIOLINKS area of BIOZONE's web site. Almost exclusively, they are narrowly focused animations and video clips directly relevant to the activity on which they are cited. They provide great support to aid student understanding of basic concepts, especially for visual learners.

Chapter in the workbook

Activity in the workbook

Hyperlink to the external website page.

Bookmark weblinks by typing in the address: it is not accessible directly from BIOZONE's website
Corrections and clarifications to current editions are always posted on the weblinks page

Using BIOZONE's Website

Access the **BIOLINKS** database of web sites directly from the homepage of our website.

Contact us with questions, feedback, ideas, and critical commentary. We welcome your input.

Use Google to search for websites of interest. The more precise your search words are, the better the list of results. Be specific, e.g. "biotechnology medicine DNA uses", rather than "biotechnology".

Biolinks is organised into easy-to-use sub-sections relating to general areas of interest. It's a great way to quickly find out more on topics of interest.

PS
MS
AT

Practical & Mathematical Skills in Biology

Also supported in AQA Biology 2

Key terms

accuracy
assumption
bar graph
chi-squared test
control
controlled variable
correlation
dependent variable
fair test
histogram
hypothesis
independent variable
line graph
mean
median
mode
observation
percentage error
precision
prediction
quantitative data
qualitative data
sample
scatter graph
standard deviation
statistical test
Student's *t* test
variable

PS AS required practical activities

Required practicals supported as indicated

Activity number

- ☐ 1 Investigate the effect of a named variable (e.g. temperature or substrate concentration) on the rate of an enzyme controlled reaction. **50 52**

- ☐ 2 Prepare stained squashes of cells from a plant root tip. Set up and use an optical microscope to identify stages of mitosis in these preparations and calculate a mitotic index. **84 85 91**

- ☐ 3 Produce a dilution series of a solute to produce a calibration curve. Use the calibration curve to determine the water potential of plant tissue. **103 104**

- ☐ 4 Investigate the effect of a named variable, e.g. temperature or organic solvents, on the permeability of plasma membranes. **99**

- ☐ 5 Dissect the gas exchange or mass transport system of a plant or animal, or an organ within one of these systems (e.g. heart or insect tracheal system). **153**

- ☐ 6 Use aseptic techniques to investigate the effect of antimicrobial substances on microbial growth. **188**

AT Use of apparatus and techniques

Learning outcomes supported as indicated and throughout AQA 1 & 2

Activity number

- ☐ a Use appropriate apparatus to record a range of quantitative data, including mass, time, volume, temperature, length, and pH. **12 86**

- ☐ b Use appropriate instrumentation, such as a colorimeter or potometer, to record quantitative data. **35 164**

- ☐ c Use laboratory glassware for a range of techniques, including serial dilution. **12 35 103**

- ☐ d Use a light microscope (including graticule) at high and low power. **83 86**

- ☐ e Make annotated scientific drawings from observations. **27 28**

- ☐ f Use qualitative reagents to identify biological molecules. **4 45**

- ☐ g Separate biological compounds using thin layer chromatography or electrophoresis. **41**

- ☐ h Record physiological functions and plant or animal responses safely and ethically. **133 154**

- ☐ i Use aseptic techniques in microbiological investigations. **188**

- ☐ j Use dissection equipment safely. **153**

- ☐ k Use sampling techniques e.g. quadrats, transects, in fieldwork. **197 200 & Book 2**

- ☐ l Use ICT, e.g in computer modelling or to collect or process data. **203-204**

PS Practical skills to be assessed in written papers
Learning outcomes supported as indicated and throughout AQA 1 & 2

Activity number

			Activity number
☐	1.1	Solve problems in practical contexts.	5 29
☐	1.2	Apply scientific knowledge to practical contexts.	1 2 4 5
☐	2.1	Comment on experimental design and evaluate scientific methods.	5 29
☐	2.2	Present data appropriately.	13-20
☐	2.3	Evaluate results and draw conclusions with reference to errors and uncertainties.	12 29
☐	2.4	Identify variables including those that must be controlled.	3 5
☐	3.1	Plot and interpret graphs.	14-21
☐	3.2	Process and analyse data using appropriate mathematical skills.	7-11 14-21
☐	3.3	Consider margins of error, and accuracy and precision of data.	6 12
☐	4.1	Know and understand how to use a range of apparatus and techniques.	12 86 164

MS Mathematical skills
Supported as indicated but also throughout AQA Biology 1 & 2

Activity number

M0: Arithmetic and numerical computation

			Activity number
☐	1	Recognise and use appropriate units in calculations.	6 7
☐	2	Recognise and use expressions in both decimal and standard form.	7 11
☐	3	Carry out calculations involving fractions, percentages, and ratios.	8 11
☐	4	Estimate results to assess if calculated values are appropriate.	7
☐	5	Use calculator to find and use power, exponential, and logarithmic functions (AL).	9

M1: Handling data

☐	1	Use an appropriate number of significant figures in reporting calculations.	6
☐	2	Find arithmetic means for a range of data.	24 29
☐	3	Represent and interpret frequency data in the form of bar graphs and histograms.	16 17 26
☐	4	Demonstrate an understanding of simple probability, e.g. as in genetic inheritance.	197
☐	5	Show understanding of the principles of sampling as applied to scientific data and analyse random data collected by an appropriate sampling method.	197 200
☐	6	Calculate or compare mean, mode, and median for sample data.	24 26 29
☐	7	Plot and interpret scatter graphs to identify correlation between two variables.	19 20
☐	8	Make order of magnitude calculations, e.g. in calculating magnification.	87
☐	9	Select and apply appropriate statistical tests to analyse and interpret data, e.g. the chi-squared test, the Student's t test, and Spearman's rank correlation.	22 23 203 204
☐	10	Understand and use measures of dispersion, e.g. standard deviation and range.	25 26
☐	11	Identify and determine uncertainties in measurements.	12

M2: Algebra

☐	1	Demonstrate understanding of the symbols =, <, <<, >>, >, ∝, ~	7
☐	2	Manipulate equations to change the subject.	87
☐	3	Substitute numerical values into algebraic equations using appropriate units.	21
☐	4	Solve algebraic equations.	8 41 132
☐	5	Use logs in relation to quantities ranging over several orders of magnitude (AL).	9

M3: Graphs

☐	1	Translate information between graphical, numerical, and algebraic forms.	21
☐	2	Select an appropriate format to plot two variables from experimental or other data.	15
☐	3	Predict or sketch the shape of a graph with a linear relationship ($y = mx + c$).	21
☐	4	Determine the intercept of a graph (AL).	21
☐	5	Calculate rate of change from a graph showing a linear relationship.	21 49
☐	6	Draw and use the slope of a tangent to a curve as a measure of rate of change.	49

M4: Geometry and trigonometry

☐	1	Calculate the circumferences, surface areas, and volumes of regular shapes.	10

1 How Do We Do Science?

Key Idea: The scientific method is a rigorous process of observation, measurement, and analysis that helps us to explain phenomena and predict changes in a system. Scientific knowledge is gained through a non-linear, dynamic process called the **scientific method**. The scientific method is not a strict set of rules to be followed, but rather a way of approaching problems in a rigorous, but open-minded way. It involves inspiration and creativity, it is dynamic and context dependent, and usually involves collaboration. The model below is one interpretation of the scientific method.

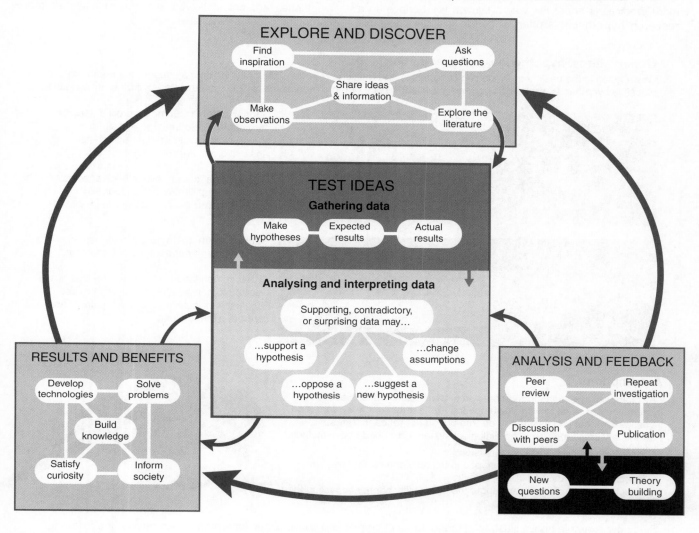

Citation and reference by numbers

Introduction

Hemoglobin is surely the most studied of all proteins. Indeed, the molecular analysis of hemoglobin has been the testing ground for many contemporary ideas and concepts in biology, particularly the understanding of the crystallographic structure and structure-function relationship of proteins, ligand binding, structural transitions between conformers, allosteric interactions, and others (1,2).

The ability of the aerobic metabolism of animals to satisfy the demands for... only possible thanks to the role... such as hemoglobins, contained i... or erythrocytes, which facilitate t... tion of large quantities of gas and...

References

1. Perutz MF. Species adaptation in a protein molecule. *Adv Protein Chem* 1984; 36: 213-244.
2. Berenbrink M. Evolution of vertebrate haemoglobins: Histidine side chains, specific buffer value and Bohr effect. *Respir Physiol Neurobiol* 2006; 154: 165-184.
3. Giardina B, Mosca D, De Rosa MC. The Bohr effect of haemoglobin

Citation and reference by authors

the long-term viability of a population. **Individual fitness, resistance to disease and parasites, and the ability of populations to respond to environmental changes may decrease as a con...** (Lacy 1997). Alt... "bottlenecks," ...

Author

Keller, L. F., P. Arcese, J. N. M. Smith, W. M. Hochachka, and S. C. Stearns. 1994. Selection against inbred Song Sparrows during a natural population bottleneck. Nature 372:356-357.

Lacy, R. C. 1997. Importance of genetic variation to the viability of mammalian populations. Journal of Mammalogy 78:320-335.

Lande, R. 1999. Extinction risks from anthropogenic, ecological and genetic factors. Pages 1-22 in L. F. Landweber and A. P. Dobson,

Year Title Publication Volume and pages

The style you choose is not as important as being consistent, thorough, and honest about drawing on other people's work. All the information needed to locate the reference should be included (above).

Citation and references

All scientific work acknowledges sources of information through citation and a list of references. Citations support the statements made in the text in context, and **all** citations are then listed alphabetically, or identified and referenced sequentially by number. Internet sites are dated and site author acknowledged.

Thorough and accurate citation and referencing shows you have explored the topic, have evidence to support your work, and you are not taking credit for work that is not your own. Each publication sets its own particular referencing style and these can vary widely. In your own work, it is most important to be consistent.

1. What is the role of citation and correct referencing when reporting on scientific investigations? _____

_____

2. Study the diagram and write a paragraph on the scientific process and the role of surprising results in the progression of science. Staple it to this page. At the end of your course, reexamine what you wrote. Have your ideas changed?

LINK **5**   LINK **2**   **KNOW**

2 Hypotheses and Predictions

Key Idea: A hypothesis is a tentative, testable explanation for an observed phenomenon. An assumption is something that is accepted as true but is not tested.

Scientific hypotheses are tentative testable explanations for observed phenomena. A hypothesis leads to one or more predictions about the way a system will behave so a **research hypothesis** is often written to include a testable prediction, i.e if X is true, then the effect of Y will be Z. For every hypothesis, there is a corresponding **null hypothesis**: a hypothesis of no difference or no effect. A null hypothesis allows a hypothesis to be tested statistically and can be rejected if the experimental results are statistically significant. Hypotheses are not static, but may be modified as more information becomes available.

Observations, hypotheses, and predictions

Observation is the basis for formulating hypotheses and making predictions. An observation may generate a number of plausible hypotheses, and each hypothesis will lead to one or more predictions, which can be tested by further investigation.

Observation 1: Some caterpillar species are brightly coloured and appear to be conspicuous to predators such as insectivorous (insect-eating) birds.

Predators appear to avoid these species. These caterpillars are often found in groups, rather than as solitary animals.

Observation 2: Some caterpillar species are cryptic in their appearance or behaviour.

Their camouflage is so convincing that, when alerted to danger, they are difficult to see against their background. Such caterpillars are often found alone.

Assumptions

Any biological investigation requires you to make assumptions about the system you are working with. Assumptions are features of the system (and investigation) that you assume to be true but do not (or cannot) test. Possible assumptions about the biological system described above include:

- insectivorous birds have colour vision;
- caterpillars that look bright or cryptic to us, also appear that way to insectivorous birds; and
- insectivorous birds can learn about the palatability of prey by tasting them.

1. Study the example above illustrating the features of cryptic and conspicuous caterpillars, then answer the following:

   (a) Generate a hypothesis to explain the observation that some caterpillars are brightly coloured and conspicuous while others are cryptic and blend into their surroundings:

   Hypothesis: _____

   _____

   _____

   (b) State the null form of this hypothesis: _____

   _____

   (c) Describe one of the **assumptions** being made in your hypothesis:_____

   _____

   _____

   (d) Based on your hypothesis, generate a **prediction** about the behaviour of insectivorous birds towards caterpillars:

   _____

   _____

3 Types of Data

Key Idea: Data is information collected during an investigation. Data may be quantitative, qualitative, or ranked.

Data is information collected during an investigation and it can be quantitative, qualitative, or ranked (below). When planning a biological investigation, it is important to consider the type of data that will be collected. It is best to collect quantitative data, because it is mathematically versatile and easier to analyse it objectively (without bias).

Types of data

Quantitative (interval or ratio)
Characteristics for which measurements or counts can be made, e.g. height, weight, number.
Summary measures: mean, median, standard deviation.

Qualitative (nominal)
Non-numerical and descriptive, e.g. sex, colour, viability (dead/alive), presence or absence of a specific feature.
Summary measures: frequencies and proportions

e.g. Sex of children in a family (male, female)

Ranked (ordinal)
Data are ranked on a scale that represents an order, although the intervals between the orders on the scale may not be equal, e.g. abundance (abundant, common, rare). Summary measures: frequencies and proportions

e.g. Birth order in a family (1, 2, 3)

Discontinuous (discrete)
e.g. Number of children in a family (3, 0, 4)

Continuous
e.g. Height of children in a family (1.5 m, 0.8 m)

Discontinuous or discrete data:
The unit of measurement cannot be split up (e.g. can't have half a child).

Continuous data:
The unit of measurement can be a part number (e.g. 5.25 kg).

1. For each of the photographic examples A-C below, classify the data as quantitative, ranked, or qualitative:

A: Skin colour

B: Eggs per nest

C: Tree trunk diameter

(a) Skin colour: _____

(b) Number of eggs per nest: _____

(c) Tree trunk diameter: _____

2. Why is it best to collect quantitative data where possible in biological studies? _____

_____

_____

3. Give an example of data that could not be collected quantitatively and explain your answer: _____

_____

_____

_____

4. Students walked a grid on a football field and ranked plant species present as abundant, common, or rare. How might they have collected and expressed this information more usefully?

_____

_____

LINK **5**   LINK **4**   WEB **3**   **KNOW**

4 Making A Qualitative Investigation

Key Idea: Qualitative data is non-numerical and descriptive. Qualitative data is more difficult to analyse and interpret objectively than quantitative data. It is also more likely to be biased. However, sometimes it is appropriate to collect qualitative data, e.g. when recording colour changes in simple tests for common components of foods. Two common tests for carbohydrates are the iodine/potassium iodide test for starch and the Benedict's test for reducing sugars, such as glucose. These tests indicate the presence of a substance with a colour change. All monosaccharides are reducing sugars as are the disaccharides, lactose and maltose. The monosaccharide fructose is a ketose, but it gives a positive test because it is converted to glucose in the reagent. When a starchy fruit ripens, the starch is converted to reducing sugars.

The aim

To investigate the effect of ripening on the relative content of starch and simple sugars in bananas.

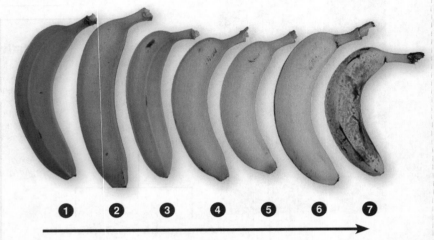

① ② ③ ④ ⑤ ⑥ ⑦

Green
unripe and
hard

bright yellow
ripening but firm
with green tip

mottled
yellow/brown
ripe and soft

The tests

Iodine-potassium iodide test for starch
The sample is covered with the iodine in potassium iodide solution. The sample turns blue-black if starch is present.

Benedict's test for reducing sugars
The sample is heated with the reagent in a boiling water bath. After 2 minutes, the sample is removed and stirred, and the colour recorded immediately after stirring. A change from a blue to a brick red colour indicates a reducing sugar.

Summary of the method

Two 1 cm thick slices of banana from each of seven stages of ripeness were cut and crushed to a paste. One slice from each stage was tested using the I/KI test for starch, and the other was tested using the Benedict's test.

The colour changes were recorded in a table. Signs (+/–) were used to indicate the intensity of the reaction relative to those in bananas that were either less or more ripe.

Stage of ripeness	Starch-iodine test		Benedict's test	
1	blue-black	+++++	blue clear	–
2	blue-black	++++	blue clear	–
3	blue-black	+++	green	+
4	blue-black	++	yellow cloudy	++
5	slight darkening	+	orange thick	+++
6	no change	–	orangey-red thick	++++
7	no change	–	brick-red thick	+++++

1. Explain why each of the following protocols was important:

   (a) All samples of banana in the Benedict's reagent were heated for 2 minutes: _____

   _____

   (b) The contents of the banana sample and Benedict's reagent were stirred after heating: _____

   _____

2. Explain what is happening to the relative levels of starch and glucose as bananas ripen: _____

   _____

   _____

3. Fructose is a ketose sugar (not an aldose with an aldehyde functional group like glucose).

   (a) Explain why fructose also gives a positive result in a Benedict's test: _____

   _____

   (b) What could this suggest to you about the results of this banana test? _____

   _____

© 2015 **BIOZONE** International
ISBN: 978-1-927309-19-3
Photocopying Prohibited

5 Making A Quantitative Investigation

Key Idea: Practical work carried out in a careful and methodical way makes analysis of the results much easier. The next stage after planning an experiment is to collect the data. Practical work may be laboratory or field based. Typical laboratory based experiments involve investigating how a biological response is affected by manipulating a particular **variable**, e.g. temperature. The data collected for a quantitative practical task should be recorded systematically, with due attention to safe practical techniques, a suitable quantitative method, and accurate measurements to an appropriate degree of precision. If your quantitative practical task is executed well, and you have taken care throughout, your evaluation of the experimental results will be much more straightforward and less problematic.

Carrying out your practical work

Preparation

Familiarise yourself with the equipment and how to set it up. If necessary, calibrate equipment to give accurate measurements.

Read through the methodology and identify key stages and how long they will take.

Execution

Identify any **assumptions** you make about your set up. Assumptions are features of the system that you assume to be true but do not (or cannot) test. Know how you will take your measurements, how often, and to what degree of precision.

Recording

Record your results systematically, in a hand-written table or on a spreadsheet.

Record your results to the appropriate number of significant figures according to the precision of your measurement.

Identifying variables

A variable is any characteristic or property able to take any one of a range of values. Investigations often look at the effect of changing one variable on another. It is important to identify all variables in an investigation: independent, dependent, and controlled, although there may be nuisance factors of which you are unaware. In all fair tests, only one variable is changed by the investigator.

Dependent variable

- Measured during the investigation.
- Recorded on the y axis of the graph.

Controlled variables

- Factors that are kept the same or controlled.
- List these in the method, as appropriate to your own investigation.

Independent variable

- Set by the experimenter.
- Recorded on the graph's x axis.

Experimental controls

A control refers to standard or reference treatment or group in an experiment. It is the same as the experimental (test) group, except that it lacks the one variable being manipulated by the experimenter. Controls are used to demonstrate that the response in the test group is due a specific variable (e.g. temperature). The control undergoes the same preparation, experimental conditions, observations, measurements, and analysis as the test group. This helps to ensure that responses observed in the treatment groups can be reliably interpreted.

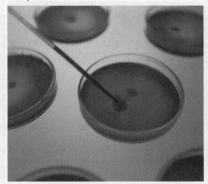

The experiment above tests the effect of a certain nutrient on microbial growth. All the agar plates are prepared in the same way, but the control plate does not have the test nutrient applied. Each plate is inoculated from the same stock solution, incubated under the same conditions, and examined at the same set periods. The control plate sets the baseline; any growth above that seen on the control plate is attributed to the presence of the nutrient.

Examples of investigations

Aim		Variables	
Investigating the effect of varying...	**on the following...**	**Independent variable**	**Dependent variable**
Temperature	Leaf width	Temperature	Leaf width
Light intensity	Activity of woodlice	Light intensity	Woodlice activity
Soil pH	Plant height at age 6 months	pH	Plant height

LINK 29   LINK 3   **KNOW**

Investigation: catalase activity

Catalase is an enzyme that converts hydrogen peroxide (H_2O_2) to oxygen and water.

An experiment to investigate the effects of temperature on the rate of the catalase reaction is described below.

- 10 cm³ test tubes were used for the reactions, each tube contained 0.5 cm³ of catalase enzyme and 4 cm³ of H_2O_2.

- Reaction rates were measured at four temperatures (10°C, 20°C, 30°C, 60°C).

- For each temperature, there were two reaction tubes (e.g. tubes 1 and 2 were both kept at 10°C).

- The height of oxygen bubbles present after one minute of reaction was used as a measure of the reaction rate. A faster reaction rate produced more bubbles than a slower reaction rate.

- The entire experiment was repeated on two separate days.

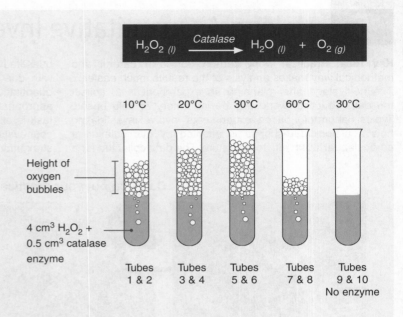

$$H_2O_2 \, {}_{(l)} \xrightarrow{\text{Catalase}} H_2O \, {}_{(l)} + O_2 \, {}_{(g)}$$

Height of oxygen bubbles

4 cm³ H_2O_2 + 0.5 cm³ catalase enzyme

10°C — Tubes 1 & 2
20°C — Tubes 3 & 4
30°C — Tubes 5 & 6
60°C — Tubes 7 & 8
30°C — Tubes 9 & 10 — No enzyme

1. Write a suitable aim for this experiment: _____

   _____

2. Write an hypothesis for this experiment: _____

   _____

3. (a) What is the independent variable in this experiment? _____

   (b) What is the range of values for the independent variable? _____

   (c) Name the unit for the independent variable: _____

   (d) List the equipment needed to set the independent variable, and describe how it was used: _____

   _____

   _____

   _____

4. (a) What is the dependent variable in this experiment? _____

   (b) Name the unit for the dependent variable: _____

   (c) List the equipment needed to measure the dependent variable, and describe how it was used: _____

   _____

5. (a) Each temperature represents a treatment/sample/trial (circle one):

   (b) How many tubes are at each temperature? _____

   (c) What is the sample size for each treatment? _____

   (d) How many times was the whole investigation repeated? _____

6. Which tubes are the control for this experiment? _____

7. Identify three variables that might have been controlled in this experiment, and how they could have been monitored:

   (a) _____

   (b) _____

   (c) _____

6 Accuracy and Precision

Key Idea: Accuracy refers to the correctness of a measurement (how true it is to the real value). Precision refers to how close the measurements are to each other.

Accuracy refers to how close a measured or derived value is to its true value. Simply put, it is the correctness of the measurement. Precision refers to the closeness of repeated measurements to each other, i.e. the ability to be exact. A balance with a fault in it could give very precise (repeatable) but inaccurate (untrue) results. Data can only be reported as accurately as the measurement of the apparatus allows and is often expressed as significant figures (the digits in a number which express meaning to a degree of accuracy.

The accuracy of a measurement refers to how close the measured (or derived) value is to the true value. The precision of a measurement relates to its repeatability. In most laboratory work, we usually have no reason to suspect a piece of equipment is giving inaccurate measurements (is biased), so making precise measures is usually the most important consideration. We can test the precision of our measurements by taking repeated measurements from individual samples.

Population studies present us with an additional problem. When a researcher makes measurements of some variable in a study (e.g. fish length), they are usually trying to obtain an estimate of the true value for a parameter of interest, e.g. the mean size (which is correlated with age) of fish. Populations are variable, so we can more accurately estimate a population parameter if we take a large number of random samples from the population.

Accurate but imprecise	**Inaccurate and imprecise**	**Precise but inaccurate**	**Accurate and precise**

The measurements are all close to the true value but quite spread apart.	The measurements are all far apart and not close to the true value.	The measurements are all clustered close together but not close to the true value.	The measurements are all close to the true value and also clustered close together.
Analogy: The arrows are all close to the bullseye.	**Analogy**: The arrows are spread around the target.	**Analogy**: The arrows are all clustered close together but not near the bullseye.	**Analogy**: The arrows are clustered close together near the bullseye.

Significant figures

Significant figures (sf) are the digits of a number that carry meaning contributing to its precision. They communicate how well you could actually measure the data.

For example, you might measure the height of 100 people to the nearest cm. When you calculate their mean height, the answer is 175.0215 cm. If you reported this number, it implies that your measurement technique was accurate to 4 decimal places. You would have to round the result to the number of significant figures you had accurately measured. In this instance the answer is 175 cm.

Non-zero numbers (1-9) are always **significant**.

All zeros between non-zero numbers are always **significant**.

$$0.005704510$$

Zeros to the left of the first non-zero digit after a decimal point are **not significant**.

Zeros at the end of number where there is a decimal place are **significant** (e.g. 4600.0 has five sf). BUT
Zeros at the end of a number where there is no decimal point are **not significant** (e.g. 4600 has two sf).

1. Distinguish between accuracy and precision: _____

_____

_____

2. State the number of significant figures in the following examples:

(a) 3.15985 _____   (d) 1000.0 _____

(b) 0.0012_____   (e) 42.3006_____

(c) 1000 _____   (f) 120 _____

© 2015 **BIOZONE** International
ISBN: 978-1-927309-19-3
Photocopying Prohibited

LINK

7

DATA

7 Working with Numbers

Key Idea: Using correct mathematical notation and being able to carry out simple calculations and conversions are fundamental skills in biology.

Mathematics is used in biology to analyse, interpret, and compare data. It is important that you are familiar with mathematical notation (the language of mathematics) and can confidently apply some basic mathematical principles and calculations to your data.

Commonly used mathematical symbols

In mathematics, universal symbols are used to represent mathematical concepts. They save time and space when writing. Some commonly used symbols are shown below.

- $=$ Equal to
- $<$ The value on the left is **less than** the value on the right
- $\ll$ The value on the left is **much less than** the value on the right
- $>$ The value on the left is **greater than** the value on the right
- $\gg$ The value on the left is **much greater than** the value on the right
- $\propto$ Proportional to. $A \propto B$ means that $A =$ a constant $\times B$
- $\sim$ Approximately equal to

Conversion factors and expressing units

Measurements can be converted from one set of units to another by the use of a **conversion factor**.

A conversion factor is a numerical factor that multiplies or divides one unit to convert it into another. Conversion factors are commonly used to convert non-SI units to SI units (e.g. converting pounds to kilograms). Note that mL and cm^3 are equivalent, as are L and dm^3.

In the space below, convert $5.6\ cm^3$ to mm^3 ($1\ cm^3 = 1000\ mm^3$):

1. _____

The value of a variable must be written with its units where possible. SI units or their derivations should be used in recording measurements: volume in cm^3 or dm^3, mass in kilograms (kg) or grams (g), length in metres (m), time in seconds (s).

For example the rate of oxygen consumption would be expressed:

Oxygen consumption$/cm^3 g^{-1} s^{-1}$

Estimates

When carrying out mathematical calculations, typing the wrong number into your calculator can put your answer out by several orders of magnitude. An **estimate** is a way of roughly calculating what answer you should get, and helps you decide if your final calculation is correct.

Numbers are often rounded to help make estimation easier. The rounding rule is, if the next digit is 5 or more, round up. If the next digit is 4 or less, it stays as it is.

For example, to estimate 6.8×704 you would round the numbers to $7 \times 700 = 4900$. The actual answer is 4787, so the estimate tells us the answer (4787) is probably right.

Use the following examples to practise estimating:

2. 43.2×1044: _____

3. $3.4 \times 72 \div 15$: _____

4. $658 \div 22$: _____

Decimal and standard form

Decimal form (also called ordinary form) is the longhand way of writing a number (e.g. 15 000 000). Very large or very small numbers can take up too much space if written in decimal form and are often expressed in a condensed **standard form**. For example, 15 000 000 is written as 1.5×10^7 in standard form.

In standard form a number is always written as $A \times 10^n$, where A is a number between 1 and 10, and n (the exponent) indicates how many places to move the decimal point. n can be positive or negative.

For the example above, $A = 1.5$ and $n = 7$ because the decimal point moved seven places (see below).

$$1\,5\,000\,000 = 1.5 \times 10^7$$

Small numbers can also be written in standard form. The exponent (n) will be negative. For example, 0.00101 is written as 1.01×10^{-3}.

$$0.00101 = 1.01 \times 10^{-3}$$

Converting can make calculations easier. Work through the following example to solve $4.5 \times 10^4 + 6.45 \times 10^5$.

5. Convert $4.5 \times 10^4 + 6.45 \times 10^5$ to decimal form:

   _____

6. Add the two numbers together: _____

7. Convert to standard form: _____

Rates

Rates are expressed as a measure per unit of time and show how a variable changes over time. Rates are used to provide meaningful comparisons of data that may have been recorded over different time periods.

Often rates are expressed as a mean rate over the duration of the measurement period, but it is also useful to calculate the rate at various times to understand how rate changes over time. The table below shows the reaction rates for a gas produced during a chemical reaction. A worked example for the rate at 4 minutes is provided below the table.

Time / Minute	Cumulative gas produced / cm^3	Rate of reaction / $cm^3\ min^{-1}$
0	0	0
2	34	17
4	42	4*
6	48	3
8	50	1
10	50	0

* Gas produced between 2 – 4 min: $42\ cm^3 - 34\ cm^3 = 8\ cm^3$

Rate of reaction between 2 – 4 mins: $8 \div 2\ minutes = 4\ cm^3\ min^{-1}$

DATA

8 Fractions, Percentages, and Ratios

Key Idea: Percentages and ratios are alternative ways to express fractions. All forms are commonly used in biology. The data collected in the field or laboratory are called raw data. Data are often expressed in ways that make them easy to understand, visualise, and work with. Fractions, ratios, and percentages are widely used in biology and are often used to provide a meaningful comparison of sample data where the sample sizes are different.

Fractions

- Fractions express how many parts of a whole are present.

- Fractions are expressed as two numbers separated by a solidus (/) (e.g. 1/2).

- The top number is the numerator. The bottom number is the denominator. The denominator can not be zero.

- Fractions are often written in their simplest form (the top and bottom numbers cannot be any smaller, while still being whole numbers). Simplifying makes working with fractions easier.

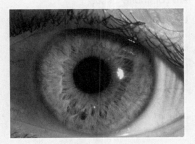

In a class of 20 students, five had blue eyes. This fraction is 5/20. To simplify this fraction, divide the numerator and denominator by a common factor (a number which both are divisible by). In this instance the lowest common factor is five (1/4). To add fractions with different denominators, obtain a common denominator, add numerators, then simplify.

Ratios

- Ratios give the relative amount of two or more quantities, and provide an easy way to identify patterns.

- Ratios do not require units.

- Ratios are usually expressed as a : b.

- Ratios are calculated by dividing all the values by the smallest number.

882 inflated

299 constricted

Pea pod shape:
Ratio = 2.95 : 1

495 round yellow

152 wrinkled yellow

158 round green

55 wrinkled green

Pea seed shape and colour:
Ratio = 9 : 2.8 : 2.9 : 1

Example: Calculating phenotype ratios in Mendelian genetics

Percentages

- Percentages are expressed as a fraction of 100 (e.g. 20/100 = 20%).

- Percentages provide a clear expression of what proportion of data fall into any particular category, e.g. for pie graphs.

- Allows meaningful comparison between different samples.

- Useful to monitor change (e.g. % increase from one year to the next).

Volume of food colouring / cm³	Volume of water / cm³	Concentration of solution / %
10	0	100
8	2	80
6	4	60
4	6	40
2	8	20
0	10	0

Example: Producing standards for a calibration curve.

1. (a) A student prepared a slide of the cells of an onion root tip and counted the cells at various stages in the cell cycle. The results are presented in the table (right). Calculate the ratio of cells in each stage (show your working):

   _____

   _____

   (b) Assuming the same ratio applies in all the slides examined in the class, calculate the number of cells in each phase for a cell total count of 4800.

Cell cycle stage	No. of cells counted	No. of cells calculated
Interphase	140	
Prophase	70	
Telophase	15	
Metaphase	10	
Anaphase	5	
Total	240	4800

2. Simplify the following fractions:

   (a) 3/9 : _____   (b) 84/90: _____   (c) 11/121: _____

3. In the fraction example pictured above 5/20 students had blue eyes. In another class, 5/12 students had blue eyes. What fraction of students had blue eyes in both classes?

   _____

4. The total body mass and lean body mass for women with different body types is presented in the table (right). Complete the table by calculating the % lean body mass column.

Women	Body mass / kg	Lean body mass / kg	% lean body mass
Athlete	50	38	
Lean	56	41	
Normal weight	65	46	
Overweight	80	48	
Obese	95	52	

DATA

9 Logs and Exponents

Key Idea: A function relates an input to an output. Functions are often defined through a formula that tells us how to compute the output for a given input. Logarithmic, power, and exponential functions are all common in biology.

A function is a rule that allows us to calculate an output for any given input. In biology, power functions are often observed in biological scaling, for example, heart beat slows with increasing size in mammals. Exponential growth is often seen in bacterial populations and also with the spread of viral diseases if intervention does not occur. The 2014 Ebola outbreak is one such example. The numbers associated with exponential growth can be very large and are often log transformed. Log transformations reduce skew in data and make data easier to analyse and interpret.

Power function

Power functions are a type of scaling function showing the relationship between two variables, one of which is usually size.

- In power functions, the base value is variable and the exponent (power number) is fixed (constant).

- The equation for an exponential function is $y = x^c$.

- Power functions are not linear, one variable changes more quickly relative to the other.

- Examples of power functions include metabolic rate versus body mass (below), or surface area to volume ratio.

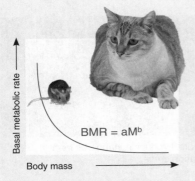

$$BMR = aM^b$$

Body mass →

Basal metabolic rate →

Example: Relationship between body mass and metabolic rate.
M = mass and a and b are constants.

Exponential function

Exponential growth occurs at an increasingly rapid rate in proportion to the growing total number or size.

- In an exponential function, the base number is fixed (constant) and the exponent is variable.

- The equation for an exponential function is $y = c^x$.

- Exponential growth is easy to identify because the curve has a J-shape appearance due to its increasing steepness over time. It grows more rapidly than a power function

- Examples of exponential growth include the growth of microorganisms in an unlimiting growth environment.

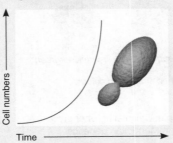

Cell numbers →

Time →

Example: Cell growth in a yeast culture in optimal growth conditions.

Log transformations

A log transformation has the effect of normalising data and making very large numbers easier to work with. Biological data often have a positive skew so log transformations can be very useful.

- The log of a number is the exponent to which a fixed value (the base) is raised to get that number. So $\log_{10}(1000) = 3$ because $10^3 = 1000$.

- Both $\log_{10}$ and $\log_e$ (natural logs or *ln*) are commonly used.

- Log transformations are useful for data where there is an exponential increase in numbers (e.g. cell growth).

- Log transformed data will plot as a straight line.

- To find the $\log_{10}$ of a number, e.g. 32, using a calculator, key in log 32 = . The answer should be 1.51.

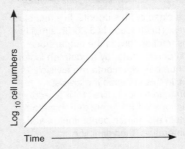

Log 10 cell numbers →

Time →

Example: Yeast cell growth plotted on logarithmic scale.

1. Describe the relationship between body mass and metabolic rate: _____
   _____

2. Describe the difference between a power function and exponential growth: _____
   _____
   _____
   _____

3. (a) On what type of data would you carry out a log transformation? _____
   _____

   (b) What is the purpose of a log transformation? _____
   _____
   _____

© 2015 **BIOZONE** International
ISBN: 978-1-927309-19-3
Photocopying Prohibited

10 Properties of Geometric Shapes

Key Idea: Circumference, surface area, and volume are useful calculations that can be applied in biological situations. Biology often requires you to evaluate the effect of a physical property, such as cell volume, on function. For example, how does surface area to volume ratio influence the transport of materials into a cell? The cells of organisms, and sometimes the organisms themselves, are often rather regular shapes, so their physical properties (e.g. cell volume or surface area) can be calculated (or approximated) using the simple formulae applicable to standard geometric shapes.

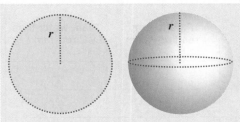

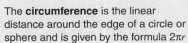

The **circumference** is the linear distance around the edge of a circle or sphere and is given by the formula $2\pi r$

r = radius l = length w = width h = height $\pi = 3.14$	

	Sphere	Cube	Rectangular prism	Cylinder
Biological example	*Staphylococcus* bacterial cell	Kidney tubule cell	Intestinal epithelial cell	Axon of neurone
Surface area: The sum of all areas of all shapes covering an object's surface.	$4\pi r^2$	$6w^2$	$2(lh + lw + hw)$	$(2\pi r^2) + (2\pi rh)$
Volume: The amount that a 3-dimensional shape can hold.	$\frac{4}{3}\pi r^3$	w^3	lwh	$\pi r^2 h$

1. For a sphere with a radius of 2 cm, calculate the:

   (a) Circumference: _____

   (b) Surface area: _____

   (c) Volume: _____

2. For a rectangular prism with the dimensions l = 3 mm, w = 0.3 mm, and h = 2 mm calculate the:

   (a) Surface area: _____

   (b) Volume: _____

3. For a cylinder with a radius of 4.9 cm and height of 11 cm, calculate the:

   (a) Surface area: _____

   (b) Volume: _____

4. Find the height of a rectangular prism with a volume of 48 cm³, a length of 4 cm, and a width of 2.5 cm: _____

   _____

5. Find the radius of a cylinder with a volume of 27 cm³ and a height of 3 cm: _____

   _____

6. A spherical bacterium with a radius of 0.2 μm divides in two. Each new cell has a radius that is 80% of the original cell.

   (a) Calculate the surface area of the 'parent' bacterial cell: _____

   (b) Calculate the volume of the 'parent' bacterial cell: _____

   (c) Calculate the surface area of each new cell: _____

   (d) Calculate the volume of each new cell: _____

   (e) Which cell has the greatest surface area to volume ratio: _____

LINK 123   LINK 78   LINK 77   **DATA**

11 Practising with Data

Key Idea: This activity allows you to practise working with data and applying the skills you have learned in previous activities.

1. Complete the transformations for each of the tables below. The first value is provided in each case.

(a) Photosynthetic rate at different light intensities

Light intensity / %	Average time for leaf disc to float / min	Reciprocal of time* / min⁻¹
100	15	0.067
50	25	
25	50	
11	93	
6	187	

(b) Plant water loss using a bubble potometer

Time / min	Pipette arm reading / cm³	Plant water loss / cm³ min⁻¹
0	9.0	–
5	8.0	0.2
10	7.2	
15	6.2	
20	4.9	

* *Reciprocal of time gives a crude measure of rate.*

(c) Incidence of cyanogenic clover in different areas

Clover plant type	Frost free area		Frost prone area		Totals
	Number	%	Number	%	
Cyanogenic	124	78	26		
Acyanogenic	35		115		
Total	159				

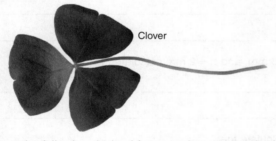

Clover

(d) Frequency of size classes in a sample of eels

Size class / mm	Frequency	Relative frequency / %
0-50	7	2.6
50-99	23	
100-149	59	
150-199	98	
200-249	50	
250-299	30	
300-349	3	
Total	270	

2. Convert the following decimal form numbers to standard form:

   (a) 8970 _____   (b) 0.046 _____   (c) 1 467 851 _____

3. Convert the following standard form numbers to decimal form:

   (a) 4.3×10^{-1} _____   (b) 0.0031×10^{-2} _____   (c) 6.2×10^{4} _____

4. (a) The table on the right shows the nutritional label found on a can of chilli beans. Use the information provided to complete the table by calculating the percentage composition for each of the nutritional groups listed:

   (b) How much of the total carbohydrates is made up of:

   Dietary fibre? _____

   Sugars? _____

   (c) Manufacturers do not have to state the volume of water, which makes up the remainder of the serving size. What percentage of the can of beans is water?

   _____

Chilli Beans Nutrition Facts Serving size 1 cup (253 g)		
Amount per serving		% Composition
Total Fat	8 g	
– Saturated Fat	3 g	
Total Carbohydrate	22 g	
– Dietary Fibre	9 g	
– Sugars	4 g	
Protein	25 g	

LINK 7 LINK 8

© 2015 **BIOZONE** International
ISBN: 978-1-927309-19-3
Photocopying Prohibited

12 Apparatus and Measurement

Key Idea: The apparatus used in experimental work must be appropriate for the experiment or analysis and it must be used correctly to eliminate experimental errors.
Using scientific equipment can generate experimental errors.

These can be reduced by selecting the right equipment for what you want to measure and by using it correctly. Some error is inevitable, but evaluating experimental error helps to interpret and assess the validity of the results.

Selecting the correct equipment

When measuring physical properties it is vital that you choose equipment that is appropriate for the type of measurement you want to take. For example, if you wanted to accurately weigh out 5.65 g of sucrose, you need a balance that accurately weighs to two decimal places. A balance that weighs to only one decimal place would not allow you to make an accurate enough measurement.

Study the glassware (right). Which would you use if you wanted to measure 225 mL? The graduated cylinder has graduations every 10 mL whereas the beaker has graduations every 50 mL. It would be more accurate to measure 225 mL in a graduated cylinder.

Percentage errors

Percentage error is a way of mathematically expressing how far out your result is from the ideal result. The equation for measuring percentage error is:

$$\frac{\text{experimental value - ideal value}}{\text{ideal value}} \times 100$$

For example, you want to know how accurate a 5 mL pipette is. You dispense 5 mL of water from a pipette and weigh the dispensed volume on a balance. The volume is 4.98 mL.

$$\frac{\text{experimental value (4.98) - ideal value (5.0)}}{\text{ideal value (5.0)}} \times 100$$

The percentage error = −0.4% (the negative sign tells you the pipette is dispensing **less** than it should).

Recognising potential sources of error

It is important to know how to use equipment correctly to reduce errors. A spectrophotometer measures the amount of light absorbed by a solution at a certain wavelength. This information can be used to determine the concentration of the absorbing molecule (e.g. density of bacteria in a culture). The more concentrated the solution, the more light is absorbed. Incorrect use of the spectrophotometer can alter the results. Common mistakes include incorrect calibration, errors in sample preparation, and errors in sample measurement.

A cuvette (left) is a small clear tube designed to hold spectrophotometer samples. Inaccurate readings occur when:

- The cuvette is dirty or scratched (light is absorbed giving a falsely high reading).

- Some cuvettes have a frosted side to aid alignment. If the cuvette is aligned incorrectly, the frosted side absorbs light, giving a false reading.

- Not enough sample is in the cuvette and the beam passes over, rather than through the sample, giving a lower absorbance reading.

---

1. Assume that you have the following measuring devices available: 50 mL beaker, 50 mL graduated cylinder, 25 mL graduated cylinder, 10 mL pipette, 10 mL beaker. What would you use to accurately measure:

   (a) 21 mL: _____   (b) 48 mL: _____   (c) 9 mL: _____

2. Calculate the percentage error for the following situations (show your working):

   (a) A 1 mL pipette delivers a measured volume of 0.98 mL: _____

   _____

   (b) A 10 mL pipette delivers a measured volume of 9.98 mL: _____

   _____

   (c) The pipettes used in (a) and (b) above both under-delivered 0.02 mL, yet the percentage errors are quite different. Use this data to describe the effect of volume on percentage error:

   _____

   _____

KNOW

13 Recording Results

Key Idea: Accurately recording results in a table makes it easier to understand and analyse your data later.

A table is a good way to record your results systematically, both during the course of your experiment and in presenting your results. A table can also be used to show calculated values, such as rates or means. An example of a table for recording results is shown below. It relates to an investigation of the net growth of plants at three pH levels, but it represents a relatively standardised layout. The labels on the columns and rows are chosen to represent the design features of the investigation. The first column shows the entire range of the independent variable. There are spaces for multiple sampling units, repeats (trials), and calculated mean values. A version of this table would be given in the write-up of the experiment.

Dependent variable and its units

Space for repeats of the experimental design (in this case, three trials).

All masses are in grams and to the nearest 0.1 g.

Space for three plants at each pH

The range of values for the independent variable are in this column

Recordings of the dependent variable

Space for calculated means

		Trial 1 / plant mass in grams						Trial 2 / plant mass in grams						Trial 3 / plant mass in grams					
		Day No.						Day No.						Day No.					
		0	2	4	6	8	10	0	2	4	6	8	10	0	2	4	6	8	10
pH 3	1	0.5	1.1																
	2	0.6	1.2																
	3	0.7	1.3																
	Mean	0.6	1.2																
pH 5	1	0.6	1.4																
	2	0.8	1.7																
	3	0.5	1.9																
	Mean	0.6	1.7																
pH 7	1	0.7	1.3																
	2	0.8	1.3																
	3	0.4	1.7																
	Mean	0.6	1.4																

1. In the box (below) design a table to collect data from the case study below. Include space for individual results and averages from the three set ups (use the table above as a guide).

CO$_2$ levels in a respiration chamber

A datalogger was used to monitor the concentrations of carbon dioxide (CO$_2$) in respiration chambers containing five green leaves from one plant species. The entire study was performed in conditions of full light (quantified) and involved three identical set-ups.

The CO$_2$ concentrations were measured every minute, over a period of 10 minutes, using a CO$_2$ sensor. A mean CO$_2$ concentration (for the three set-ups) was calculated. The study was carried out two more times, two days apart.

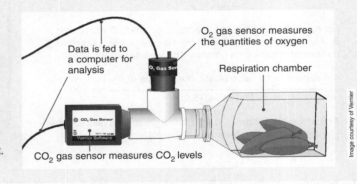

Data is fed to a computer for analysis

O$_2$ gas sensor measures the quantities of oxygen

Respiration chamber

CO$_2$ gas sensor measures CO$_2$ levels

Image courtesy of Vernier

2. Next, the effect of various light intensities (low light, half-light, and full light) on CO$_2$ concentration was investigated. How would the results table for this investigation differ from the one you have drawn above (for full light only):

© 2015 **BIOZONE** International
ISBN: 978-1-927309-19-3
Photocopying Prohibited

14 Constructing Tables and Graphs

Key Idea: Tables and graphs provide a way to organise and visualise data in a way that helps to identify trends.

Tables and graphs are ways to present data and they have different purposes. **Tables** provide an accurate record of numerical values and allow you to organise your data so that relationships and trends are apparent. **Graphs** provide a visual image of trends in the data in a minimum of space.

It is useful to plot your data as soon as possible, even during your experiment, as this will help you to evaluate your results as you proceed and make adjustments as necessary (e.g. to the sampling interval). The choice between graphing or tabulation in the final report depends on the type and complexity of the data and the information that you are wanting to convey. Usually, both are appropriate.

Presenting data in tables

An accurate, descriptive title.

Independent variable in left column.

Control values (if present) should be placed at the beginning of the table.

Each row should show a different experimental treatment, organism, sampling site etc.

Table 1: Length and growth of the third internode of bean plants receiving three different hormone treatments (data are given ± standard deviation).

Treatment	Sample size	Mean rate of internode growth / mm day^{-1}	Mean internode length / mm	Mean mass of tissue added / g day^{-1} ± SD)
Control	50	0.60 ± 0.025	32.3 ± 2.3	0.36 ± 0.025
Hormone 1	46	1.52 ± 0.030	41.6 ± 3.4	0.51 ± 0.030
Hormone 2	98	0.82 ± 0.018	38.4 ± 0.9	0.56 ± 0.028
Hormone 3	85	2.06 ± 0.019	50.2 ± 1.4	0.68 ± 0.020

Heading and subheadings identify each set of data and show units of measurement.

Tables can show a calculated measure of data variability (e.g. standard deviation).

Show values only to the level of significance allowable by your measuring technique.

Columns that need to be compared should be placed alongside each other.

Organise the columns so that each category of like numbers or attributes is listed vertically.

Presenting data in graph format

Plot points accurately. Different responses can be distinguished using different symbols, lines or bar colours.

Label both axes (provide SI units of measurement if necessary).

Place the dependent variable, e.g. biological response, on the vertical (y) axis (if you are drawing a scatter graph it does not matter).

A break in an axis allows economical use of space if there are no data in the "broken" area. A floating axis (where zero points do not meet) allows data points to be plotted away from the vertical axis.

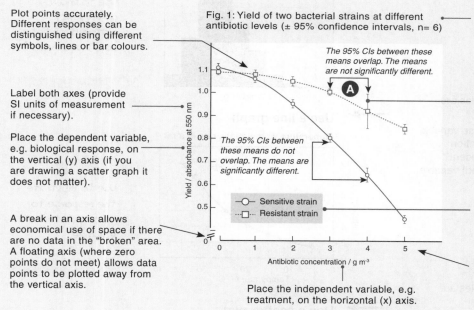

Fig. 1: Yield of two bacterial strains at different antibiotic levels (± 95% confidence intervals, n= 6)

The 95% CIs between these means overlap. The means are not significantly different. **A**

The 95% CIs between these means do not overlap. The means are significantly different.

Key:
- ○ Sensitive strain
- □ Resistant strain

Place the independent variable, e.g. treatment, on the horizontal (x) axis.

Graphs (called figures) should have a concise, explanatory title. If several graphs appear in your report they should be numbered consecutively.

Measures of spread about the plotted mean value can be shown on the graph. Such measures include standard deviation and 95% confidence intervals (CI). The values are plotted as **error bars** and give an indication of the reliability of the mean value. If the 95% confidence intervals do not overlap between points, then these means will be significantly different.

A key identifies symbols. This information sometimes appears in the title or the legend.

Each axis should have an appropriate scale. Decide on the scale by finding the maximum and minimum values for each variable.

1. What can you conclude about the difference (labelled A) between the two means plotted above? Explain your answer:

_____

2. Explain the reasons for including both graphs and tables in a final report: _____

_____

_____

_____

LINK 15 KNOW

15 Which Graph to Use?

Key Idea: The type of graph you choose to display your data depends on the type of data you have collected.

Before you graph your data, it is important to identify what type of data you have. Choosing the correct type of graph can highlight trends or reveal relationships between variables. Choosing the wrong type of graph can obscure information and make the data difficult to interpret. Examples of common types of graphs and when to use them are provided below.

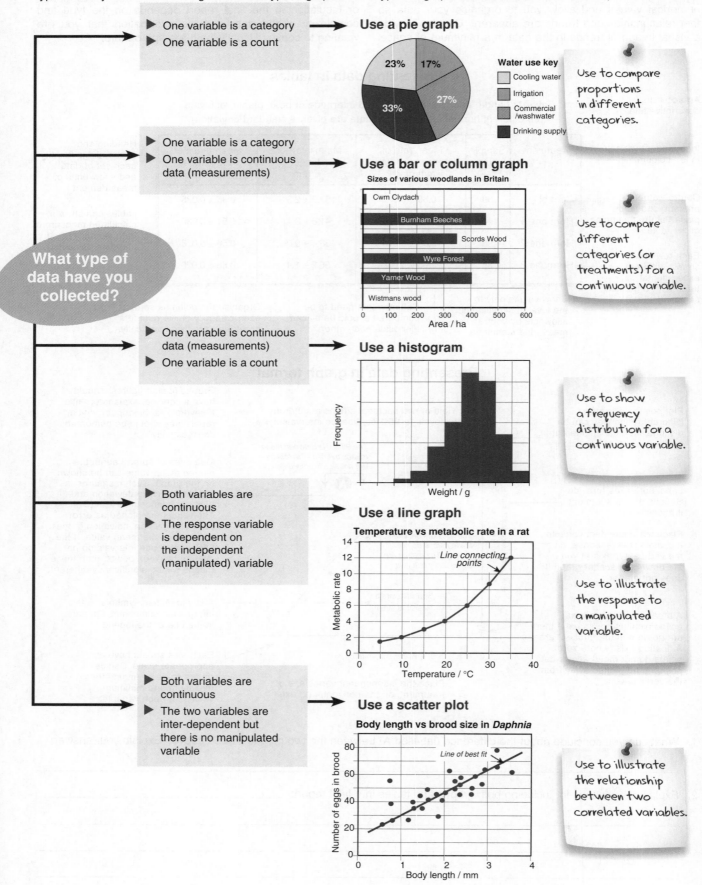

What type of data have you collected?

▶ One variable is a category
▶ One variable is a count

Use a pie graph

Water use key
- Cooling water
- Irrigation
- Commercial /washwater
- Drinking supply

17% 23% 27% 33%

Use to compare proportions in different categories.

▶ One variable is a category
▶ One variable is continuous data (measurements)

Use a bar or column graph

Sizes of various woodlands in Britain

Cwm Clydach
Burnham Beeches
Scords Wood
Wyre Forest
Yarner Wood
Wistmans wood

Area / ha

Use to compare different categories (or treatments) for a continuous variable.

▶ One variable is continuous data (measurements)
▶ One variable is a count

Use a histogram

Frequency

Weight / g

Use to show a frequency distribution for a continuous variable.

▶ Both variables are continuous
▶ The response variable is dependent on the independent (manipulated) variable

Use a line graph

Temperature vs metabolic rate in a rat

Line connecting points

Metabolic rate

Temperature / °C

Use to illustrate the response to a manipulated variable.

▶ Both variables are continuous
▶ The two variables are inter-dependent but there is no manipulated variable

Use a scatter plot

Body length vs brood size in *Daphnia*

Line of best fit

Number of eggs in brood

Body length / mm

Use to illustrate the relationship between two correlated variables.

REFER   LINK 16   LINK 17   LINK 18   LINK 20

© 2015 **BIOZONE** International
ISBN: 978-1-927309-19-3
Photocopying Prohibited

16 Drawing Bar Graphs

Key Idea: Bar graphs are used to plot data that is non-numerical or discrete for at least one variable.

Guidelines for bar graphs

Bar graphs are appropriate for data that are non-numerical and **discrete** for at least one variable, i.e. they are grouped into categories. There are no dependent or independent variables. Important features of this type of graph include:

- Data are collected for discontinuous, non-numerical categories (e.g. colour, species), so the bars do not touch.

- Data values may be entered on or above the bars.

- Multiple sets of data can be displayed side by side for comparison (e.g. males and females).

- Axes may be reversed so that the categories are on the x axis, i.e. bars can be vertical or horizontal. When they are vertical, these graphs are called column graphs.

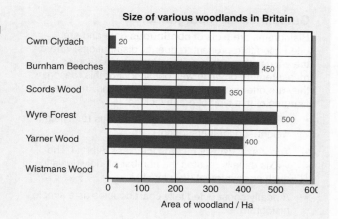

Size of various woodlands in Britain

1. Counts of eight mollusc species were made from a series of quadrat samples at two sites on a rocky shore. The summary data are presented here.

   (a) Tabulate the mean (**average**) numbers per square metre at each site in Table 1 (below left).

   (b) Plot a **bar graph** of the tabulated data on the grid below. For each species, plot the data from both sites side by side using different colours to distinguish the sites.

Mean abundance of 8 molluscan species from two sites along a rocky shore.

Species	Mean / no. m^{-2}	
	Site 1	Site 2

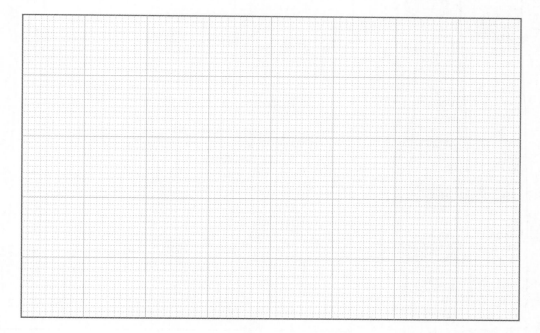

Field data notebook

Total counts at site 1 (11 quadrats) and site 2 (10 quadrats). Quadrats 1 sq. m.

	Site 1			Site 2	
	No m^{-2}			No m^{-2}	
Species	Total	Mean		Total	Mean
Ornate limpet	232	21		299	30
Radiate limpet	68	6		344	34
Limpet sp. A	420	38		0	0
Cats-eye	68	6		16	2
Top shell	16	2		43	4
Limpet sp. B	628	57		389	39
Limpet sp. C	0	0		22	2
Chiton	12	1		30	3

17 Drawing Histograms

Key Idea: Histograms graphically show the frequency distribution of continuous data.

Guidelines for histograms

Histograms are plots of **continuous** data and are often used to represent frequency distributions, where the y-axis shows the number of times a particular measurement or value was obtained. For this reason, they are often called frequency histograms. Important features of this type of graph include:

- The data are numerical and continuous (e.g. height or weight), so the bars touch.

- The x-axis usually records the class interval. The y-axis usually records the number of individuals in each class interval (frequency).

- A neatly constructed tally chart doubles as a simple histogram.

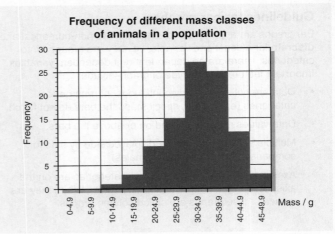

Frequency of different mass classes of animals in a population

1. The weight data provided below were recorded from 95 individuals (male and female), older than 17 years.

   (a) Create a tally chart (frequency table) in the frame provided, organising the weight data into a form suitable for plotting. An example of the tally for the weight grouping 55-59.9 kg has been completed for you as an example. Note that the raw data values are crossed off the data set in the notebook once they are recorded as counts on the tally chart. It is important to do this in order to prevent data entry errors.

   (b) Plot a **frequency histogram** of the tallied data on the grid provided below.

Weight / kg	Tally	Total
45-49.9		
50-54.9		
55-59.9	ⅢⅡ	7
60-64.9		
65-69.9		
70-74.9		
75-79.9		
80-84.9		
85-89.9		
90-94.9		
95-99.9		
100-104.9		
105-109.9		

Lab notebook

Weight (in kg) of 95 individuals

63.4	81.2	65
56.5	83.3	75.6
84	95	76.8
81.5	105.5	67.8
73.4	82	68.3
56	73.5	63.5
60.4	75.2	58
83.5	63	58.5
82	70.4	50
61	82.2	92
55.2	87.8	91.5
48	86.5	88.3
53.5	85.5	81
63.8	87	72
69	98	66.5
82.8	71	61.5
68.5	76	66
67.2	72.5	65.5
82.5	61	67.4
83	60.5	73
78.4	67	67
76.5	86	71
83.4	85	70.5
77.5	93.5	65.5
77	62	68
87	62.5	90
89	63	83.5
93.4	60	73
83	71.5	66
80	73.8	57.5
76	77.5	76
56	74	

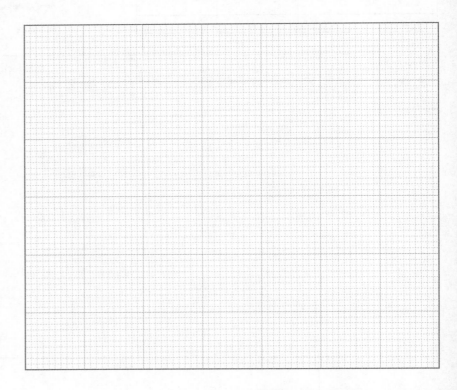

LINK

DATA 26

© 2015 **BIOZONE** International
ISBN: 978-1-927309-19-3
Photocopying Prohibited

18 Drawing Line Graphs

Key Idea: Line graphs are used to plot continuous data in which one variable (the independent variable) directly affects the other (dependent) variable. They are appropriate for data in which the independent variable is manipulated.

Guidelines for line graphs

Line graphs are used when one variable (the independent variable) affects another, the dependent variable. Line graphs can be drawn without a measure of spread (top figure, right) or with some calculated measure of data variability (bottom figure, right). Important features of line graphs include:

- The data must be continuous for both variables.

- The dependent variable is usually the biological response.

- The independent variable is often time or experimental treatment.

- In cases where there is an implied trend (e.g. one variable increases with the other), a line of best fit is usually plotted through the data points to show the relationship.

- If fluctuations in the data are likely to be important (e.g. with climate and other environmental data) the data points are usually connected directly (point to point).

- Line graphs may be drawn with measure of error. The data are presented as points (which are the calculated means), with bars above and below, indicating a measure of variability or spread in the data (e.g. standard error, standard deviation, or 95% confidence intervals).

- Where no error value has been calculated, the scatter can be shown by plotting the individual data points vertically above and below the mean. By convention, bars are not used to indicate the range of raw values in a data set.

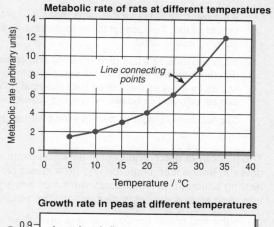

Metabolic rate of rats at different temperatures

Line connecting points

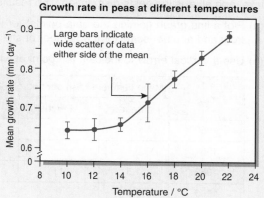

Growth rate in peas at different temperatures

Large bars indicate wide scatter of data either side of the mean

1. The results (shown right) were collected in a study investigating the effect of temperature on the activity of an enzyme.

   (a) Using the results provided (right), plot a line graph on the grid below:

   (b) Estimate the rate of reaction at 15°C: _____

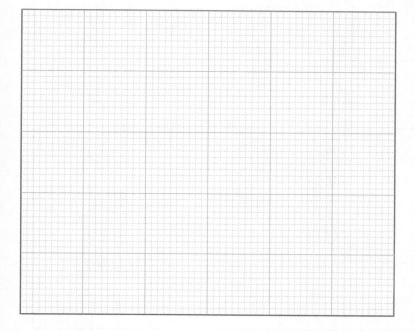

Lab Notebook

An enzyme's activity at different temperatures

Temperature / °C	Rate of reaction (mg of product formed per minute)
10	1.0
20	2.1
30	3.2
35	3.7
40	4.1
45	3.7
50	2.7
60	0

LINK

29 **DATA**

Plotting multiple data sets

A single figure can be used to show two or more data sets, i.e. more than one curve can be plotted per set of axes. This type of presentation is useful when comparing the trends for two or more treatments, or the response of one species against the response of another. Important points regarding this format are:

- If the two data sets use the same measurement units and a similar range of values for the independent variable, one scale on the y axis is used.

- If the two data sets use different units and/or have a very different range of values for the independent variable, two scales for the y axis are used (see example right). The scales can be adjusted if necessary to avoid overlapping plots

- The two curves must be distinguished with a key.

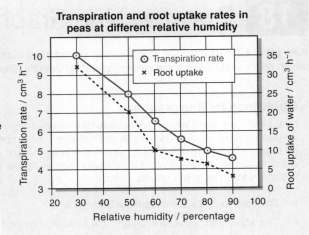

Transpiration and root uptake rates in peas at different relative humidity

2. The number of perch and trout in a hydro-electric reservoir were monitored over 19 years. A colony of black shag was also present. Shags feed on perch and (to a lesser extent) trout. In 1960-61, 424 shags were removed from the lake during the nesting season and nest counts were made every spring in subsequent years. In 1971, 60 shags were removed from the lake, and all existing nests dismantled. The results of the population survey are tabulated below.

(a) Plot a line graph (joining the data points) for the survey results. Use one scale (on the left) for numbers of perch and trout and another scale for the number of shag nests. Use different symbols to distinguish the lines and include a key.

(b) Use a vertical arrow to indicate the point at which shags and their nests were removed.

Year	Mean number of fish per haul		Shag nest numbers	Year (continued)	Mean number of fish per haul		Shag nest numbers
	Trout	Perch			Trout	Perch	
1960	–	–	16	1970	1.5	6	1.5
1961	–	–	4	1971	0.5	0.7	1.5
1962	1.5	11	5	1972	1	0.8	0
1963	0.8	9	10	1973	0.2	4	0
1964	0	5	22	1974	0.5	6.5	0
1965	1	1	25	1975	0.6	7.6	2
1966	1	2.9	35	1976	1	1.2	10
1967	2	5	40	1977	1.2	1.5	32
1968	1.5	4.6	26	1978	0.7	1.2	28
1969	1.5	6	32				

19 Correlation or Causation

Key Idea: A correlation is a mutual relationship or association between two or more variables. A correlation between two variables does not imply that one causes change in the other. Researchers often want to know if two variables have any **correlation** (relationship) to each other. This can be achieved by plotting the data as a scatter graph and drawing a line of best fit through the data, or by testing for correlation using a statistical test. The strength of a correlation is indicated by the correlation coefficient (r), which varies between 1 and -1. A value of 1 indicates a perfect (1:1) relationship between the variables. A value of -1 indicates a 1:1 negative relationship and 0 indicates no relationship between the variables.

Correlation does not imply causation

You may come across the phrase "correlation does not necessarily imply causation". This means that even when there is a strong correlation between variables (they vary together in a predictable way), you cannot assume that change in one variable caused change in the other.

Example: When data from the organic food association and the office of special education programmes is plotted (below), there is a strong correlation between the increase in organic food and rates of diagnosed autism. However it is unlikely that eating organic food causes autism, so we can not assume a causative effect here.

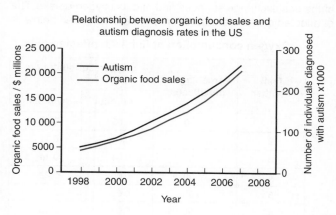

Relationship between organic food sales and autism diagnosis rates in the US

Drawing the line of best fit

Some simple guidelines need to be followed when drawing a line of best fit on your scatter plot.

► Your line should follow the trend of the data points.

► Roughly half of your data points should be above the line of best fit, and half below.

► The line of best fit does not necessarily pass through any particular point.

► The line of best fit should pivot around the point which represents the mean of the x and the mean of the y variables.

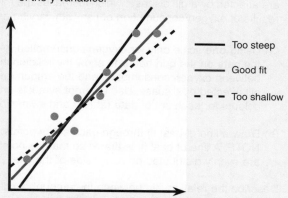

1. What does the phrase "correlation does not imply causation" mean? _____

_____

_____

2. A student measured the hand span and foot length measurements of 21 adults and plotted the data as a scatter graph (right).

(a) Draw a line of best fit through the data:

(b) Describe the results: _____

_____

_____

_____

_____

(c) Using your line of best fit as a guide, comment on the correlation between handspan and foot length:

_____

_____

_____

_____

_____

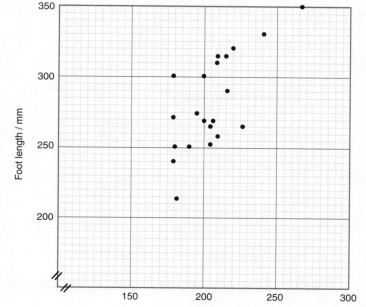

Hand span vs foot length in adults

20 Drawing Scatter Plots

Key Idea: Scatter graphs are used to plot continuous data where there is a relationship between two interdependent variables.

Guidelines for scatter graphs

A scatter graph is used to display continuous data where there is a relationship between two interdependent variables.

- The data must be continuous for both variables.

- There is no independent (manipulated) variable, but the variables are often correlated, i.e. they vary together in some predictable way.

- Scatter graphs are useful for determining the relationship (correlation) between two variables. A relationship does not imply that change in one variable causes change in the other variable.

- The points on the graph need not be connected, but a line of best fit is often drawn through the points to show the relationship between the variables (this may be drawn by eye or computer generated).

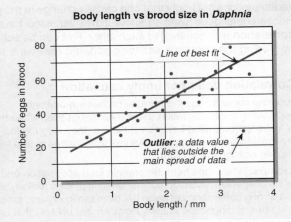
Body length vs brood size in *Daphnia*

1. In the example below, metabolic measurements were taken from seven Antarctic fish *Pagothenia borchgrevinski*. The fish are affected by a gill disease, which increases the thickness of the gas exchange surfaces and affects oxygen uptake. The results of oxygen consumption of fish with varying amounts of affected gill (at rest and swimming) are tabulated below.

   (a) Using **one** scale only for oxygen consumption, plot the data on the grid below to show the relationship between oxygen consumption and the amount of gill affected by disease. Use different symbols or colours for each set of data (at rest and swimming).

   (b) Draw a line of best fit through each set of points. NOTE: A line of best fit is drawn so that the points are evenly distributed on either side of the line.

2. Describe the relationship between the amount of gill affected and oxygen consumption in the fish:

   (a) For the **at rest** data set:

   _____

   _____

   _____

   _____

   _____

   _____

   (b) For the **swimming** data set:

   _____

   _____

   _____

   _____

   _____

   _____

   _____

Oxygen consumption of fish with affected gills

Fish number	Percentage of gill affected	Oxygen consumption / cm³ g⁻¹ h⁻¹	
		At rest	Swimming
1	0	0.05	0.29
2	95	0.04	0.11
3	60	0.04	0.14
4	30	0.05	0.22
5	90	0.05	0.08
6	65	0.04	0.18
7	45	0.04	0.20

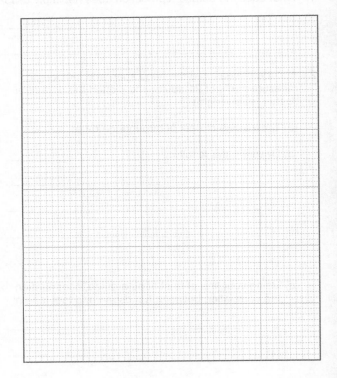

3. How does the gill disease affect oxygen uptake in resting fish? _____

_____

© 2015 **BIOZONE** International
ISBN: 978-1-927309-19-3
Photocopying Prohibited

DATA

21 Interpreting Line Graphs

Key Idea: The equation for a straight line is y = mx + c. A line may have a positive, negative, or zero slope.
The equation for a linear (straight) line on a graph is y = mx + c. The equation can be used to calculate the gradient (slope) of a straight line and tells us about the relationship between x and y (how fast y is changing relative to x). For a straight line, the rate of change of y relative to x is always constant. A line may have a positive, negative, or zero slope.

Measuring gradients and intercepts

The equation for a straight line is written as:

y = mx + c

Where :

y = the y-axis value

m = the slope (or gradient)

x = the x-axis value

c = the y intercept (where the line cross the y-axis).

Determining "m" and "c"

To find "c" just find where the line crosses the y-axis.

To find m:

1. Choose any two points on the line.

2. Draw a right-angled triangle between the two points on the line.

3. Use the scale on each axis to find the triangle's vertical length and horizontal length.

4. Calculate the gradient of the line using the following equation:

$$\frac{\text{change in y}}{\text{change in x}}$$

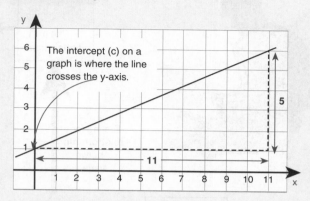

The intercept (c) on a graph is where the line crosses the y-axis.

For the example above:

c = 1

m = 0.45 (5 ÷11)

Once c and m have been determined you can choose any value for x and find the corresponding value for y.

For example, when x = 9, the equation would be:

y = 9 x 0.45 + 1

y = 5.05

Interpreting gradients

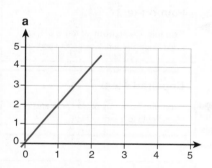

Positive gradients: the line slopes upward to the right (y is increasing as x increases).

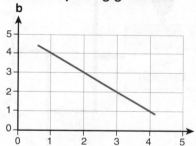

Negative gradients: the line slopes downward to the right (y is decreasing as x increases).

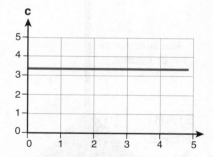

Zero gradients: the line is horizontal (y does not change as x increases).

1. State the gradient for graphs a, b, and c (above): (a) _____ (b) _____ (c) _____

2. For a straight line y = 3x + 2,

   (a) Identify the value of c: _____ (b) Determine y if x = 4: _____

3. For the graph (right):

   (a) Identify the value of c: _____

   (b) Calculate the value of m: _____

   (c) Determine y if x = 2: _____

   _____

   (d) Describe the slope of the line: _____

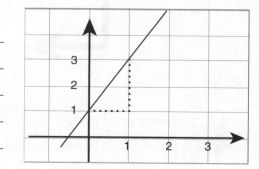

22 What Test to Use?

Key Idea: How your data is analysed depends on the type of data you have collected. Plotting your initial data can help you to decide what statistical analysis to carry out. Data analysis provides information on the biological significance of your investigation. Never under-estimate the value of plotting your data, even at a very early stage. This will help you decide on the best type of data analysis. Sometimes, statistical analysis may not be required.

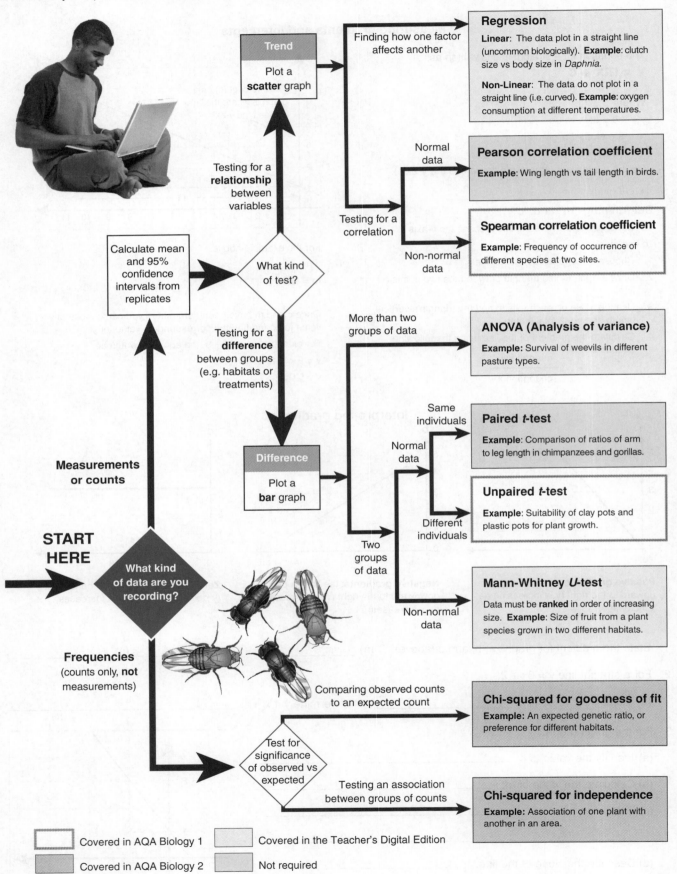

Trend

Plot a **scatter** graph

Finding how one factor affects another

Regression

Linear: The data plot in a straight line (uncommon biologically). **Example**: clutch size vs body size in *Daphnia*.

Non-Linear: The data do not plot in a straight line (i.e. curved). **Example**: oxygen consumption at different temperatures.

Testing for a relationship between variables

Testing for a correlation

Normal data

Pearson correlation coefficient

Example: Wing length vs tail length in birds.

Non-normal data

Spearman correlation coefficient

Example: Frequency of occurrence of different species at two sites.

Calculate mean and 95% confidence intervals from replicates

What kind of test?

Testing for a difference between groups (e.g. habitats or treatments)

More than two groups of data

ANOVA (Analysis of variance)

Example: Survival of weevils in different pasture types.

Measurements or counts

Difference

Plot a **bar** graph

Normal data

Same individuals

Paired *t*-test

Example: Comparison of ratios of arm to leg length in chimpanzees and gorillas.

Different individuals

Unpaired *t*-test

Example: Suitability of clay pots and plastic pots for plant growth.

Two groups of data

Non-normal data

Mann-Whitney *U*-test

Data must be **ranked** in order of increasing size. **Example**: Size of fruit from a plant species grown in two different habitats.

START HERE

What kind of data are you recording?

Frequencies (counts only, **not** measurements)

Comparing observed counts to an expected count

Chi-squared for goodness of fit

Example: An expected genetic ratio, or preference for different habitats.

Test for significance of observed vs expected

Testing an association between groups of counts

Chi-squared for independence

Example: Association of one plant with another in an area.

	Covered in AQA Biology 1		Covered in the Teacher's Digital Edition
	Covered in AQA Biology 2		Not required

REFER

23 Spearman Rank Correlation

Key Idea: The Spearman rank correlation is a test used to determine if there is a statistical dependence (correlation) between two variables.

The Spearman rank correlation is appropriate for data that have a non-normal distribution (or where the distribution is not known) and assesses the degree of association between the X and Y variables (if they are correlated). For the test to work, the values used must be monotonic i.e. the values must increase or decrease together or one increases while the other decreases. A value of 1 indicates a perfect correlation; a value of 0 indicates no correlation between the variables. The example below examines the relationship between the frequency of the drumming sound made by male frigatebirds (Y) and the volume of their throat pouch (X).

Spearman's rank data for frigate bird pouch volume and drumming frequency

Bird	Volume of pouch / cm³	Rank (R_1)	Frequency of drumming sound / Hz	Rank (R_2)	Difference (D) (R_1-R_2)	D^2
1	2550		461			
2	2440	I	473	6	-5	25
3	2740		532			
4	2730		465			
5	3010		485			
6	3370		488			
7	3080		527			
8	4910		478			
9	3740		485			
10	5090		434			
11	5090		468			
12	5380		449			

Based on Madsen et al 2004

ΣD^2

r_s value

Step one: Rank the data for each variable. For each variable, the numbers are ranked in descending order, e.g. for the variable, volume, the highest value 5380 cm³ is given the rank of 12 while its corresponding frequency value is given the rank of 2. Fill in the rank columns in the table above in the same way. If two numbers have the same rank value, then use the mean rank of the two values (e.g. 1+2 = 3. 3/2= 1.5).

Step two: Calculate the difference (D) between each pair of ranks (R_1-R_2) and enter the value in the table (as a check, the sum of all differences should be 0).

Step three: Square the differences and enter them into the table above (this removes any negative values).

Step four: Sum all the D^2 values and enter the total into the table.

Analysing the data

Step five: Use the formula below to calculate the Spearman Rank Correlation Coefficient (r_s). Enter the r_s value in the box above.

$$r_s = 1 - \left(\frac{6 \Sigma D^2}{n(n^2-1)} \right)$$

Spearman rank correlation coefficient

Step six: Compare the r_s value to the table of critical values (right) for the appropriate number of pairs. If the r_s value (ignoring sign) is greater than or equal to the critical value then there is a significant correlation. If r_s is positive then there is a positive correlation. If r_s is negative then there is a negative correlation.

Number of pairs of measurements	Critical value
5	1.00
6	0.89
7	0.79
8	0.74
9	0.68
10	0.65
12	0.59
14	0.54
16	0.51
18	0.48
20	0.45

1. State the null hypothesis for the data set. _____

_____

_____

2 (a) Identify the critical value for the frigate bird data: _____

   (b) State if the correlation is positive or negative: _____

   (c) State whether the correlation is significant: _____

3. In your class, gather data on heart rate (beats per minute measured by carotid or radial pulse) and breathing rate (breaths per minute). Use the Spearman rank coefficient to determine if there is a relationship between these variables. Complete your analysis and staple it to this page.

KNOW

24 Mean, Median, and Mode

Key Idea: Mean, median, and mode are measures of the central tendency of data. The distribution of the data will determine which measurement of central tendency you use. Measures of a biological response are usually made from more than one sampling unit. In lab-based investigations, the sample size (the number of sampling units) may be as small as three or four (e.g. three test-tubes in each of four treatments). In field studies, each individual may be a sampling unit, and the sample size can be very large (e.g. 100 individuals). It is useful to summarise data using **descriptive statistics.** Descriptive statistics, such as mean, median, and mode, can identify the central tendency of a data set. Each of these statistics is appropriate to certain types of data or distribution (as indicated by a frequency distribution).

Variation in data

Whether they are obtained from observation or experiments, most biological data show variability. In a set of data values, it is useful to know the value about which most of the data are grouped, i.e. the centre value. This value can be the mean, median, or mode depending on the type of variable involved (see below). The main purpose of these statistics is to summarise important features of your data and to provide the basis for statistical analyses.

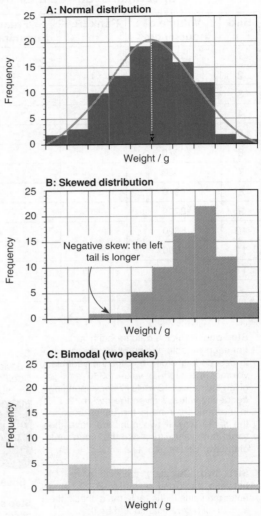

A: Normal distribution

B: Skewed distribution

Negative skew: the left tail is longer

C: Bimodal (two peaks)

Weight / g

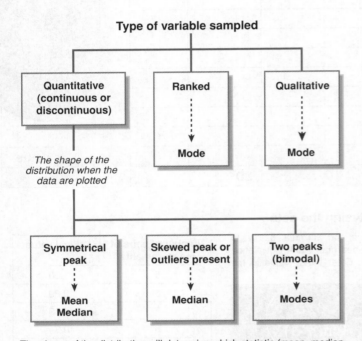

Type of variable sampled

- Quantitative (continuous or discontinuous)
- Ranked → Mode
- Qualitative → Mode

The shape of the distribution when the data are plotted

- Symmetrical peak → Mean Median
- Skewed peak or outliers present → Median
- Two peaks (bimodal) → Modes

The shape of the distribution will determine which statistic (mean, median, or mode) best describes the central tendency of the sample data.

Statistic	Definition and use	Method of calculation
Mean	• The average of all data entries. • Measure of central tendency for normally distributed data.	• Add up all the data entries. • Divide by the total number of data entries.
Median	• The middle value when data entries are placed in rank order. • A good measure of central tendency for skewed distributions.	• Arrange the data in increasing rank order. • Identify the middle value. • For an even number of entries, find the mid point of the two middle values.
Mode	• The most common data value. • Suitable for bimodal distributions and qualitative data.	• Identify the category with the highest number of data entries using a tally chart or a bar graph.
Range	• The difference between the smallest and largest data values. • Provides a crude indication of data spread.	• Identify the smallest and largest values and find the difference between them.

When NOT to calculate a mean:

In some situations, calculation of a simple arithmetic mean is not appropriate.

Remember:

- *DO NOT* calculate a mean from values that are already means (averages) themselves.

- *DO NOT* calculate a mean of ratios (e.g. percentages) for several groups of different sizes. Go back to the raw values and recalculate.

- *DO NOT* calculate a mean when the measurement scale is not linear, e.g. pH units are not measured on a linear scale.

© 2015 **BIOZONE** International
ISBN: 978-1-927309-19-3
Photocopying Prohibited

Total of data entries	=	5221	=	180	cm
Number of entries		29			

Mean

Case study: height of swimmers

Data (below) and descriptive statistics (left) from a survey of the height of 29 members of a male swim squad.

Height of swimmers (in rank order)		
174	177	185
175	177	185
175	178	185
175	178	186
176	178	186
176	178	186
176	180	188
176	180	188
176	180	189
177	181	

Mode

Median

Height (cm)	Tally	Total
174	✔	1
175	✔ ✔ ✔	3
176	✔ ✔ ✔ ✔ ✔	5
177	✔ ✔ ✔	3
178	✔ ✔ ✔ ✔	4
179		0
180	✔ ✔ ✔	3
181	✔	1
182		0
183		0
184		0
185	✔ ✔ ✔	3
186	✔ ✔ ✔	3
187		0
188	✔ ✔	2
189	✔	1

Raw data: Height / cm					
178	177	188	176	186	175
180	181	178	178	176	175
180	185	185	175	189	174
178	186	176	185	177	176
176	188	180	186	177	

1. Give a reason for the difference between the mean, median, and mode for the swimmers' height data:

_____

_____

_____

Case study: fern reproduction

Fern spores

Raw data (below) and descriptive statistics (right) from a survey of the number of sori found on the fronds of a fern plant.

Raw data: Number of sori per frond							
64	60	64	62	68	66	66	63
69	70	63	70	70	63	63	62
71	69	59	70	66	61	61	70
67	64	63	64				

Total of data entries	=	1641	=	66	sori
Number of entries		25			

Mean

2. Give a reason for the difference between the mean, median, and mode for the fern sori data:

_____

_____

_____

_____

Number of sori per frond (in rank order)	
59	66
60	66
61	67
62	68
62	69
63	69
63	70
63	70
63	70
64	70
64	70
64	71
64	

Median

Mode

Sori per frond	Tally	Total
59	✔	1
60	✔	1
61	✔	1
62	✔ ✔	2
63	✔ ✔ ✔ ✔	4
64	✔ ✔ ✔ ✔	4
65		0
66	✔ ✔	2
67	✔	1
68	✔	1
69	✔ ✔	2
70	✔ ✔ ✔ ✔ ✔	5
71	✔	1

3. Calculate the mean, median, and mode for the data on ladybird masses below. Draw up a tally chart and show all calculations:

Ladybird mass / mg		
10.1	8.2	7.7
8.0	8.8	7.8
6.7	7.7	8.8
9.8	8.8	8.9
6.2	8.8	8.4

_____

_____

_____

_____

_____

25 Spread of Data

Key Idea: Standard deviation is used to quantify the variability around the central value and evaluate the reliability of estimates of the true mean.

While it is important to know the central tendency (e.g. mean) of a data set, it is also important to know how well the mean represents the data set. This is determined by measuring the spread of data around the central measure. The variance (s^2) or its square root, standard deviation (s) are often used to give a simple measure of the spread or dispersion in data. In general, if the spread of values in a data set around the mean is small, the mean will more accurately represent the data than if the spread of data is large.

Standard deviation

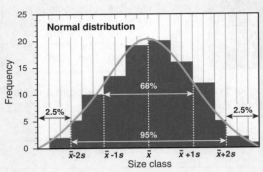

The **standard deviation** is a frequently used measure of the variability (spread) in a set of data. It is usually presented in the form $\bar{x} \pm s$. In a normally distributed set of data, 68% of all data values will lie within one standard deviation (s) of the mean ($\bar{x}$) and 95% of all data values will lie within two standard deviations of the mean (left).

Two different sets of data can have the same mean and range, yet the distribution of data within the range can be quite different. In both the data sets pictured in the histograms below, 68% of the values lie within the range $\bar{x} \pm 1s$ and 95% of the values lie within $\bar{x} \pm 2s$. However, in B, the data values are more tightly clustered around the mean.

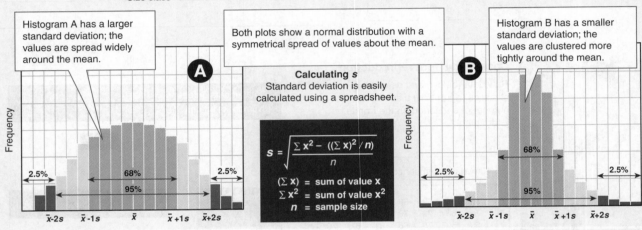

Histogram A has a larger standard deviation; the values are spread widely around the mean.

Both plots show a normal distribution with a symmetrical spread of values about the mean.

Histogram B has a smaller standard deviation; the values are clustered more tightly around the mean.

Calculating s
Standard deviation is easily calculated using a spreadsheet.

$$s = \sqrt{\frac{\sum x^2 - ((\sum x)^2 / n)}{n}}$$

$(\sum x)$ = sum of value x
$\sum x^2$ = sum of value x^2
n = sample size

NOTE: you may sometimes see the standard deviation equation written as

$$s = \sqrt{\frac{\sum(x - \bar{x})^2}{n}}$$

This equation will give you the same answer as the first equation (above), but the first equation is often used because it is easier to calculate.

Birth weights / kg		
3.740	3.810	3.220
3.830	2.640	3.135
3.530	2.980	3.090
3.095	3.350	3.830
1.560	3.780	3.840
3.910	3.260	4.710
4.180	3.800	4.050
3.570	4.170	4.560
3.150	4.400	3.380
3.400	3.770	3.690
3.380	3.825	1.495
2.660	3.130	3.260
3.840	3.400	
3.630	3.260	

1. Two data sets have the same mean. The standard deviation of the first data set is much larger than the standard deviation of the second data set. What does this tell you about the spread of data around the central measure for each set?

_____

_____

_____

2. The data on the left are the birth weights of 40 newborn babies.

(a) Calculate the mean for the data: _____

_____

(b) Calculate the standard deviation (s) for the data: _____

(c) State the mean ± 1s: _____

(d) What percentage of values are within 1s of the mean? _____

(e) What does this tell you about the spread of the data? _____

_____

26 Interpreting Sample Variability

Key Idea: The sampling method can affect the results of the study, especially if it has an unknown bias.

The **standard deviation** (s) gives a simple measure of the spread or **dispersion** in data. It is usually preferred over the **variance** (s^2) because it is expressed in the original units. Two data sets could have the same mean, but very different values of dispersion. If we simply used the mean to compare these data sets, the results would (incorrectly) suggest that they were alike. The assumptions we make about a population will be affected by what the sample data tell us. This is why it is important that sample data are unbiased (e.g. collected by **random sampling**) and that the sample set is as large as practicable. This exercise will help to illustrate this principle.

Complete sample set $n = 689$ (random)

Length in mm	Freq
25	1
26	0
27	0
28	0
29	0
30	0
31	0
32	2
33	3
34	3
35	4
36	5
37	10
38	23
39	22
40	33
41	39
42	41
43	41
44	36
45	49
46	32
47	14
48	32
49	27
50	25
51	24
52	17
53	18
54	27
55	21
56	20
57	11
58	18
59	16
60	22
61	13
62	8
63	10
64	5
65	7
66	2
67	3
68	3
69	1
70	0
71	1
	689

Random sampling, sample size, and dispersion in data

Sample size and sampling bias can both affect the information we obtain when we sample a population. In this exercise you will calculate some descriptive statistics for some sample data. The complete set of sample data we are working with comprises 689 length measurements of year zero (young of the year) perch (column left). Basic descriptive statistics for the data have been calculated for you below and the frequency histogram has also been plotted.

Look at this data set and then complete the exercise to calculate the same statistics from each of two smaller data sets (tabulated right) drawn from the same population. This exercise shows how random sampling, large sample size, and sampling bias affect our statistical assessment of variation in a population.

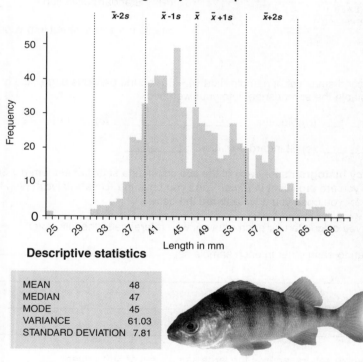

Length of year zero perch

$\bar{x} - 2s$ $\bar{x} - 1s$ $\bar{x}$ $\bar{x} + 1s$ $\bar{x} + 2s$

(Frequency vs Length in mm)

Descriptive statistics

MEAN	48
MEDIAN	47
MODE	45
VARIANCE	61.03
STANDARD DEVIATION	7.81

Small sample set $n = 30$ (random)

Length in mm	Freq
25	1
26	0
27	0
28	0
29	0
30	0
31	0
32	0
33	0
34	0
35	2
36	0
37	0
38	3
39	2
40	1
41	3
42	0
43	0
44	0
45	0
46	1
47	0
48	2
49	0
50	0
51	1
52	3
53	0
54	0
55	0
56	0
57	1
58	0
59	3
60	2
61	2
62	0
63	0
64	0
65	0
66	0
67	2
68	1
	30

Small sample set $n = 50$ (bias)

Length in mm	Freq
46	1
47	0
48	0
49	1
50	0
51	0
52	1
53	1
54	1
55	1
56	0
57	2
58	2
59	4
60	1
61	0
62	8
63	10
64	13
65	2
66	0
67	2
	50

The person gathering this set of data was biased towards selecting larger fish because the mesh size on the net was too large to retain small fish

This population was sampled randomly to obtain this data set

This column records the number of fish of each size

Number of fish in the sample

1. For the complete data set ($n = 689$) calculate the percentage of data falling within:

   (a) ± one standard deviation of the mean: _____

   (b) ± two standard deviations of the mean: _____

   (c) Explain what this information tells you about the distribution of year zero perch from this site: _____

   _____

2. Give another reason why you might reach the same conclusion about the distribution: _____

   _____

LINK 25 LINK 24 DATA

34

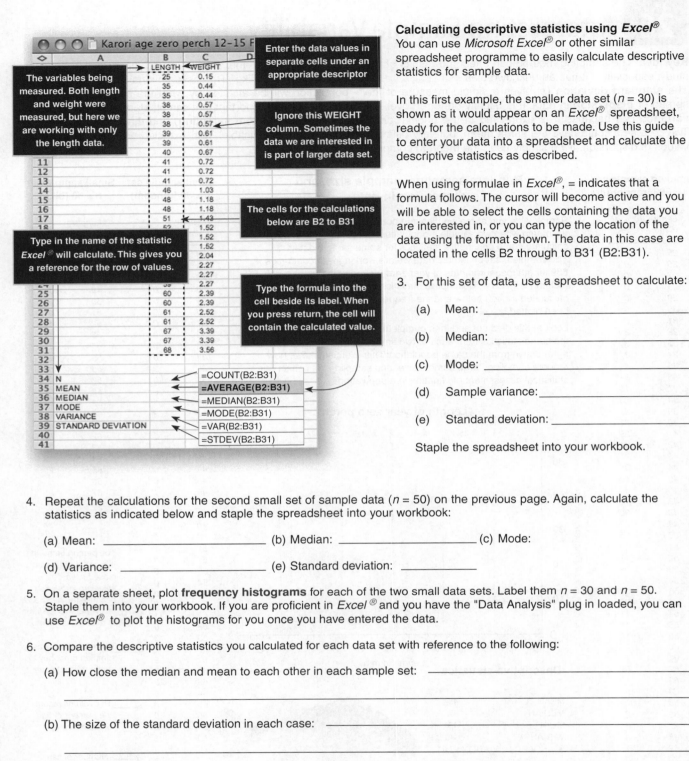

Calculating descriptive statistics using *Excel*®

You can use *Microsoft Excel*® or other similar spreadsheet programme to easily calculate descriptive statistics for sample data.

In this first example, the smaller data set ($n = 30$) is shown as it would appear on an *Excel*® spreadsheet, ready for the calculations to be made. Use this guide to enter your data into a spreadsheet and calculate the descriptive statistics as described.

When using formulae in *Excel*®, = indicates that a formula follows. The cursor will become active and you will be able to select the cells containing the data you are interested in, or you can type the location of the data using the format shown. The data in this case are located in the cells B2 through to B31 (B2:B31).

3. For this set of data, use a spreadsheet to calculate:

   (a) Mean: _____

   (b) Median: _____

   (c) Mode: _____

   (d) Sample variance: _____

   (e) Standard deviation: _____

   Staple the spreadsheet into your workbook.

Labels in spreadsheet image:

The variables being measured. Both length and weight were measured, but here we are working with only the length data.

Enter the data values in separate cells under an appropriate descriptor

Ignore this WEIGHT column. Sometimes the data we are interested in is part of larger data set.

The cells for the calculations below are B2 to B31

Type in the name of the statistic *Excel*® will calculate. This gives you a reference for the row of values.

Type the formula into the cell beside its label. When you press return, the cell will contain the calculated value.

	LENGTH	WEIGHT
	25	0.15
	35	0.44
	35	0.44
	38	0.57
	38	0.57
	38	0.57
	39	0.61
	39	0.61
	40	0.67
11	41	0.72
12	41	0.72
13	41	0.72
14	46	1.03
15	48	1.18
16	48	1.18
17	51	1.43
18	52	1.52
		1.52
		1.52
		2.04
		2.27
		2.27
		2.27
25	60	2.39
26	60	2.39
27	61	2.52
28	61	2.52
29	67	3.39
30	67	3.39
31	68	3.56
32		
33		
34	N	=COUNT(B2:B31)
35	MEAN	=AVERAGE(B2:B31)
36	MEDIAN	=MEDIAN(B2:B31)
37	MODE	=MODE(B2:B31)
38	VARIANCE	=VAR(B2:B31)
39	STANDARD DEVIATION	=STDEV(B2:B31)
40		
41		

4. Repeat the calculations for the second small set of sample data ($n = 50$) on the previous page. Again, calculate the statistics as indicated below and staple the spreadsheet into your workbook:

   (a) Mean: _____ (b) Median: _____ (c) Mode: _____

   (d) Variance: _____ (e) Standard deviation: _____

5. On a separate sheet, plot **frequency histograms** for each of the two small data sets. Label them $n = 30$ and $n = 50$. Staple them into your workbook. If you are proficient in *Excel*® and you have the "Data Analysis" plug in loaded, you can use *Excel*® to plot the histograms for you once you have entered the data.

6. Compare the descriptive statistics you calculated for each data set with reference to the following:

   (a) How close the median and mean to each other in each sample set: _____

   _____

   (b) The size of the standard deviation in each case: _____

   _____

   (c) How close each small of the sample sets resembles the large sample set of 689 values: _____

   _____

   _____

7. (a) Compare the two frequency histograms you have plotted for the two smaller sample data sets: _____

   _____

   _____

   (b) Why do you think two histograms look so different? _____

   _____

   _____

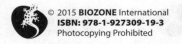

27 | Biological Drawings

Key Idea: Good biological drawings provide an accurate record of the specimen you are studying and enable you to make a record of its important features.

Drawing is a very important skill to have in biology. Drawings record what a specimen looks like and give you an opportunity to record its important features. Often drawing something will help you remember its features at a later date (e.g. in a test). Annotated drawings provide explanatory notes about the labelled structures, while plan diagrams label the main structures observed, but provide no additional detail.

▶ Biological drawings require you to pay attention to detail. It is very important that you draw what you actually see, and not what you think you should see.

▶ Biological drawings should include as much detail as you need to distinguish different structures and types of tissue, but avoid unnecessary detail which can make your drawing confusing.

▶ Attention should be given to the symmetry and proportions of your specimen. Accurate labeling, a statement of magnification or scale, the view (section type), and type of stain used (if applicable) should all be noted on your drawing.

▶ Some key points for making good biological drawing are described on the example below. The drawing of *Drosophila* (right) is well executed but lacks the information required to make it a good biological drawing.

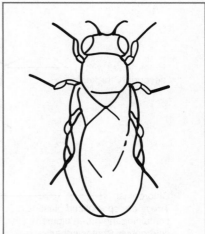

This drawing of *Drosophila* is a fair representation of the animal, but has no labels, title, or scale.

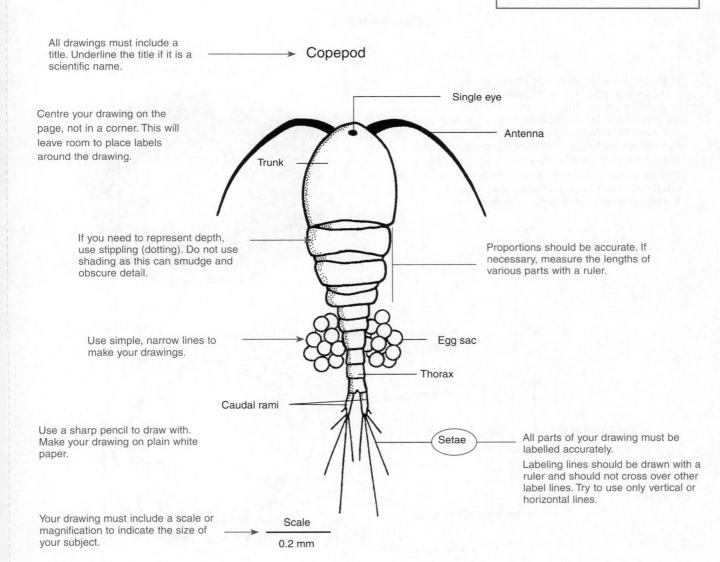

All drawings must include a title. Underline the title if it is a scientific name.

Copepod

Centre your drawing on the page, not in a corner. This will leave room to place labels around the drawing.

If you need to represent depth, use stippling (dotting). Do not use shading as this can smudge and obscure detail.

Use simple, narrow lines to make your drawings.

Use a sharp pencil to draw with. Make your drawing on plain white paper.

Your drawing must include a scale or magnification to indicate the size of your subject.

Single eye

Antenna

Trunk

Proportions should be accurate. If necessary, measure the lengths of various parts with a ruler.

Egg sac

Thorax

Caudal rami

Setae

All parts of your drawing must be labelled accurately.

Labeling lines should be drawn with a ruler and should not cross over other label lines. Try to use only vertical or horizontal lines.

Scale

0.2 mm

REFER

Annotated diagrams

An annotated diagram is a diagram that includes a series of explanatory notes. These provide important or useful information about your subject.

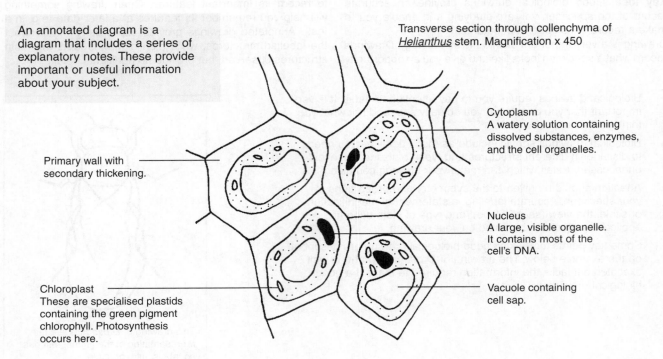

Transverse section through collenchyma of *Helianthus* stem. Magnification x 450

Primary wall with secondary thickening.

Cytoplasm
A watery solution containing dissolved substances, enzymes, and the cell organelles.

Nucleus
A large, visible organelle. It contains most of the cell's DNA.

Chloroplast
These are specialised plastids containing the green pigment chlorophyll. Photosynthesis occurs here.

Vacuole containing cell sap.

Plan diagrams

Plan diagrams are drawings made of samples viewed under a microscope at low or medium power. They are used to show the distribution of the different tissue types in a sample without any cellular detail. The tissues are identified, but no detail about the cells within them is included.

The example here shows a plan diagram produced after viewing a light micrograph of a transverse section through a dicot stem.

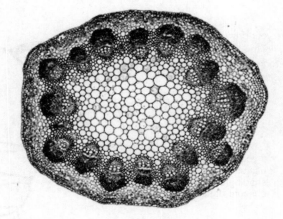

Light micrograph of a transverse section through a dicot stem.

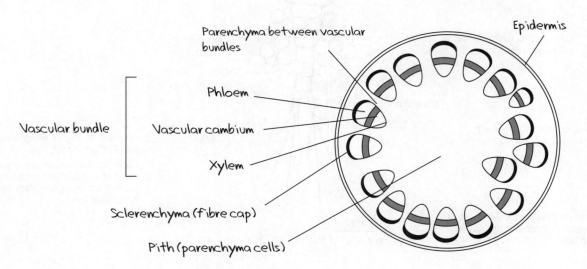

Parenchyma between vascular bundles

Epidermis

Phloem

Vascular bundle

Vascular cambium

Xylem

Sclerenchyma (fibre cap)

Pith (parenchyma cells)

© 2015 **BIOZONE** International
ISBN: 978-1-927309-19-3
Photocopying Prohibited

28 Practising Biological Drawings

Key Idea: Attention to detail is vital when making accurate and useful biological drawings.

In this activity, you will practise the skills required to translate what is viewed into a good biological drawing.

Above: Use relaxed viewing when drawing at the microscope. Use one eye (the left for right handers) to view and the right eye to look at your drawing.

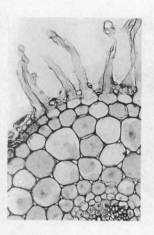

Above: Light micrograph Transverse section (TS) through a *Ranunculus* root.

Right: A biological drawing of the same section.

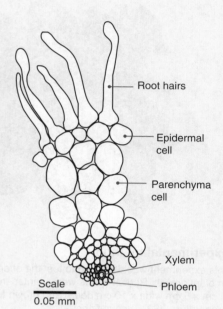

- Root hairs
- Epidermal cell
- Parenchyma cell
- Xylem
- Phloem

Scale
0.05 mm

1. During your course of study, you will investigate cells and mass transport systems, and you may be required to identify and draw cells in a prepared blood smear viewed with a light microscope. It can be difficult to identify cell types in prepared smears under the magnification commonly used in school microscopes (X400). An example of what you might see is shown below.

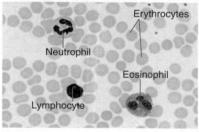

Erythrocytes
Neutrophil
Eosinophil
Lymphocyte

Looking at your slide, draw what you can see and try to identify as many cell types as you can. Use the picture (below, right) to help you. The drawn cells are organised from left to right in order of most common to least common. White blood cells are framed by the rectangle. Platelets are cell fragments and may not be visible. White blood cells are distinguished by the presence and staining of granules in the cytoplasm and the shape of the nucleus. Lymphocytes and monocytes do not have a granular cytoplasm.

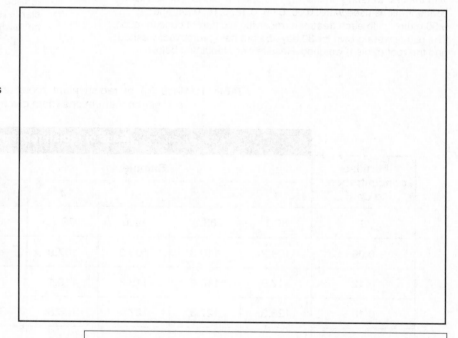

Platelets

Erythrocyte

Most common

Neutrophil
Light staining granules

Lymphocyte
Smaller, rounder, agranular

Monocyte
Agranular, lobed nucleus

Eosinophil
Stains dark pink

Basophil
Stains dark purple

Least common

LINK
142
LINK
111
LINK
27

PRAC

29 Test Your Understanding

Key Idea: Systematic recording and analysis of results can help identify trends and draw conclusions about a biological response in an experiment.

Using the information below, analyse results and draw conclusions about the effect of a nitrogen fertiliser on the growth of radish plants.

Radishes

The Aim

To investigate the effect of a nitrogen fertiliser on the growth of radish plants.

Hypothesis

If plants need nitrogen to grow, radish growth will increase with increasing nitrogen concentration.

Background

Inorganic fertilisers revolutionised crop farming when they were introduced during the late 19th and early 20th century. Crop yields soared and today it is estimated around 50% of crop yield is attributable to the use of fertiliser. Nitrogen is a very important element for plant growth and several types of purely nitrogen fertiliser are manufactured to supply it, e.g. urea.

Experimental method

This experiment was designed to test the effect of nitrogen fertiliser on plant growth. Radish seeds were planted in separate identical pots (5 cm x 5 cm wide x 10 cm deep) and grown together in normal room temperature (22°C) conditions.

The radishes were watered every day at 10 am and 3 pm with 1.25 L per treatment. Water soluble fertiliser was mixed and added with the first watering on the 1st, 11th and 21st days. The fertiliser concentrations used were: 0.00, 0.06, 0.12, 0.18, 0.24, and 0.30 g dm^{-3} with each treatment receiving a different concentration. The plants were grown for 30 days before being removed, washed, and the root (radish) weighed. Results were tabulated below:

To investigate the effect of nitrogen on plant growth, a group of students set up an experiment using different concentrations of nitrogen fertiliser. Radish seeds were planted into a standard soil mixture and divided into six groups, each with five sample plants (30 plants in total).

Table 1: Mass (g) of radish plant roots under six different fertiliser concentrations (data given to 1 dp).

Fertiliser concentration / g dm^{-3}	Mass of radish root / g† Sample / n					Total mass	Mean mass
	1	2	3	4	5		
0	80.1	83.2	82.0	79.1	84.1	408.5	81.7
0.06	109.2	110.3	108.2	107.9	110.7		
0.12	117.9	118.9	118.3	119.1	117.2		
0.18	128.3	127.3	127.7	126.8	DNG*		
0.24	23.6	140.3	139.6	137.9	141.1		
0.30	122.3	121.1	122.6	121.3	123.1		

† Based on data from M S Jilani, et al Journal Agricultural Research

* DNG: Did not germinate

1. Identify the independent variable for the experiment and its range: _____

_____

2. What is the sample size for each concentration of fertiliser? _____

© 2015 **BIOZONE** International
ISBN: 978-1-927309-19-3
Photocopying Prohibited

3. One of the radishes recorded in Table 1 did not grow as expected and produced an extreme value. Record the **outlying value** here and decide whether or not you should include it in future calculations:

_____

_____

_____

4. Complete the table on the previous page by calculating the **total mass** and **mean mass** of the radish roots:

5. Use the grid below to draw a **line graph** of the experimental results. Use your calculated means and remember to include a title and correctly labelled axes.

6. The students recorded the wet mass of the root (the root still containing water) in their table. What mass should they have actually recorded to get a better representation of the effect of the fertiliser on root mass?

_____

_____

_____

7. Why would measuring just root mass not be a totally accurate way of measuring the effect of fertiliser on radish growth?

_____

_____

8. Describe some other measurements the students could have taken to make their experiment more complete:

_____

_____

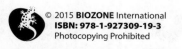

9. Complete Table 2 by calculating the mean, median and mode for each concentration of fertiliser:

The students decided to further their experiment by recording the number of leaves on each radish plant:

Table 2: Number of leaves on radish plant under six different fertiliser concentrations.

| Fertiliser concentration / g dm^{-3} | Number of leaves | | | | | Mean | Median | Mode |
| | Sample / n | | | | | | | |
	1	2	3	4	5			
0	9	9	10	8	7			
0.06	15	16	15	16	16			
0.12	16	17	17	17	16			
0.18	18	18	19	18	DNG*			
0.24	6	19	19	18	18			
0.30	18	17	18	19	19			

* DNG: Did not germinate

10. (a) Identify the outlier in the table above: _____

(b) Recalculate the mean if the outlier was included: _____

(c) Calculate the standard deviation for the fertiliser concentration affected by an outlier:

With the outlier included: _____

Without the outlier included: _____

(d) Compare the results in (c). What can you conclude about how accurately the mean reflects the data set when the outlier is included?

_____

_____

11. Which concentration of fertiliser appeared to produce the best growth results? _____

12. Describe some sources of error for the experiment: _____

_____

_____

_____

13. Write a conclusion for the experiment with reference to the aim, hypothesis, and results: _____

_____

_____

_____

_____

14. The students decided to replicate the experiment (carry it out again). How might this improve the experiment's results?

_____

_____

_____

© 2015 **BIOZONE** International
ISBN: 978-1-927309-19-3
Photocopying Prohibited

Biological Molecules

Key terms

activation energy

amino acid

base pairing rule

Benedict's test

biuret test

carbohydrate

chromatography

colorimetry

condensation

denaturation

dipeptide

disaccharide

DNA

emulsion test

enzyme

fatty acid

fibrous protein

hydrolysis

globular protein

glycerol

hydrogen bond

inhibition

inorganic ion

iodine/potassium iodide test

isomer

lipid

macromolecule

monomer

monosaccharide

nucleic acid

phospholipid

polymer

polypeptide

polysaccharide

primary structure

protein

quaternary structure

RNA

secondary structure

tertiary structure

triglyceride

water

1.1 Monomers and polymers
Learning outcomes

Activity number

□ 1 Identify the organic compounds around which life is based Comment on the commonalities in the biochemical basis of all life on Earth. — 30 31 32

□ 2 Giving examples, describe the nature of monomers and polymers. — 31

□ 3 Describe how condensation and hydrolysis reactions are involved in the formation and breakdown of polymers. — 34 38 40 53 54

1.2 Carbohydrates
Learning outcomes

Activity number

□ 4 Recognise glucose, galactose, and fructose as common monosaccharides. — 33

□ 5 Describe how glycosidic bonds are formed and broken in the synthesis (by condensation) and hydrolysis of disaccharides (e.g. sucrose, lactose, and maltose) and polysaccharides (e.g. amylose of starch). — 34 36

□ 6 Describe the ring structure and properties of glucose (hexose monosaccharide). Recognise isomers of glucose (α-glucose and β-glucose). — 33

□ 7 **AT** Produce a dilution series of glucose solutions and use colorimetry to produce a calibration curve with which to identify the concentration of glucose in an unknown solution. — 35

□ 8 Compare and contrast the structure of glucose polymers: starch, cellulose, and glycogen. Relate the structure to their biological function in each case. — 36 37

□ 9 **AT** Use chromatography to separate a mixture of monosaccharides. — 41

□ 10 **AT** Use and interpret the results of qualitative tests for carbohydrates. — 45

Catalase

Pyruvate dehydrogenase
FontanaCG cc 3.0

Restriction enzyme

1.3 Lipids
Learning outcomes

Activity number

□ 11 Recognise triglycerides and phospholipids as classes of lipid and describe the basic structure of each. Relate the properties and roles of triglycerides and phospholipids to their different structures. — 38 39

□ 12 Explain how triglycerides are formed by condensation from fatty acids and glycerol with the formation of ester bonds. Describe the structure of fatty acids, distinguishing saturated, monounsaturated, and polyunsaturated fatty acids. — 38

□ 13 **AT** Use and interpret the results of the emulsion test for lipids. — 45

1.4 Proteins
Learning outcomes

Activity number

□ 14 Describe the structure of an amino acid, including the significance of the R group. Explain how dipeptides and polypeptides are formed and broken apart by condensation and hydrolysis. — 40

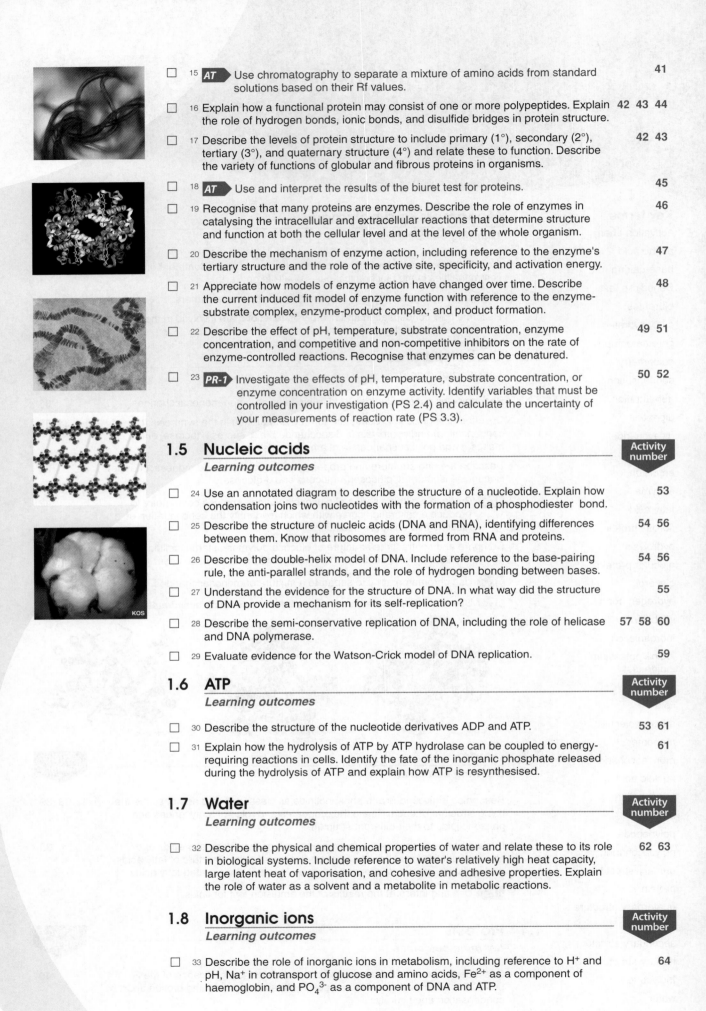

30 Organic Molecules

Key Idea: Organic molecules are those with carbon-hydrogen bonds. They make up most of the chemicals found in living organisms and can be portrayed as formulae or models. Molecular biology is a branch of science that studies the molecular basis of biological activity. All life is based around carbon, which is able to combine with many other elements to form a large number of carbon-based (or organic) molecules.

Specific groups of atoms, called functional groups, attach to a C-H core and determine the specific chemical properties of the molecule. The organic macromolecules (large complex molecules) that make up living things can be grouped into four classes: carbohydrates, lipids, proteins, and nucleic acids. The diagram (bottom) illustrates some of the common ways in which organic molecules are portrayed.

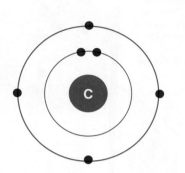

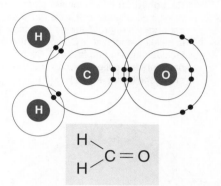

Organic macromolecule	Structural unit	Elements
Carbohydrates	Sugar monomer	C, H, O
Proteins	Amino acid	C, H, O, N, S
Lipids	Not applicable	C, H, O
Nucleic acids	Nucleotide	C, H, O, N, P

A carbon atom (above) has four electrons that are available to form up to four **covalent bonds** with other atoms. A covalent bond forms when two atoms share a pair of electrons. The number of covalent bonds formed between atoms in a molecule determines the shape and chemical properties of the molecule.

Methanal (molecular formula CH_2O) is a simple organic molecule. A carbon (C) atom bonds with two hydrogen (H) atoms and an oxygen (O) atom. In the structural formula (blue box), the bonds between atoms are represented by lines. Covalent bonds are very strong, so the molecules formed are very stable.

The most common elements found in organic molecules are carbon, hydrogen, and oxygen, but organic molecules may also contain other elements, such as nitrogen, phosphorus, and sulfur. Most organic macromolecules are built up of one type of repeating unit or 'building block', except lipids, which are quite diverse in structure.

Portraying organic molecules

The numbers next to the carbon atoms are used for identification when the molecule changes shape →

$C_6H_{12}O_6$

Glucose

Molecular formula

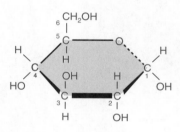

Structural formula
Glucose (straight form)

Structural formula
α-glucose (ring form)

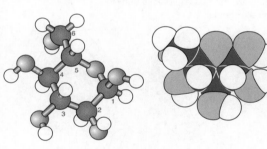

Ball and stick model
Glucose

Space filling model
β-D-glucose

The molecular formula expresses the number of atoms in a molecule, but does not convey its structure. This is indicated by the structural formula.

A ball and stick model shows the arrangement of bonds while a space filling model gives a more realistic appearance of a molecule.

1. Study the table above and state the three main elements that make up the structure of organic molecules: _____

_____

2. Name two other elements that are also frequently part of organic molecules: _____

3. (a) On the diagram of the carbon atom top left, mark with arrows the electrons that are available to form covalent bonds with other atoms.

   (b) State how many covalent bonds a carbon atom can form with neighbouring atoms: _____

4. Distinguish between molecular and structural formulae for a given molecule: _____

_____

_____

LINK
31

WEB
30

KNOW

31 The Biochemical Nature of Cells

Key Idea: The main components of cells are water and organic compounds of carbon, hydrogen, nitrogen and oxygen. Monomers can join together to form larger polymers. About 70% or more of a cell's mass is water. The remainder comprises molecules made up mainly of carbon, hydrogen, oxygen, and nitrogen. The combination of carbon with other elements provides a wide variety of molecular structures, called organic molecules. The organic molecules that make up living things can be grouped into four broad classes: carbohydrates, lipids, proteins, and nucleic acids. Organic molecules often consist of single units (**monomers**), which are joined to form large molecules of many units (**polymers**).

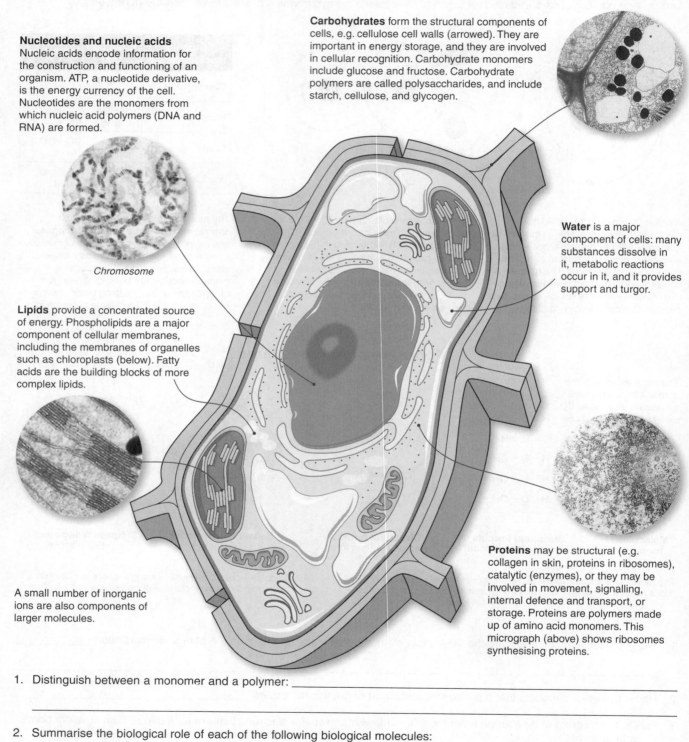

Nucleotides and nucleic acids
Nucleic acids encode information for the construction and functioning of an organism. ATP, a nucleotide derivative, is the energy currency of the cell. Nucleotides are the monomers from which nucleic acid polymers (DNA and RNA) are formed.

Chromosome

Lipids provide a concentrated source of energy. Phospholipids are a major component of cellular membranes, including the membranes of organelles such as chloroplasts (below). Fatty acids are the building blocks of more complex lipids.

A small number of inorganic ions are also components of larger molecules.

Carbohydrates form the structural components of cells, e.g. cellulose cell walls (arrowed). They are important in energy storage, and they are involved in cellular recognition. Carbohydrate monomers include glucose and fructose. Carbohydrate polymers are called polysaccharides, and include starch, cellulose, and glycogen.

Water is a major component of cells: many substances dissolve in it, metabolic reactions occur in it, and it provides support and turgor.

Proteins may be structural (e.g. collagen in skin, proteins in ribosomes), catalytic (enzymes), or they may be involved in movement, signalling, internal defence and transport, or storage. Proteins are polymers made up of amino acid monomers. This micrograph (above) shows ribosomes synthesising proteins.

1. Distinguish between a monomer and a polymer: _____

_____

2. Summarise the biological role of each of the following biological molecules:

(a) Carbohydrates: _____

(b) Lipids: _____

(c) Proteins: _____

(d) Nucleic acids: _____

LINK 33   LINK 36   LINK 38   LINK 40   LINK 53   LINK 54

KNOW

© 2015 **BIOZONE** International
ISBN: 978-1-927309-19-3
Photocopying Prohibited

32 The Common Ancestry of Life

Key Idea: Molecular similarities have allowed scientists to trace the evolutionary history of the three domains of life. Despite the diversity of life on Earth, all organisms (with a few exceptions), share the same universal genetic code, i.e. the same combination of three DNA bases code for the same amino acid in almost all organisms. The universality of the genetic code and similarities in the molecular machinery of all cells provide evidence for a common ancestor to all life. The analysis of DNA, RNA, and proteins has provided detailed information about how all life is related (below).

The tree of life

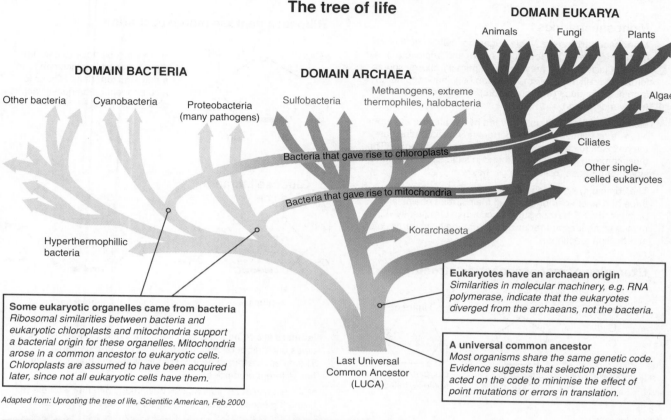

Some eukaryotic organelles came from bacteria
Ribosomal similarities between bacteria and eukaryotic chloroplasts and mitochondria support a bacterial origin for these organelles. Mitochondria arose in a common ancestor to eukaryotic cells. Chloroplasts are assumed to have been acquired later, since not all eukaryotic cells have them.

Eukaryotes have an archaean origin
Similarities in molecular machinery, e.g. RNA polymerase, indicate that the eukaryotes diverged from the archaeans, not the bacteria.

A universal common ancestor
Most organisms share the same genetic code. Evidence suggests that selection pressure acted on the code to minimise the effect of point mutations or errors in translation.

Adapted from: Uprooting the tree of life, Scientific American, Feb 2000

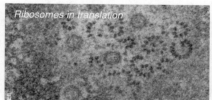

In all living systems, the genetic machinery consists of self-replicating DNA molecules. Some DNA is transcribed into RNA, some of which is translated into proteins. The machinery for translation (above) involves proteins and RNA. Ribosomal RNA analyses support a universal common ancestor.

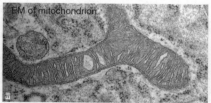

The mitochondria of eukaryotes are thought to have been acquired when a pre-eukaryote engulfed a bacterial cell to form an endosymbiosis. The endosymbiotic origin of eukaryotic mitochondria is supported by the evidence from mitochondrial gene sequences, ribosomes, and protein synthesis.

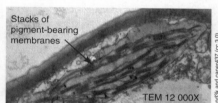

Similarities between chloroplasts and cyanobacteria suggest that they too were acquired by endosymbiosis, probably independently from more than one type of cyanobacterial cell in different photosynthetic lineages. The prokaryotic origin of chloroplasts is supported by ribosomal evidence.

1. Describe the chemical evidence that supports a common ancestor for life on Earth: _____

_____

2. Identify one line of evidence supporting a bacterial origin for chloroplast and mitochondria in eukaryotes: _____

_____

3. Describe the contribution of molecular techniques, e.g. DNA analysis, to our understanding of evolutionary relationships:

_____

33 Sugars

Key Idea: Monosaccharides are the building blocks for larger carbohydrates. They can exist as isomers.

Sugars (monosaccharides and disaccharides) play a central role in cells, providing energy and joining together to form carbohydrate macromolecules, such as starch and glycogen.

Monosaccharide polymers form the major component of most plants (as cellulose). Monosaccharides are important as a primary energy source for cellular metabolism. Carbohydrates have the general formula $C_x(H_2O)_y$, where x and y are variable numbers (often but not always the same).

Monosaccharides

Monosaccharides are single-sugar molecules and include glucose (grape sugar and blood sugar) and fructose (honey and fruit juices). They are used as a primary energy source for fuelling cell metabolism. They can be joined together to form disaccharides (two monomers) and polysaccharides (many monomers).

Monosaccharides can be classified by the number of carbon atoms they contain. Some important monosaccharides are the hexoses (6 carbons) and the pentoses (5 carbons). The most common arrangements found in sugars are hexose (6 sided) or pentose (5 sided) rings (below).

The commonly occurring monosaccharides contain between three and seven carbon atoms in their carbon chains and, of these, the 6C hexose sugars occur most frequently. All monosaccharides are reducing sugars (they can participate in reduction reactions).

Examples of monosaccharide structures

Triose	Pentose	Hexose
C C C		
e.g. glyceraldehyde	e.g. ribose, deoxyribose	e.g. glucose, fructose, galactose

Ribose: a pentose monosaccharide

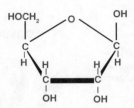

Ribose is a pentose (5 carbon) monosaccharide which can form a ring structure (left). Ribose is a component of the nucleic acid ribonucleic acid (RNA).

Glucose isomers

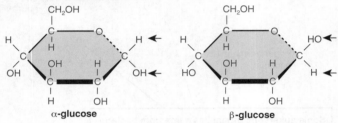

α-glucose   β-glucose

Isomers are compounds with the same chemical formula (same types and numbers of atoms) but different arrangements of atoms. The different arrangement of the atoms means that each isomer has different properties.

Molecules such as glucose can have many different isomers (e.g. α and β glucose, above) including straight and ring forms.

Glucose is a versatile molecule. It provides energy to power cellular reactions, can form energy storage molecules such as glycogen, or it can be used to build structural molecules.

Plants make their glucose via the process of photosynthesis. Animals and other heterotrophic organisms obtain their glucose by consuming plants or other organisms.

Fructose, often called fruit sugar, is a simple monosaccharide. It is often derived from sugar cane (above). Both fructose and glucose can be directly absorbed into the bloodstream.

1. Describe the two major functions of monosaccharides:

   (a) _____

   (b) _____

2. Describe the structural differences between the ring forms of glucose and ribose: _____

   _____

   _____

3. Using glucose as an example, define the term **isomer** and state its importance: _____

   _____

   _____

© 2015 **BIOZONE** International
ISBN: 978-1-927309-19-3
Photocopying Prohibited

34 Condensation and Hydrolysis of Sugars

Key Idea: Condensation reactions join monosaccharides together to form disaccharides and polysaccharides. Hydrolysis reactions split disaccharides and polysaccharides into smaller molecules.

Monosaccharide monomers can be linked together by **condensation reactions** to produce larger molecules

(disaccharides and polysaccharides). The reverse reaction, **hydrolysis**, breaks compound sugars down into their constituent monosaccharides. **Disaccharides** (double-sugars) are produced when two monosaccharides are joined together. Different disaccharides are formed by joining together different combinations of monosaccharides (below).

Condensation and Hydrolysis Reactions

Monosaccharides can combine to form compound sugars in what is called a condensation reaction. Compound sugars can be broken down by hydrolysis to simple monosaccharides.

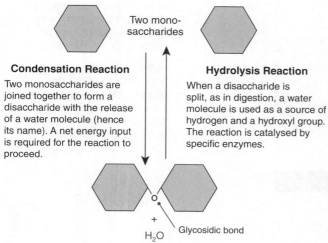

Two mono-saccharides

Condensation Reaction

Two monosaccharides are joined together to form a disaccharide with the release of a water molecule (hence its name). A net energy input is required for the reaction to proceed.

Hydrolysis Reaction

When a disaccharide is split, as in digestion, a water molecule is used as a source of hydrogen and a hydroxyl group. The reaction is catalysed by specific enzymes.

+ H_2O — Glycosidic bond

Disaccharide + water

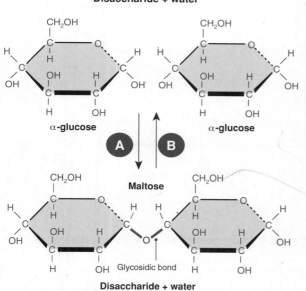

α-glucose   α-glucose

A   **B**

Maltose

Glycosidic bond

Disaccharide + water

Disaccharides

Disaccharides (below) are double-sugar molecules and are used as energy sources and as building blocks for larger molecules. They are important in human nutrition and are found in milk (lactose), table sugar (sucrose), and malt (maltose).

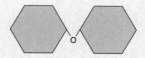

The type of disaccharide formed depends on the monomers involved and whether they are in their α- or β- form. Only a few disaccharides (e.g. lactose) are classified as reducing sugars. Some common disaccharides are described below.

Lactose, a milk sugar, is made up of β-glucose + β-galactose. Milk contains 2-8% lactose by weight. It is the primary carbohydrate source for suckling mammalian infants.

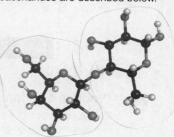

Maltose is composed of two α-glucose molecules. Germinating seeds contain maltose because the plant breaks down their starch stores to use it for food.

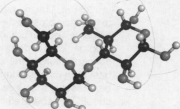

Sucrose (table sugar) is a simple sugar derived from plants such as sugar cane, sugar beet, or maple sap. It is composed of an α-glucose molecule and a β-fructose molecule.

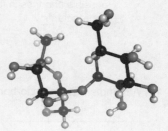

1. Explain briefly how disaccharide sugars are formed and broken down: _____

_____

_____

_____

2. On the diagram above, name the reaction occurring at points **A** and **B** and name the product that is formed:

_____

_____

3. On the lactose, maltose, and sucrose molecules (above right), circle the two monomers on each molecule.

LINK **41**   LINK **37**   LINK **36**   WEB **34**   **KNOW**

35 Colorimetry

Key Idea: Colorimetric analysis can be used to determine the concentration of a substance in a solution.

Colorimetric analysis is a simple quantitative technique used to determine the concentration of a specific substance in a solution. A specific reagent is added to the test solution where it reacts with the substance of interest to produce a colour. The samples are placed in a colorimeter, which measures the solution's absorbance at a specific wavelength. A dilution series can be used to produce a calibration curve, which can then be used to quantify that substance in samples of unknown concentration. This is illustrated for glucose in the example below.

1 **Prepare glucose standards**

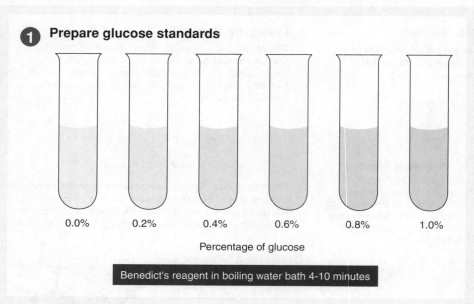

0.0%   0.2%   0.4%   0.6%   0.8%   1.0%

Percentage of glucose

Benedict's reagent in boiling water bath 4-10 minutes

Solutions containing a range of known glucose concentrations are prepared in test tubes. Benedict's reagent (used to detect the presence of a reducing sugar) is added and the test tubes are heated in a boiling waterbath for 4-10 minutes.

At the end of the reaction time, samples containing glucose will have undergone a colour change. The samples are cooled, then filtered or centrifuged to remove suspended particles.

2 **Produce a calibration curve**

The absorbance of each standard is measured in a colorimeter (or sometimes a spectrophotometer) at 735 nm. These values are used to produce a calibration curve for glucose. The calibration curve can then be used to determine the glucose concentration of any 'unknown' based on its absorbance. For the best results, a new calibration curve should be generated for each new analysis. This accounts for any possible changes in the conditions of the reactants.

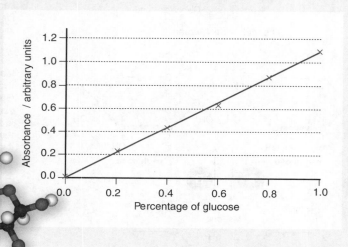

Glucose

1. (a) A sample has an absorbance of 0.5. Use the calibration curve above to estimate how much glucose it contains.

_____

(b) What would you do if the absorbance values you obtained for most of your 'unknowns' were outside the range of your calibration curve?

_____

_____

2. How could you quantify the amount of glucose in a range of commercially available glucose drinks? _____

_____

_____

3. Why is it important to remove suspended solids from a sample before measuring its absorbance? _____

_____

LINK
45
LINK
103

KNOW

© 2015 **BIOZONE** International
ISBN: 978-1-927309-19-3
Photocopying Prohibited

36 Polysaccharides

Key Idea: Polysaccharides consist of many monosaccharides joined together through condensation reactions. Their composition and isomerisation alter their functional properties. **Polysaccharides** (complex carbohydrates) are straight or branched chains of many monosaccharides joined together. They can consist of one or more types of monosaccharides.

The most common polysaccharides, cellulose, starch, and glycogen contain only glucose, but their properties are very different. These differences are a function of the glucose isomer involved and the types of linkages joining them. Different polysaccharides can thus be a source of readily available glucose or a structural material that resists digestion.

Cellulose

Cellulose is a structural material found in the cell walls of plants. It is made up of unbranched chains of β-glucose molecules held together by β-1,4 glycosidic links. As many as 10 000 glucose molecules may be linked together to form a straight chain. Parallel chains become cross-linked with hydrogen bonds and form bundles of 60-70 molecules called **microfibrils**. Cellulose microfibrils are very strong and are a major structural component of plants, e.g. as the cell wall. Few organisms can break the β-linkages so cellulose is an ideal structural material.

Starch

Starch is also a polymer of glucose, but it is made up of long chains of α-glucose molecules linked together. It contains a mixture of 25-30% amylose (unbranched chains linked by α-1,4 glycosidic bonds) and 70-75% amylopectin (branched chains with α-1, 6 glycosidic bonds every 24-30 glucose units). Starch is an energy storage molecule in plants and is found concentrated in insoluble starch granules within specialised plastids called amyloplasts in plant cells (see photo, right). Starch can be easily hydrolysed by enzymes to soluble sugars when required.

Glycogen

Glycogen, like starch, is a branched polysaccharide. It is chemically similar to amylopectin, being composed of α-glucose molecules, but there are more α-1,6 glycosidic links mixed with α-1,4 links. This makes it more highly branched and more water-soluble than starch. Glycogen is a storage compound in animal tissues and is found mainly in liver and muscle cells (photo, right). It is readily hydrolysed by enzymes to form glucose making it an ideal energy storage molecule for active animals.

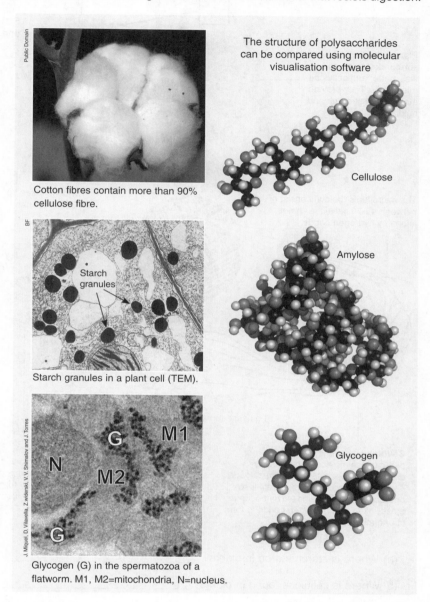

The structure of polysaccharides can be compared using molecular visualisation software

Cellulose

Amylose

Glycogen

Cotton fibres contain more than 90% cellulose fibre.

Starch granules in a plant cell (TEM).

Glycogen (G) in the spermatozoa of a flatworm. M1, M2=mitochondria, N=nucleus.

1. (a) Why are polysaccharides such a good source of energy?_____

_____

(b) How is the energy stored in polysaccharides mobilised?_____

_____

2. Contrast the properties of the polysaccharides starch, cellulose, and glycogen and relate these to their roles in the cell:

_____

_____

_____

_____

_____

© 2015 **BIOZONE** International
ISBN: 978-1-927309-19-3
Photocopying Prohibited

LINK **45** LINK **37** WEB **36** **KNOW**

37 Starch and Cellulose

Key Idea: Starch and cellulose are important polysaccharides in plants. Starch is a storage carbohydrate made up of two α-glucose polymers, amylose and amylopectin. Cellulose is a β-glucose polymer which forms the plant cell wall.

Glucose monomers can be linked in condensation reactions to form large structural and energy storage polysaccharides. The glucose isomer involved and the type of glycosidic linkage determines the properties of the molecule.

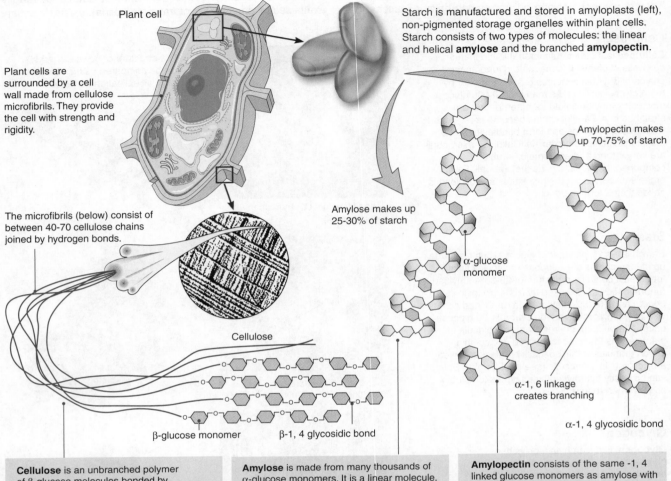

Plant cell

Plant cells are surrounded by a cell wall made from cellulose microfibrils. They provide the cell with strength and rigidity.

Starch is manufactured and stored in amyloplasts (left), non-pigmented storage organelles within plant cells. Starch consists of two types of molecules: the linear and helical **amylose** and the branched **amylopectin**.

Amylopectin makes up 70-75% of starch

The microfibrils (below) consist of between 40-70 cellulose chains joined by hydrogen bonds.

Amylose makes up 25-30% of starch

α-glucose monomer

Cellulose

α-1, 6 linkage creates branching

β-glucose monomer   β-1, 4 glycosidic bond

α-1, 4 glycosidic bond

Cellulose is an unbranched polymer of β-glucose molecules bonded by extremely stable β-1, 4 glycosidic bonds. The unbranched structure of cellulose produces parallel chains which become cross linked with hydrogen bonds to form strong microfibrils.

Amylose is made from many thousands of α-glucose monomers. It is a linear molecule, which forms a helix as a result of the angle of the α-1, 4 glycosidic bonds. Every turn of the amylose helix requires six α-glucose molecules. Amylose forms 25-30% of the structure of starch.

Amylopectin consists of the same -1, 4 linked glucose monomers as amylose with occasional -1,6 glycosidic bonds which provide branching points around every 24-30 glucose residues. This branching allows many millions of glucose molecules to be stored in a compact form.

1. (a) Where is starch stored in plants? _____

    (b) Where is cellulose found in plants? _____

2. Compare and contrast the structure of amylose and amylopectin: _____

    _____

    _____

    _____

3. Account for the differences in structure between cellulose and starch: _____

    _____

    _____

    _____

4. Amylopectin is very similar in structure to glycogen but is less soluble. Explain why: _____

    _____

LINK
36

© 2015 **BIOZONE** International
ISBN: 978-1-927309-19-3
Photocopying Prohibited

38 Lipids

Key Idea: Lipids are non-polar, hydrophobic organic molecules, which have many important biological functions. Fatty acids are the building blocks of more complex lipids.
Lipids are organic compounds which are mostly nonpolar (have no overall charge) and hydrophobic, so they do not readily dissolve in water. Lipids include fats, waxes, sterols, and phospholipids. Fatty acids are a major component of neutral fats and phospholipids. Most fatty acids consist of an even number of carbon atoms, with hydrogen bound along the length of the chain. The carboxyl group (–COOH) at one end makes them an acid. They are generally classified as saturated or unsaturated fatty acids (below).

Triglycerides

Glycerol Ester bond Fatty acids

Triglyceride: an example of a neutral fat

Neutral fats and oils are the most abundant lipids in living things. They make up the fats and oils found in plants and animals. They consist of a glycerol attached to one (mono-), two (di-) or three (tri-) fatty acids by **ester bonds**. Lipids have a high proportion of hydrogen present in the fatty acid chains. When the molecule is metabolised, the chemical energy is released. Being so reduced and anhydrous, they are an economical way to store fuel reserves, and provide more than twice as much energy as the same quantity of carbohydrate.

Lipids containing a high proportion of saturated fatty acids tend to be solids at room temperature (e.g. butter). Lipids with a high proportion of unsaturated fatty acids are oils and tend to be liquid at room temperature (e.g. olive oil). This is because the unsaturation causes kinks in the straight chains so that the fatty acid chains do not pack closely together.

Saturated and unsaturated fatty acids

Fatty acids are carboxylic acids with long hydrocarbon chains. They are classed as either saturated or unsaturated. **Saturated fatty acids** contain the maximum number of hydrogen atoms. **Unsaturated fatty acids** contain some double-bonds between carbon atoms and are not fully saturated with hydrogens. A chain with only one double bond is called monounsaturated, whereas a chain with two or more double bonds is called polyunsaturated.

Formula (above) and molecular model (below) for a saturated fatty acid (palmitic acid).

Formula (above) and molecular model (right) for an unsaturated fatty acid (linoleic acid). The arrows indicate double bonded carbon atoms that are not fully saturated with hydrogens.

1. Identify the main components (a-c) of the symbolic triglyceride below:

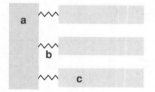

(a) _____

(b) _____

(c) _____

2. Why do lipids have such a high energy content? _____

_____

_____

3. (a) Distinguish between saturated and unsaturated fatty acids: _____

_____

(b) Relate the properties of a neutral fat to the type of fatty acid present: _____

_____

_____

LINK 45 LINK 39 WEB 38 KNOW

Triglycerides are formed by condensation reactions

Triglycerides form when glycerol bonds with three fatty acids. Glycerol is an alcohol containing three carbons. Each of these carbons is bonded to a hydroxyl (-OH) group.

When glycerol bonds with the fatty acid, an **ester bond** is formed and water is released. Three separate condensation reactions are involved in producing a triglyceride.

Esterification: A condensation reaction of an alcohol (e.g. glycerol) with an acid (e.g. fatty acid) to produce an ester and water. In the diagram right, the ester bonds are indicated by blue lines.

Lipolysis: The breakdown of lipids. It involves hydrolysis of triglycerides into glycerol molecules and free fatty acids.

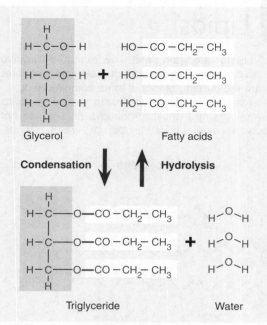

Glycerol   Fatty acids

Condensation ↓   ↑ **Hydrolysis**

Triglyceride   Water

Biological functions of lipids

Lipids are concentrated sources of energy and provide fuel for aerobic respiration.

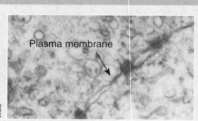

Phospholipids form the structure of cellular membranes in eukaryotes and prokaryotes.

Waxes and oils secreted onto surfaces provide waterproofing in plants and animals.

Fat absorbs shocks. Organs that are prone to bumps and shocks (e.g. kidneys) are cushioned with a relatively thick layer of fat.

Lipids are a source of metabolic water. During respiration stored lipids are metabolized for energy, producing water and carbon dioxide.

Stored lipids provide insulation. Increased body fat levels in winter reduce heat losses to the environment.

4. (a) Describe what happens during the esterification (condensation) process to produce a triglyceride:

_____

_____

(b) Describe what happens when a triglyceride is hydrolysed: _____

_____

_____

5. Discuss the biological role of lipids: _____

_____

_____

_____

_____

© 2015 **BIOZONE** International
ISBN: 978-1-927309-19-3
Photocopying Prohibited

39 Phospholipids

Key Idea: Phospholipids are modified triglycerides. They are important components of cellular membranes.

Phospholipids are similar in structure to a triglyceride except that a phosphate group replaces one of the fatty acids attached to the glycerol. Phospholipids naturally form bilayers in aqueous solutions and are the main component of all cellular membranes. The fatty acid tails can be saturated (forming straight chains) or unsaturated (kinked chains). The level of phospholipids with saturated or unsaturated tails affects the fluidity of the phospholipid bilayer.

Phospholipids

Phospholipids consist of a glycerol attached to two fatty acid chains and a phosphate (PO_4^{3-}) group. The phosphate end of the molecule is attracted to water (it is hydrophilic) while the fatty acid end is repelled (hydrophobic). The hydrophobic ends turn inwards in the membrane to form a **phospholipid bilayer.**

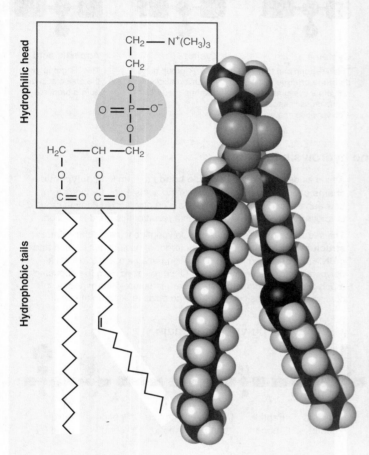

Phospholipids and membranes

The amphipathic (having hydrophobic and hydrophilic ends) nature of phospholipids means that when in water they spontaneously form bilayers. This bilayer structure forms the outer boundary of cells or organelles. Modifications to the different hydrophobic ends of the phospholipids cause the bilayer to change its behaviour. The greater the number of double bonds in the hydrophobic tails, the greater the fluidity of the membrane.

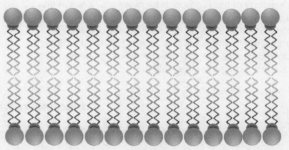

Membrane containing only phospholipids with saturated fatty acid tails.

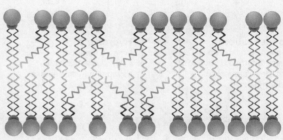

Membrane containing phospholipids with unsaturated fatty acid tails. The fact that the phospholipids do not stack neatly together produces a more fluid membrane.

1. (a) Relate the structure of phospholipids to their chemical properties and their functional role in cellular membranes:

_____

_____

_____

(b) Suggest how the cell membrane structure of an Arctic fish might differ from that of tropical fish species: _____

_____

_____

2. Explain why phospholipid bilayers containing many phospholipids with unsaturated tails are particularly fluid:

_____

_____

_____

LINK **97** | WEB **39** | **KNOW**

40 Amino Acids

Key Idea: Amino acids join together in a linear chain by condensation reactions to form polypeptides. The sequence of amino acids in a protein is defined by a gene and encoded in the genetic code. In the presence of water, they can be broken apart by hydrolysis into their constituent amino acids.

Amino acids are the basic units from which proteins are made. Twenty amino acids commonly occur in proteins and they can be linked in many different ways by peptide bonds to form a huge variety of polypeptides. Proteins are made up of one or more polypeptide molecules.

The structure and properties of amino acids

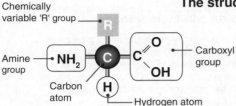

Chemically variable 'R' group

Amine group — NH₂

Carbon atom

Hydrogen atom

Carboxyl group

All amino acids have a common structure (above), but the R group is different in each kind of amino acid (right). The property of the R group determines how it will interact with other amino acids and ultimately determines how the amino acid chain folds up into a functional protein. For example, the hydrophobic R groups of soluble proteins are folded into the protein's interior, while the hydrophilic groups are arranged on the outside.

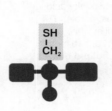

Cysteine
This 'R' group can form **disulfide bridges** with other cysteines to create cross linkages in a polypeptide chain.

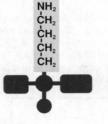

Lysine
This 'R' group gives the amino acid an **alkaline** property.

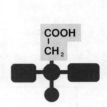

Aspartic acid
This 'R' group gives the amino acid an **acidic** property.

Condensation and hydrolysis reactions

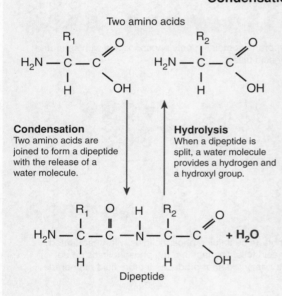

Two amino acids

Condensation
Two amino acids are joined to form a dipeptide with the release of a water molecule.

Hydrolysis
When a dipeptide is split, a water molecule provides a hydrogen and a hydroxyl group.

Dipeptide

Amino acids are linked by **peptide bonds** to form long **polypeptide chains** of up to several thousand amino acids. Peptide bonds form between the carboxyl group of one amino acid and the amine group of another (left). Water is formed as a result of this bond formation.

The sequence of amino acids in a polypeptide is called the **primary structure** and is determined by the order of nucleotides in DNA and mRNA (the gene sequence). The linking of amino acids to form a polypeptide occurs on ribosomes. Once released from the ribosome, a polypeptide will fold into a secondary structure determined by the composition and position of the amino acids making up the chain.

A polypeptide chain

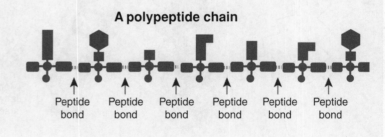

Peptide bond   Peptide bond   Peptide bond   Peptide bond   Peptide bond   Peptide bond

---

1. (a) What makes each of the amino acids in proteins unique? _____

   (b) What is the primary structure of a protein? _____

   (c) What determines the primary structure? _____

   _____

   (d) How do the sequence and composition of amino acids in a protein influence how a protein folds up? _____

   _____

   _____

2. (a) What type of bond joins neighbouring amino acids together? _____

   (b) How is this bond formed? _____

   (c) Circle this bond in the dipeptide above: _____

   (d) How are di- and polypeptides broken down? _____

© 2015 **BIOZONE** International
ISBN: 978-1-927309-19-3
Photocopying Prohibited

41 Chromatography

Key Idea: Paper chromatography is used to separate substances in a sample solution.

Chromatography is a technique used to separate a mixture of molecules. Chromatography involves passing a mixture dissolved in a mobile phase (a solvent) through a stationary phase, which separates the molecules according to their specific characteristics (e.g. size or charge). Paper chromatography is a simple technique in which porous paper serves as the stationary phase, and a solvent, either water or ethanol, serves as the mobile phase.

Paper chromatography

Set up and procedure

The chromatography paper is folded so it can be secured by the bung inside the test tube. The bung also prevents the solvent evaporating.

Chromatography paper may be treated with chemicals to stain normally invisible pigments.

A spot of concentrated sample is added using a pipette and suspended above the solvent. As the solvent travels up the paper it will carry the sample with it. The distance the sample travels depends on its solubility.

A pencil line is used to show the starting point.

Solvent

Determining Rf values

To identify the substances in a mixture an Rf value is calculated using the equation:

$$R_f = \frac{\text{Distance travelled by the spot (x)}}{\text{Distance travelled by the solvent (y)}}$$

These Rf values can then be compared with Rf values from known samples or standards, for example Rf values for the the following carbohydrates are:

Fructose = 0.68
Glucose = 0.64
Sucrose = 0.62
Maltose = 0.50
Lactose = 0.46

Using chromatography to separate amino acids

Mixtures of amino acids can be separated by paper chromatography. The R_f values for amino acids separated using paper chromatography are given below:

Glycine: 0.50
Alanine: 0.70
Arginine: 0.72
Leucine: 0.91

A student was given a solution containing two unknown amino acids. They separated them by paper chromatography and obtained the results below.

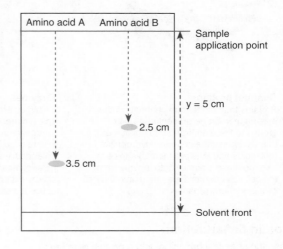

1. Calculate the R_f value for **spot X** in the example given above left (show your working): _____

_____

2. Why is the R_f value of a substance always less than 1? _____

_____

3. Predict what would happen if a sample was immersed in the chromatography solvent, instead of suspended above it:

_____

_____

4. (a) Calculate the R_f values for the two unknown amino acid samples (above right): _____

_____

(b) Based on the R_f values calculated in (a), identify the two amino acids:

Amino acid A: _____   Amino acid B: _____

5. (a) Which two amino acids could be difficult to separate by chromatography?_____

(b) Explain your reasoning: _____

_____

LINK   LINK   WEB

40 **33** **41**   K.

42 Protein Shape is Related to Function

Key idea: Interactions between amino acid R groups direct a polypeptide chain to fold into its functional shape. When a protein is denatured, it loses its functionality.

A protein may consist of one polypeptide chain, or several polypeptide chains linked together. Hydrogen bonds between amino acids cause it to form its **secondary structure**, either an α-helix or a β-pleated sheet. The interaction between R groups causes a polypeptide to fold into its **tertiary structure**, a three dimensional shape held by ionic bonds and disulfide bridges (bonds formed between sulfur containing amino acids). If bonds are broken (through denaturation), the protein loses its tertiary structure, and its functionality.

The shape of a protein reflects its biological role

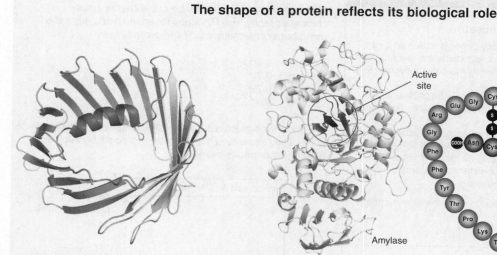
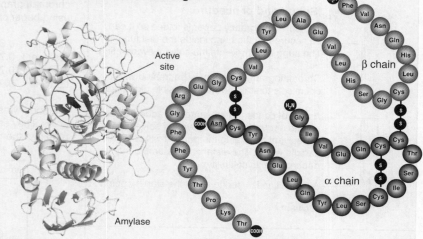

Active site

Amylase

β chain

α chain

Channel proteins
Proteins that fold to form channels in the plasma membrane present non-polar R groups to the membrane and polar R groups to the inside of the channel. Hydrophilic molecules and ions are then able to pass through these channels into the interior of the cell. Ion channels are found in nearly all cells and many organelles.

Enzymes
Enzymes are globular proteins that catalyse specific reactions. Enzymes that are folded to present polar R groups at the active site will be specific for polar substances. Nonpolar active sites will be specific for non-polar substances. Alteration of the active site by extremes of temperature or pH cause a loss of function.

Sub-unit proteins
Many proteins, e.g. insulin and haemoglobin, consist of two or more subunits in a complex quaternary structure, often in association with a metal ion. Active insulin is formed by two polypeptide chains stabilised by disulfide bridges between neighbouring cysteines. Insulin stimulates glucose uptake by cells.

Protein denaturation

When the chemical bonds holding a protein together become broken the protein can no longer hold its three dimensional shape. This process is called **denaturation**, and the protein usually loses its ability to carry out its biological function.

There are many causes of denaturation including exposure to heat or pH outside of the protein's optimum range. The main protein in egg white is albumin. It has a clear, thick fluid appearance in a raw egg (right). Heat (cooking) denatures the albumin protein and it becomes insoluble, clumping together to form a thick white substance (far right).

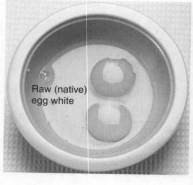

Raw (native) egg white

Cooked (denatured) egg white

1. Explain the importance of the amino acid sequence in protein folding: _____

_____

_____

2. Why do channel proteins often fold with non-polar R groups to the channel's exterior and polar R groups to its interior?

_____

_____

3. Why does **denaturation** often result in the loss of protein functionality? _____

_____

_____

_____

© 2015 **BIOZONE** International
ISBN: 978-1-927309-19-3
Photocopying Prohibited

43 Protein Structure

Key Idea: The sequence and type of amino acids in a protein determines the protein's three-dimensional shape and function.

Proteins are large, complex **macromolecules**, built up from a linear sequence of repeating units called **amino acids**. Proteins are molecules of central importance in the chemistry of life. They account for more than 50% of the dry weight of most cells, and they are important in virtually every cellular process. The folding of a protein into its functional form creates a three dimensional arrangement of the active 'R' groups. It is this **tertiary structure** that gives a protein its unique chemical properties. If a protein loses this precise structure (through **denaturation**), it is usually unable to carry out its biological function.

Primary (1°) structure
(amino acid sequence)

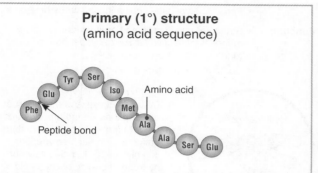

Hundreds of amino acids are linked together by peptide bonds to form polypeptide chains. The attractive and repulsive charges on the amino acids determines the higher levels of organisation in the protein and its biological function.

Secondary (2°) structure
(α-helix or β pleated sheet)

2° structure is maintained by hydrogen bonds, which are individually weak but collectively strong

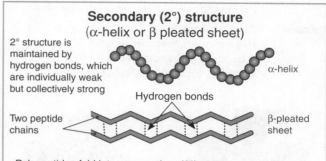

Polypeptides fold into a secondary (2°) structure, usually a coiled α-helix or a β-pleated sheet. Secondary structures are maintained by hydrogen bonds between neighbouring CO and NH groups. Most globular proteins contain regions of α-helices together with β-sheets.

Tertiary (3°) structure
(folding of the **2°** structure)

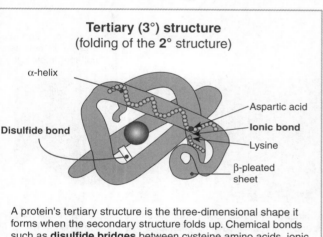

A protein's tertiary structure is the three-dimensional shape it forms when the secondary structure folds up. Chemical bonds such as **disulfide bridges** between cysteine amino acids, ionic bonds, hydrogen bonds, and hydrophobic interactions result in protein folding. These bonds can be destroyed by heavy metals or some solvents, and extremes of pH and temperature.

Quaternary (4°) structure

In haemoglobin, each polypeptide chain encloses an iron-containing prosthetic group (haem group).

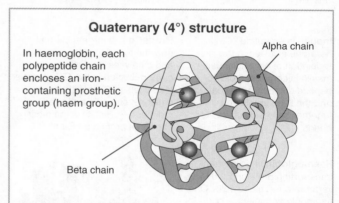

Many complex proteins exist as groups of polypeptide chains. The arrangement of the polypeptide chains into a functional protein is termed the quaternary structure. The example (above) shows haemoglobin, which has a quaternary structure comprising two alpha and two beta polypeptide chains, each enclosing a complex iron-containing prosthetic group.

---

1. Describe the main features that aid the formation of each part of a protein's structure:

(a) Primary structure: _____

(b) Secondary structure: _____

_____

(c) Tertiary structure: _____

_____

(d) Quaternary structure: _____

_____

2. How are proteins built up into a functional structure? _____

_____

_____

LINK 44   WEB 43

44 Comparing Globular and Fibrous Proteins

Key Idea: Protein structure is related to its biological function. Proteins can be classified according to their structure or their function. **Globular proteins** are spherical and soluble in water (e.g. enzymes). **Fibrous proteins** have an elongated structure and are not water soluble. They are often made up of repeating units and provide stiffness and rigidity to the more fluid components of cells and tissues. They have important structural and contractile roles.

Globular proteins

Properties
- Easily water soluble
- Tertiary structure critical to function
- Polypeptide chains folded into a spherical shape

Function
- Catalytic, *e.g. enzymes*
- Regulatory, *e.g. hormones (insulin)*
- Transport, *e.g. haemoglobin*
- Protective, *e.g. immunoglobulins (antibodies)*

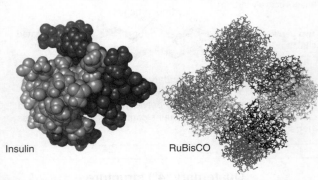

Insulin   RuBisCO

Insulin is a peptide hormone involved in the regulation of blood glucose. Insulin is composed of two peptide chains (the A chain and the B chain) linked together by two disulfide bonds.

RuBisCo is a large multi-unit enzyme found in green plants and catalyses the first step of carbon fixation in the Calvin cycle. It consists of 8 large (L) and 8 small (S) subunits arranged as 4 dimers. RuBisCO is the most abundant protein on Earth.

Haemoglobin is an oxygen-transporting protein found in vertebrate red blood cells. One haemoglobin molecule consists of four polypeptide chains (two identical alpha chains and two identical beta chains). Each polypeptide subunit contains a non-protein prosthetic group, an iron-containing haem group, which binds oxygen.

Haemoglobin

Fibrous proteins

Properties
- Water insoluble
- Very tough physically; may be supple or stretchy
- Parallel polypeptide chains in long fibres or sheets

Function
- Structural role in cells and organisms e.g. *collagen found in connective tissue, cartilage, bones, tendons, and blood vessel walls.*
- Contractile e.g. *myosin, actin*

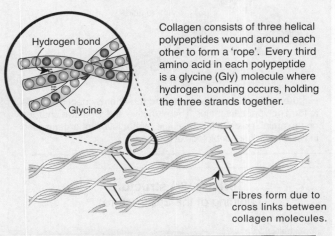

Hydrogen bond

Glycine

Collagen consists of three helical polypeptides wound around each other to form a 'rope'. Every third amino acid in each polypeptide is a glycine (Gly) molecule where hydrogen bonding occurs, holding the three strands together.

Fibres form due to cross links between collagen molecules.

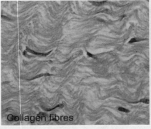

Collagen fibres

This rhinoceros' horn is keratin

Collagen is the main component of connective tissue, and is mostly found in fibrous tissues (e.g. tendons, ligaments, and skin). The elastic properties of **elastin** allows tissues to resume their shape after stretching. Skin, arteries, lungs, and bladder all contain elastin. **Keratin** is found in hair, nails, horn, hooves, wool, feathers, and the outer layers of the skin. The polypeptide chains of keratin are arranged in parallel sheets held together by hydrogen bonding.

1. How are proteins involved in the following roles? Give examples to help illustrate your answer:

    (a) Structural tissues of the body: _____

    _____

    _____

    (b) Catalysing metabolic reactions in cells: _____

    _____

    _____

2. How does the shape of a fibrous protein relate to its functional role? _____

    _____

3. How does the shape of a catalytic protein (enzyme) relate to its functional role? _____

    _____

WEB   LINK

NOW   44   46

© 2015 **BIOZONE** International
ISBN: 978-1-927309-19-3
Photocopying Prohibited

45 Biochemical Tests

Key Idea: Qualitative biochemical tests detect the presence of a specific molecule in food.

Qualitative biochemical tests can be used to detect the presence of molecules such as lipids, proteins, or carbohydrates (sugars and starch). However, they cannot be used directly to determine absolute concentrations or distinguish between different molecules of the same type (e.g. different sugars in a mixed solution).

Simple food tests

Proteins: The Biuret Test

Reagent:	Biuret solution.
Procedure:	A sample is added to biuret solution and gently heated.
Positive result:	Solution turns from blue to lilac.

Starch: The Iodine Test

Reagent:	Iodine.
Procedure:	Iodine solution is added to the sample.
Positive result:	Blue-black staining occurs.

Lipids: The Emulsion Test

Reagent:	Ethanol.
Procedure:	The sample is shaken with ethanol. After settling, the liquid portion is distilled and mixed with water.
Positive result:	The solution turns into a cloudy-white emulsion of suspended lipid molecules.

Sugars: The Benedict's Test

Reagent:	Benedict's solution.
Procedure:	Non reducing sugars: The sample is boiled with dilute hydrochloric acid (acid hydrolysis), then cooled and neutralised. A test for reducing sugars is then performed.
	Reducing sugar: Benedict's solution is added, and the sample is placed in a water bath.
Positive result:	Solution turns from blue to orange to red-brown.

A qualitative test for reducing sugar

To determine whether this muffin contains any reducing sugars (e.g. glucose), the **Benedict's test** for reducing sugar is carried out.

The muffin is placed in a blender with some water and mixed until it forms an homogenous (uniform) mixture.

2-3 mL of the muffin mixture is placed into a test tube with 1 mL of Benedict's solution. The tubes are heated for 4 -10 minutes.

The intensity of the colour depends on the concentration of glucose present in the sample. The darker the colour, the more glucose is present. A **colorimetric analysis** enables the amount of glucose present to be quantified (see the following activity).

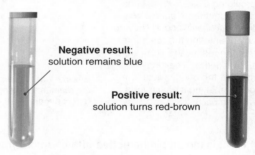

Negative result: solution remains blue

Positive result: solution turns red-brown

---

1. Explain why lipids must be mixed in ethanol before they will form an emulsion in water: _____

_____

_____

2. Explain why the emulsion of lipids, ethanol, and water appears cloudy: _____

_____

_____

3. What is the purpose of the acid hydrolysis step when testing for non-reducing sugars with Benedict's reagent?

_____

_____

4. What are the limitations of qualitative tests such as those described above? _____

_____

_____

LINK 43 LINK 38 LINK 37 LINK 33 WEB 45

46 Enzymes

Key Idea: Enzymes are biological catalysts. The active site is critical to this functional role.

Most enzymes are proteins. Enzymes are called biological catalysts because they speed up biochemical reactions, but the enzyme itself remains unchanged. The substrate in a reaction binds to a region of the enzyme called the active site, which is formed by the precise folding of the enzyme's amino acid chain. Enzymes control metabolic pathways. One enzyme will act on a substance to produce the next reactant in a pathway, which will be acted on by a different enzyme.

The active site

Enzymes have an **active site** to which specific substrates bind. The shape and chemistry of the active site is specific to an enzyme, and is a function of the polypeptide's complex tertiary structure.

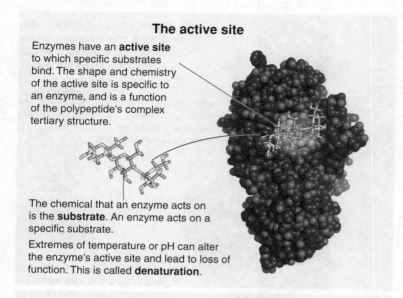

The chemical that an enzyme acts on is the **substrate**. An enzyme acts on a specific substrate.

Extremes of temperature or pH can alter the enzyme's active site and lead to loss of function. This is called **denaturation**.

Substrates collide with an enzyme's active site

For a reaction to occur reactants must collide with sufficient speed and with the correct orientation. Enzymes enhance reaction rates by providing a site for reactants to come together in such a way that a reaction will occur. They do this by orientating the reactants so that the reactive regions are brought together. They may also destabilise the bonds within the reactants making it easier for a reaction to occur.

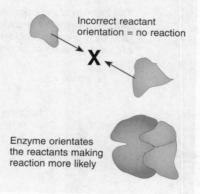

Incorrect reactant orientation = no reaction

X

Enzyme orientates the reactants making reaction more likely

Enzymes can be intracellular or extracellular

Enzymes can be defined based on where they are produced relative to where they are active.

An **intracellular enzyme** is an enzyme that performs its function within the cell that produces it. Most enzymes are intracellular enzymes, e.g. respiratory enzymes. **Example**: Catalase.

Many metabolic processes produce hydrogen peroxide, which is harmful to cells. Catalase converts hydrogen peroxide into water and oxygen (below) to prevent damage to cells and tissues.

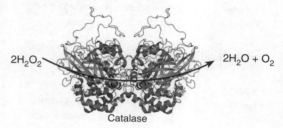

$2H_2O_2$ → $2H_2O + O_2$

Catalase

An **extracellular enzyme** is an enzyme that functions outside the cell from which it originates (i.e. it is produced in one location but active in another). **Examples**: Amylase and trypsin.

Amylase is a digestive enzyme produced in the salivary glands and pancreas in humans. However, it acts in the mouth and small intestine respectively to hydrolyse starch into sugars.

Trypsin is a protein-digesting enzyme and hydrolyses the peptide bond immediately after a basic residue (e.g. arginine). It is produced in an inactive form (called trypsinogen) and secreted into the small intestine by the pancreas. It is activated in the intestine by the enzyme enteropeptidase to form trypsin. Active trypsin can convert more trypsinogen to trypsin.

---

1. (a) What is meant by the **active site** of an enzyme and relate it to the enzyme's tertiary structure: _____

_____

_____

_____

   (b) Why are enzymes specific to one substrate (or group of closely related substrates)? _____

_____

_____ _____

2. How do substrate molecules come into contact with an enzyme's active site? _____

_____

3. (a) Suggest why digestion (the breakdown of large macromolecules) is largely performed by extracellular enzymes:

_____

   (b) Why would an extracellular enzyme be produced and secreted in an inactive form? _____

_____

© 2015 **BIOZONE** International
ISBN: 978-1-927309-19-3
Photocopying Prohibited

47 | How Enzymes Work

Key Idea: Enzymes increase the rate of biological reactions by lowering the reaction's activation energy.

Chemical reactions in cells are accompanied by energy changes. The amount of energy released or taken up is directly related to the tendency of a reaction to run to completion (for all the reactants to form products). Any reaction needs to raise the energy of the substrate to an unstable transition state before the reaction will proceed (below). The amount of energy needed to do this is the **activation energy** (Ea). Enzymes lower the Ea by destabilising bonds in the substrate so that it is more reactive. Enzyme reactions can break down a single substrate molecule into simpler substances (catabolic reactions), or join two or more substrate molecules together (anabolic reactions).

Lowering the activation energy

The presence of an enzyme simply makes it easier for a reaction to take place. All catalysts speed up reactions by influencing the stability of bonds in the reactants. They may also provide an alternative reaction pathway, thus lowering the activation energy (Ea) needed for a reaction to take place (see the graph below).

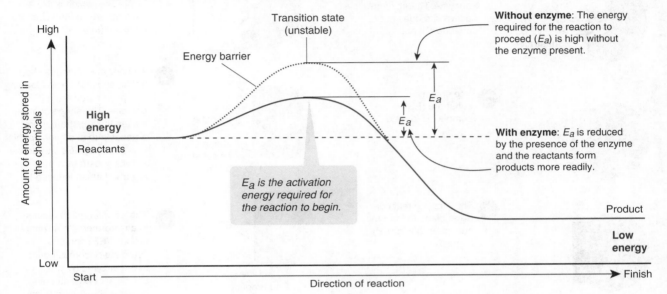

Without enzyme: The energy required for the reaction to proceed (Ea) is high without the enzyme present.

With enzyme: Ea is reduced by the presence of the enzyme and the reactants form products more readily.

Ea is the activation energy required for the reaction to begin.

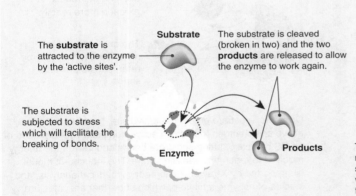

Catabolic reactions

Some enzymes can cause a single substrate molecule to be drawn into the active site. Chemical bonds are broken, causing the substrate molecule to break apart to become two separate molecules. Catabolic reactions break down complex molecules into simpler ones and involve a net release of energy, so they are called exergonic.
Examples: *hydrolysis, cellular respiration*.

Anabolic reactions

Some enzymes can cause two substrate molecules to be drawn into the active site. Chemical bonds are formed, causing the two substrate molecules to form bonds and become a single molecule. Anabolic reactions involve a net use of energy (they are endergonic) and build more complex molecules and structures from simpler ones.
Examples: *protein synthesis, photosynthesis*.

1. How do enzymes lower the activation energy for a reaction? _____

_____

_____

2. Describe the difference between a catabolic and anabolic reaction: _____

_____

LINK 49 LINK 48 WEB 47

48 | Models of Enzyme Activity

Key Idea: Enzymes catalyse reactions by providing a reaction site for a substrate. The model that describes the behaviour of enzymes the best is the induced fit model.

The initial model of enzyme activity was the lock and key model proposed by Emil Fischer in the 1890s. Fischer proposed enzymes were rigid structures, similar to a lock, and the substrate was the key. While some aspects of

Fischer's model were correct, for example, substrates align with enzymes in a way that is likely to make a reaction more likely, the model has been adapted as techniques to study molecular structures have developed. The current 'induced-fit' model of enzyme function is supported by studies of enzyme inhibitors, which show that enzymes are flexible and change shape when interacting with the substrate.

The lock and key model of enzyme function

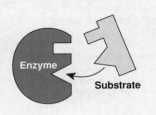

1. The substrate molecule is drawn into site of the enzyme. The enzyme's active site does not change shape.

2. The enzyme-substrate (ES) complex is formed.

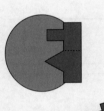

3. The enzyme reaction takes place to form the enzyme-product (EP) complex.

4. The products are released from the enzyme. Note there has been no change in the shape of the active site throughout the reaction.

The **lock and key model** proposed earlier last century suggested that the (perfectly fitting) substrate was simply drawn into a matching site on the enzyme molecule. If the substrate did not perfectly fit the active site, the reaction did not proceed. This model was supported by early X-ray crystallography studies but has since been modified to recognise the flexibility of enzymes (the induced fit model).

The current induced fit model

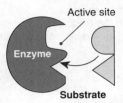

1. A substrate molecule is drawn into the enzyme's active site, which is like a cleft into which the substrate molecule(s) fit.

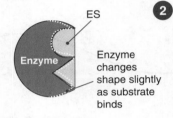

2. The enzyme changes shape as the substrate binds forming an enzyme-substrate (ES) complex. The shape change makes the substrate more amenable to alteration. In this way, the enzyme's interaction with its substrate is best regarded as an induced fit.

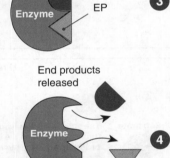

3. The ES interaction results in an intermediate enzyme-product (EP) complex. The substrate becomes bound to the enzyme by weak chemical bonds, straining bonds in the substrate and allowing the reaction to proceed more readily.

4. The end products are released and the enzyme returns to its previous shape.

Once the substrate enters the active site, the shape of the active site changes to form an active complex. The formation of an ES complex strains substrate bonds and lowers the energy required to reach the transition state. The induced-fit model is supported by X-ray crystallography, chemical analysis, and studies of enzyme inhibitors, which show that enzymes are flexible and change shape when interacting with the substrate.

1. Describe the key features of the current '**induced fit**' model of enzyme action: _____

_____

_____

_____

2. With reference to an example, explain how ideas about enzyme function have changed in the light of evidence:

_____

_____

_____

_____

49 Enzyme Kinetics

Key Idea: Enzymes operate most effectively within a narrow range of conditions. The rate of enzyme-catalysed reactions is influenced by both enzyme and substrate concentration. Enzymes usually have an optimum set of conditions (e.g. of pH and temperature) under which their activity is greatest. Many plant and animal enzymes show little activity at low temperatures. Enzyme activity increases with increasing temperature, but falls off after the optimum temperature is exceeded and the enzyme is denatured. Extremes in pH can also cause denaturation. Within their normal operating conditions, enzyme reaction rates are influenced by enzyme and substrate concentration in a predictable way.

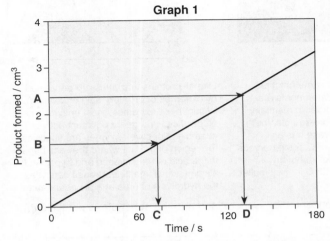

Graph 1

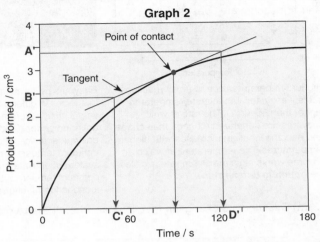

Graph 2

The rate of a reaction can be calculated from the amount of product produced during a given time period. For a reaction in which the rate does not vary (graph 1) the reaction rate calculated at any one point in time will be the same. For example: B/C = A/D = A-B/D-C = (Δp/Δt) (the change in product divided by the change in time).

In a reaction in which the rate varies (graph 2) a reaction rate can be calculated for any instantaneous moment in time by using a tangent. The tangent must touch the curve at only one point. The gradient of the tangent can then be used to calculate the rate of reaction at that point in time (A'-B'/D'-C').

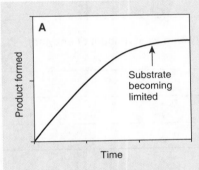

A

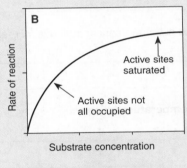

B

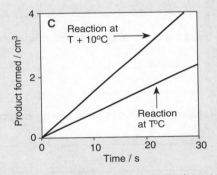

C

In a reaction where there is a limited amount of substrate, the reaction rate will slow down over time as the substrate is used up (graph A).

If there is unlimited substrate but the enzyme is limited, the reaction rate will increase until the enzyme is saturated, at which point the rate will remain static (graph B).

The effect of temperature on a reaction rate is expressed as the temperature coefficient, usually given as the Q_{10}. Q_{10} expresses the increase in the rate of reaction for every rise of 10°C. **Q_{10} = rate of reaction at (T + 10°C)/ rate of reaction at T**, where T is the temperature in °C (graph C).

1. Calculate the reaction rate in graph 1: _____

2. For graph 2, A Level students calculate:

   (a) The reaction rate at 90 seconds: _____

   (b) The reaction rate at 30 seconds: _____

3. (a) What would need to be happening to the reaction mix in graph 1 to produce a straight line (constant reaction rate)?

   _____

   _____

   (b) Explain why the reaction rate in graph 2 changes over time: _____

   _____

LINK 52   LINK 50   WEB 49

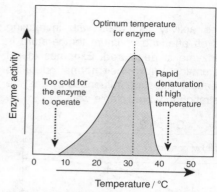

Antarctic icefish

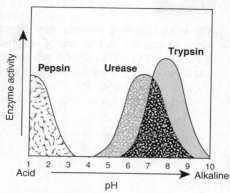

Higher temperatures speed up all reactions, but few enzymes can tolerate temperatures higher than 50–60°C. The rate at which enzymes are denatured (change their shape and become inactive) increases with higher temperatures. The temperature at which an enzyme works at its maximum rate is called the **optimum temperature**.

Enzymes performing the same function in species in different environments are very slightly different in order to maintain optimum performance. For example, the enzyme acetylcholinesterase has an optimum temperature of -2°C in the nervous system of an Antarctic icefish but an optimum temperature of 25°C in grey mullet found in the Mediterranean.

Like all proteins, enzymes are denatured by extremes of pH (very acid or alkaline). Within these extremes, most enzymes have a specific pH range for optimum activity. For example, digestive enzymes are specific to the region of the gut where they act: pepsin in the acid of the stomach and trypsin in the alkaline small intestine. Urease catalyses the hydrolysis of urea at a pH near neutral.

4. (a) Describe the change in reaction rate when the enzyme concentration is increased and the substrate is not limiting:

_____

_____

(b) Suggest how a cell may vary the amount of enzyme present: _____

_____

_____

5. Describe the change in reaction rate when the substrate concentration is increased (with a fixed amount of enzyme):

_____

_____

6. (a) Describe what is meant by an **optimum temperature** for enzyme activity: _____

_____

_____

(b) Explain why most enzymes perform poorly at low temperatures: _____

_____

_____

(c) For graph C opposite, calculate the Q_{10} for the reaction: _____

_____

_____

_____

7. (a) State the optimum pH for each of the enzymes:

Pepsin: _____ Trypsin: _____ Urease: _____

(b) Explain how the pH optima of each of these enzymes is suited to its working environment: _____

_____

_____

_____

© 2015 **BIOZONE** International
ISBN: 978-1-927309-19-3
Photocopying Prohibited

50 Investigating Enzyme Reaction Rates

Key Idea: The rate of a reaction can be measured indirectly by measuring the volume of reaction products.
A group of students decided to use cubes of potato, which naturally contain the enzyme catalase, placed in hydrogen peroxide to test the effect of enzyme concentration on reaction rate. The reaction rate could be measured by the volume of oxygen produced as the hydrogen peroxide was decomposed into oxygen and water.

Aim
To investigate the effect of potato mass (and therefore enzyme concentration) on the rate of H_2O_2 decomposition.

Hypothesis
A greater mass of potato will have more enzyme present and will produce a greater reaction rate.

Method
The students cut raw potato into cubes with a mass of one gram. These were placed a conical flask with excess hydrogen peroxide (right). The reaction was left for five minutes and the volume of oxygen produced recorded. The students recorded the results for three replicates each of 1, 2, 3, 4, and 5 cubes of potato below:

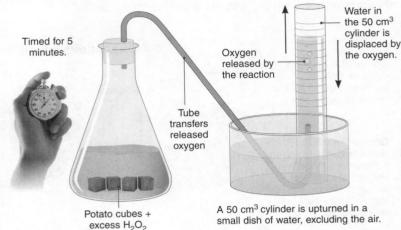

Timed for 5 minutes.

Oxygen released by the reaction

Water in the 50 cm³ cylinder is displaced by the oxygen.

Tube transfers released oxygen

Potato cubes + excess H_2O_2

A 50 cm³ cylinder is upturned in a small dish of water, excluding the air.

Mass of potato / g	Volume oxygen / cm³ (5 minutes)			Mean	Mean rate of O_2 production / cm³ min⁻¹
	Test 1	Test 2	Test 3		
1	6	5	6		
2	10	9	9		
3	14	15	15		
4	21	20	20		
5	24	23	25		

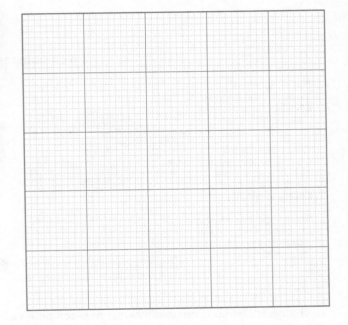

1. Complete the table by filling in the mean volume of oxygen produced and the rate of oxygen production.

2. Plot the mass of the potato vs the rate of production on the grid (right):

3. Relate the rate of the reaction to the amount of enzyme present.

_____

_____

_____

4. Why did the students add excess H_2O_2 to the reaction? _____

_____

5. State one extra reaction that should have been carried out by the students: _____

_____

6. (a) The students decide to cook some potato and carry out the test again with two grams of potato. Predict the result:

_____

_____

(b) Explain this result: _____

_____

LINK 52   LINK 49   WEB 50

51 Enzyme Inhibitors

Key Idea: Enzymes activity can be reduced or stopped by inhibitors. These may be competitive or non-competitive. Enzyme activity can be stopped, temporarily or permanently, by chemicals called enzyme inhibitors. **Competitive inhibitors** compete directly with the substrate for the active site and their effect can be overcome by increasing the concentration of available substrate. A **non-competitive inhibitor** does not occupy the active site, but distorts it so that the substrate and enzyme can no longer interact.

Competitive inhibition

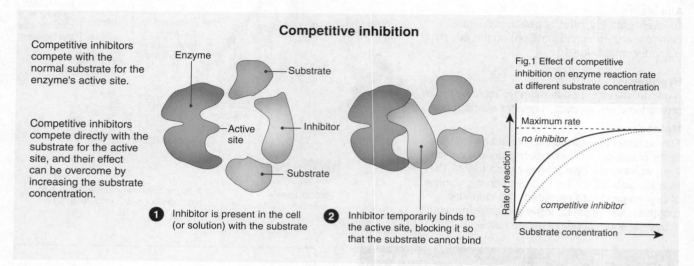

Competitive inhibitors compete with the normal substrate for the enzyme's active site.

Competitive inhibitors compete directly with the substrate for the active site, and their effect can be overcome by increasing the substrate concentration.

1 Inhibitor is present in the cell (or solution) with the substrate

2 Inhibitor temporarily binds to the active site, blocking it so that the substrate cannot bind

Fig.1 Effect of competitive inhibition on enzyme reaction rate at different substrate concentration

Non-competitive inhibition

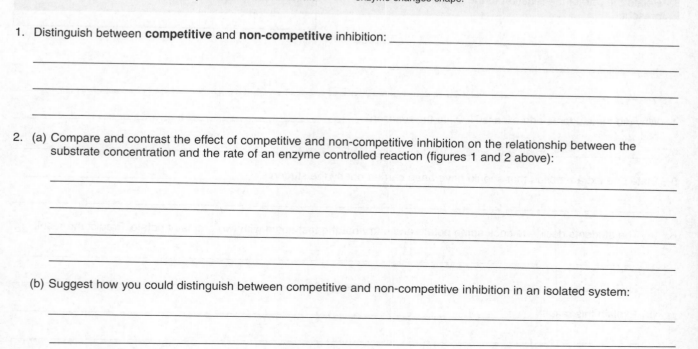

Non-competitive inhibitors bind with the enzyme at a site other than the active site.

They inactivate the enzyme by altering its shape so that the substrate and enzyme can no longer interact.

Non-competitive inhibition cannot be overcome by increasing the substrate concentration.

1 Without the inhibitor bound, the enzyme can bind the substrate

2 When the inhibitor binds, the enzyme changes shape.

Fig.2 Effect of non-competitive inhibition on enzyme reaction rate at different substrate concentration

1. Distinguish between **competitive** and **non-competitive** inhibition: _____
   _____
   _____
   _____

2. (a) Compare and contrast the effect of competitive and non-competitive inhibition on the relationship between the substrate concentration and the rate of an enzyme controlled reaction (figures 1 and 2 above):
   _____
   _____
   _____
   _____

   (b) Suggest how you could distinguish between competitive and non-competitive inhibition in an isolated system:
   _____
   _____

© 2015 **BIOZONE** International
ISBN: 978-1-927309-19-3
Photocopying Prohibited

52 Investigating Catalase Activity

Key Idea: Catalase activity can be measured in germinating seeds. Activity changes with stage of germination.

Enzyme activity can be measured easily in simple experiments. This activity describes an experiment in which germinating seeds of different ages were tested for their level of **catalase**

activity using hydrogen peroxide solution as the substrate and a simple apparatus to measure oxygen production (see background). Completing this activity, which involves a critical evaluation of the second-hand data provided, will help to prepare you for making your own similar investigations.

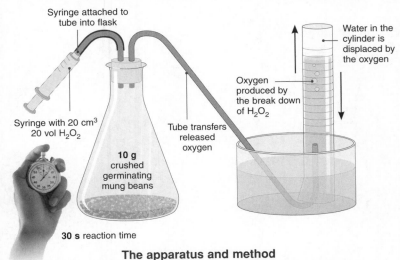

Syringe attached to tube into flask

Water in the cylinder is displaced by the oxygen

Oxygen produced by the break down of H_2O_2

Syringe with 20 cm³ 20 vol H_2O_2

Tube transfers released oxygen

10 g crushed germinating mung beans

30 s reaction time

The apparatus and method

In this experiment, 10 g germinating mung bean seeds (0.5, 2, 4, 6, or 10 days old) were ground by hand with a mortar and pestle and placed in a conical flask as above. There were six trials at each of the five seedling ages. With each trial, 20 cm³ of 20 vol H_2O_2 was added to the flask at time 0 and the reaction was allowed to run for 30 seconds. The oxygen released by the decomposition of the H_2O_2 by catalase in the seedlings was collected via a tube into an inverted measuring cylinder. The volume of oxygen produced is measured by the amount of water displaced from the cylinder. The results from all trials are tabulated below:

The aim and hypothesis

To investigate the effect of germination age on the level of catalase activity in mung beans. The students hypothesised that if metabolic activity increased with germination age, catalase activity would also increase with germination age.

Background

Germinating seeds are metabolically very active and this metabolism inevitably produces reactive oxygen species, including hydrogen peroxide (H_2O_2). H_2O_2 helps germination by breaking dormancy, but it is also toxic. To counter the toxic effects of H_2O_2 and prevent cellular damage, germinating seeds also produce **catalase**, an enzyme that catalyses the breakdown of H_2O_2 to water and oxygen.

A class was divided into six groups with each group testing the seedlings of each age. Each group's set of results (for 0.5, 2, 4, 6, and 10 days) therefore represents one trial.

Stage of germination / days	Group (trial) # 1	2	3	4	5	6	Mean	Standard deviation	Mean rate / cm³ s⁻¹ g⁻¹
	Volume of oxygen collected after 30 s / cm³								
0.5	9.5	10	10.7	9.5	10.2	10.5			
2	36.2	30	31.5	37.5	34	40			
4	59	66	69	60.5	66.5	72			
6	39	31.5	32.5	41	40.3	36			
10	20	18.6	24.3	23.2	23.5	25.5			

1. Write the equation for the catalase reaction with hydrogen peroxide: _____

2. Complete the table above to summarise the data from the six trials:

    (a) Calculate the mean volume of oxygen for each stage of germination and enter the values in the table.

    (b) Calculate the standard deviation for each mean and enter the values in the table (you may use a spreadsheet).

    (c) Calculate the mean rate of oxygen production in cm³ per second per gram. For the purposes of this exercise, assume that the weight of germinating seed in every case was 10.0 g.

3. In another scenario, group (trial) #2 obtained the following measurements for volume of oxygen produced: 0.5 d: 4.8 cm³, 2 d: 29.0 cm³, 4 d: 70 cm³, 6 d: 30.0 cm³, 10 d: 8.8 cm³ (pencil these values in beside the other group 2 data set).

    (a) Describe how group 2's new data compares with the measurements obtained from the other group: _____

    _____

    (b) Describe how you would approach a reanalysis of the data set incorporating group 2's new data: _____

    _____

    _____

LINK 50   LINK 49   WEB 52   D.

(c) Explain the rationale for your approach _____

_____

4. Use the tabulated data to plot an appropriate graph of the results on the grid provided below:

[Graph grid]

5. (a) Describe the trend in the data: _____

_____

_____

(b) Explain the relationship between stage of germination and catalase activity shown in the data: _____

_____

_____

(c) Do the results support the students' hypothesis? _____

_____

6. Describe any potential sources of errors in the apparatus or the procedure: _____

_____

_____

_____

7. Describe two things that might affect the validity of findings in this experimental design: _____

_____

_____

_____

53 Nucleotides

Key Idea: Nucleotides make up nucleic acids. A nucleotide is made up of a base, a sugar, and a phosphate group.
Nucleotides are the building blocks of the nucleic acids DNA and RNA, which are involved in the transmission of inherited information. Nucleotide derivatives, such as ATP and GTP, are involved in energy transfers in cells. A nucleotide has

three components: a base, a sugar, and a phosphate group. Nucleotides may contain one of five bases. The combination of bases in the nucleotides making up DNA or RNA stores the information controlling the cell's activity. The bases in DNA are the same as RNA except that thymine (T) in DNA is replaced with uracil (U) in RNA.

Pyrimidines

Thymine   **Cytosine**   **Uracil**

Pyrimidines are single ringed bases. DNA contains the pyrimidines cytosine (C) and thymine (T). RNA contains the pyrimidines cytosine and uracil (U).

Purines

Guanine   **Adenine**

Purines are double ringed bases. Both DNA and RNA contain the purines adenine (A) and guanine (G).

Phosphate

Phosphate groups are represented by circles. Along with the pentose sugar they form the "backbone" of the DNA or RNA molecule.

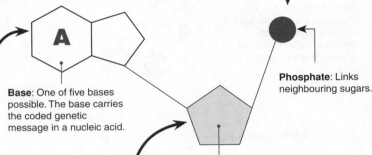

Base: One of five bases possible. The base carries the coded genetic message in a nucleic acid.

Phosphate: Links neighbouring sugars.

Sugar: One of two types: ribose in RNA and deoxyribose in DNA.

Nucleotide derivatives

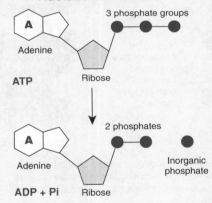

3 phosphate groups

Adenine

ATP   Ribose

2 phosphates

Adenine   Inorganic phosphate

ADP + Pi   Ribose

ATP is a nucleotide derivative used to provide chemical energy for metabolism. It consists of an adenine linked to a ribose sugar and 3 phosphate groups. Energy is made available when a phosphate group is transferred to a target molecule. Other nucleoside triphosphates (NTPs) have similar roles.

Sugars

deoxyribose   **ribose**

Nucleotides contain one of two different sorts of sugars. **Deoxyribose** sugar is only found in DNA. **Ribose** sugar is found in RNA.

Nucleotide formation

Condensation (water removed)

H_2O

H_2O

Phosphoric acid and a base are chemically bonded to a sugar molecule by a **condensation** reaction in which water is given off. The reverse reaction is **hydrolysis**.

1. List the nucleotide bases present:

   (a) In DNA: _____

   (b) In RNA: _____

2. Name the sugar present: (a) In DNA: _____ (b) In RNA: _____

3. How can simple nucleotide units combine to store genetic information? _____

   _____

   _____

LINK   LINK   WEB
61   **54**   **53**

54 Nucleic Acids

Key Idea: Nucleic acids are long chains of nucleotides, which store and transmit genetic information. DNA and RNA are nucleic acids.

DNA and RNA are nucleic acids involved in the transmission of inherited information. Nucleic acids have the capacity to store the information that controls cellular activity. The central nucleic acid is called **deoxyribonucleic acid** (DNA). **Ribonucleic acids** (RNA) are involved in the 'reading' of the DNA information. All nucleic acids are made up of nucleotides linked together to form chains or strands. The strands vary in the sequence of the bases found on each nucleotide. It is this sequence which provides the 'genetic code' for the cell.

Joining nucleotides

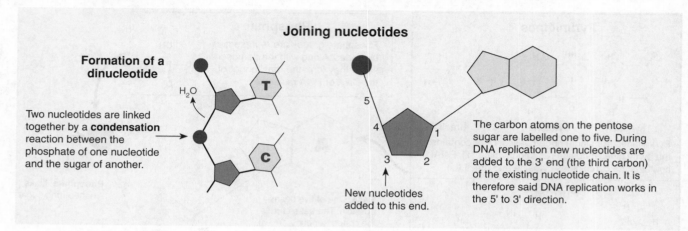

Formation of a dinucleotide

Two nucleotides are linked together by a **condensation** reaction between the phosphate of one nucleotide and the sugar of another.

New nucleotides added to this end.

The carbon atoms on the pentose sugar are labelled one to five. During DNA replication new nucleotides are added to the 3' end (the third carbon) of the existing nucleotide chain. It is therefore said DNA replication works in the 5' to 3' direction.

RNA molecule

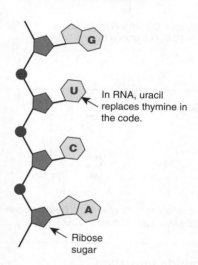

In RNA, uracil replaces thymine in the code.

Ribose sugar

Ribonucleic acid (RNA) comprises a single strand of nucleotides linked together. Although it is single stranded, it is often found folded back on itself, with complementary bases joined by hydrogen bonds.

DNA molecule

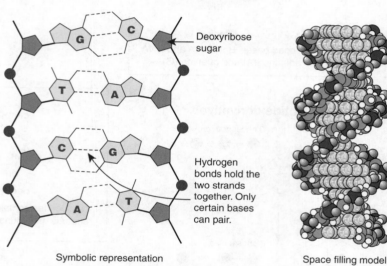

Deoxyribose sugar

Hydrogen bonds hold the two strands together. Only certain bases can pair.

Symbolic representation

Space filling model

Deoxyribonucleic acid (DNA) comprises a double strand of nucleotides linked together. It is shown unwound in the symbolic representation (above left). The DNA molecule takes on a twisted, double helix shape as shown in the space filling model above right.

Double-stranded DNA

The double-helix structure of DNA is like a ladder twisted into a corkscrew shape around its longitudinal axis. It is 'unwound' here to show the relationships between the bases.

▸ The DNA backbone is made up of alternating phosphate and sugar molecules, giving the DNA molecule an asymmetrical structure.

▸ The asymmetrical structure gives a DNA strand **direction**. Each strand runs in the opposite direction to the other.

▸ The ends of a DNA strand are labelled the 5' (five prime) and 3' (three prime) ends. The **5'** end has a terminal phosphate group (off carbon 5), the **3'** end has a terminal hydroxyl group (off carbon 3).

▸ The way the pairs of bases come together to form hydrogen bonds is determined by the number of bonds they can form and the configuration of the bases.

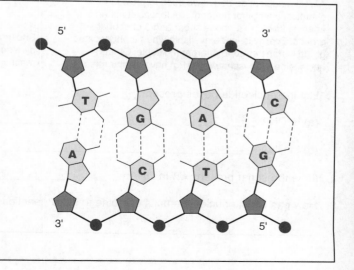

WEB 54   LINK 55

© 2015 **BIOZONE** International
ISBN: 978-1-927309-19-3
Photocopying Prohibited

RNAs are involved in decoding the genetic information in DNA, as messenger RNA (mRNA), transfer RNA (tRNA), and ribosomal RNA (rRNA). RNA is also involved in modifying mRNA after transcription and in regulating translation.

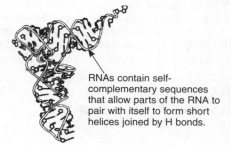

RNAs contain self-complementary sequences that allow parts of the RNA to pair with itself to form short helices joined by H bonds.

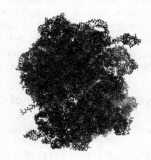

Messenger RNA (above) is transcribed (written) from DNA. It carries a copy of the genetic instructions from the DNA to ribosomes in the cytoplasm, where it is translated into a polypeptide chain.

Transfer RNA (above) carries amino acids to the growing polypeptide chain. One end of the tRNA carries the genetic code in a three-nucleotide sequence called the **anticodon**. The amino acid links to the 3' end of the tRNA.

Ribosomal RNA (above) forms ribosomes from two separate ribosomal components (the large and small subunits) and assembles amino acids into a polypeptide chain.

1. Label the following parts on the diagram of the double-stranded DNA molecule at the bottom of page 70:

    (a) Deoxyribose   (b) Phosphate   (c) Hydrogen bonds   (d) Purine bases   (e) Pyrimidine bases

2. (a) Explain the **base-pairing rule** that applies in double-stranded DNA: _____

    _____

    _____

    (b) How is the base-pairing rule for mRNA different? _____

    (c) What is the purpose of the hydrogen bonds in double-stranded DNA? _____

    _____

3. Briefly describe the roles of RNA: _____

    _____

4. (a) If you wanted to use a radioactive or fluorescent tag to label only the RNA in a cell and not the DNA, what molecule(s) would you label?

    _____

    (b) If you wanted to use a radioactive or fluorescent tag to label only the DNA in a cell and not the RNA, what molecule(s) would you label?

    _____

5. (a) Why do the DNA strands have an asymmetrical structure? _____

    _____

    (b) What are the differences between the 5' and 3' ends of a DNA strand? _____

    _____

6. Complete the following table summarising the differences between DNA and RNA molecules:

	DNA	RNA
Sugar present		
Bases present		
Number of strands		
Relative length		

55 Determining the Structure of DNA

Key Idea: Once the structure of DNA was known, it immediately suggested a mechanism for its replication.

DNA is easily extracted and isolated from cells (see below). This was first done in 1869, but it took the work of many scientists working in different areas many years to determine DNA's structure. The final pieces of evidence came from a photographic technique called X-ray crystallography in which X-rays are shone through crystallised molecules to produce a pattern on a film. The pattern can be used to understand the structure of the molecule. The focus of much subsequent research on DNA has been on DNA products, i.e. proteins and non-protein regulatory molecules (regulatory RNAs).

Discovering the structure of DNA

Although James Watson and Francis Crick are often credited with the discovery of the structure of DNA, at least two other scientists were instrumental in acquiring the images on which Watson and Crick based their discovery.

Maurice Wilkins and Rosalind Franklin produced X-ray diffraction patterns of the DNA molecule. The patterns provided measurements of different parts of the molecule and the position of different groups of atoms. Wilkins showed Franklin's X-ray image (photo 51) to Watson and Crick who then correctly interpreted the image and produced a model of the DNA molecule.

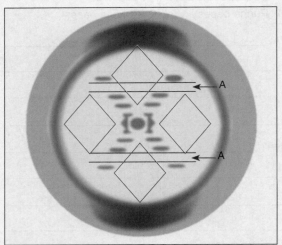

Diagram representing the image produced by Rosalind Franklin

Numerous distinct parts of the X-ray image indicate specific qualities of the DNA. The distinct X pattern indicates a helix structure, but Watson and Crick realised that the apparent gaps in the X (labelled **A**) were due to the repeating pattern of a *double* helix. The diamond shapes (in blue) indicate the helix is continuous and of constant dimensions and that the sugar-phosphate backbone is on the outside of the helix. The distance between the dark horizontal bands allows the calculation of the length of one full turn of the helix.

Structure and replication

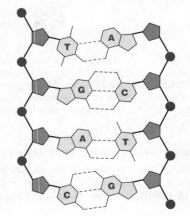

The realisation that DNA was a double helix consisting of antiparallel strands made of bases that followed a strict base pairing rule suggested a mechanism for its replication.

Watson and Crick hypothesised that each strand served as a template and that DNA replication was semi-conservative, producing two daughter strands consisting of half new and half parent material. This was confirmed by Meselson and Stahl.

DNA extraction by ethanol precipitation

DNA is easily extracted and precipitated out of solution using ice cold ethanol. Tissue is macerated in an extraction buffer and then cold ethanol is added so that the DNA precipitates out of the filtered suspension as visible whitish, glue-like strands (below left). The DNA can then be centrifuged with ethanol to form a pellet. Full methodologies are readily available through texts and online.

DNA extraction buffer contains water, detergent, and salt. The **detergent** helps to dissolve the cellular membranes of the tissue and deactivate DNases, which would chop up the DNA. The **salt** helps to remove the proteins bound to the DNA and keeps them in solution. Cations in the salt also neutralise negative charge of the DNA. **Ethanol** causes the DNA to precipitate out by removing the water from around the molecule. Low temperatures speed up the precipitation and limit DNase activity.

Strawberries are good candidates for DNA because they are octaploid (8 sets of chromosomes) and their colour makes it easy to see the precipitating DNA.

1. What made Watson and Crick realise that DNA was a double helix? _____

_____

2. In the extraction and isolation of DNA:

   (a) Why is it necessary to dissolve the cellular membranes? _____

   (b) Why does the DNA precipitate out in ethanol? _____

   (c) For a DNA extraction, why is it helpful that strawberries are octaploid? _____

3. In a DNA extraction, student A obtained DNA in long threads, whereas student B obtained DNA that appeared fluffy. Account for the differences in these two results and suggest what student B might have done incorrectly?

_____

_____

56 Constructing a DNA Model

Key Idea: Nucleotides pair together in a specific way called the base pairing rule. In DNA, adenine always pairs with thymine, and cytosine always pairs with guanine.
DNA molecules are double stranded. Each strand is made up of nucleotides. The chemical properties of each nucleotide mean it can only bind with a one other type of nucleotide. This is called the **base pairing rule** and is explained in the table below. This exercise will help you to learn this rule.

DNA base pairing rule			
Adenine	is always attracted to	**Thymine**	A ⟷ T
Thymine	is always attracted to	**Adenine**	T ⟷ A
Cytosine	is always attracted to	**Guanine**	C ⟷ G
Guanine	is always attracted to	**Cytosine**	G ⟷ C

1. Cut around the nucleotides on page 75 and separate each of the 24 nucleotides by cutting along the columns and rows (see arrows indicating two such cutting points). Although drawn as geometric shapes, these symbols represent chemical structures.

2. Place one of each of the four kinds of nucleotide on their correct spaces below:

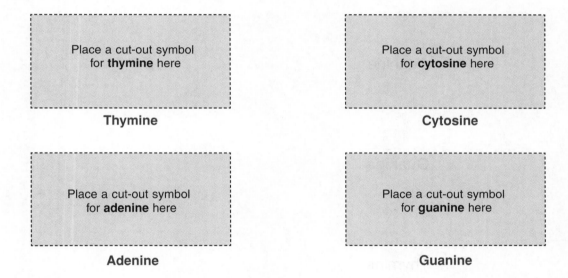

Place a cut-out symbol for **thymine** here

Thymine

Place a cut-out symbol for **cytosine** here

Cytosine

Place a cut-out symbol for **adenine** here

Adenine

Place a cut-out symbol for **guanine** here

Guanine

3. Identify and **label** each of the following features on the adenine nucleotide immediately above:
    phosphate, **sugar**, **base**, **hydrogen bonds**

4. Create one strand of the DNA molecule by placing the 9 correct 'cut out' nucleotides in the labelled spaces on the following page (DNA molecule). Make sure these are the right way up (with the **P** on the left) and are aligned with the left hand edge of each box. Begin with thymine and end with guanine.

5. Create the complementary strand of DNA by using the base pairing rule above. Note that the nucleotides have to be arranged upside down.

6. Under normal circumstances, it is not possible for adenine to pair up with guanine or cytosine, nor for any other mismatches to occur. Describe the **two factors** that prevent a mismatch from occurring:

Factor 1: _____

_____

Factor 2: _____

_____

7. Once you have checked that the arrangement is correct, you may glue, paste or tape these nucleotides in place.

> **NOTE:** There may be some value in keeping these pieces loose in order to practise the base pairing rule. For this purpose, *removable tape* would be best.

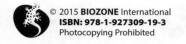

© 2015 **BIOZONE** International
ISBN: 978-1-927309-19-3

PRAC

DNA molecule

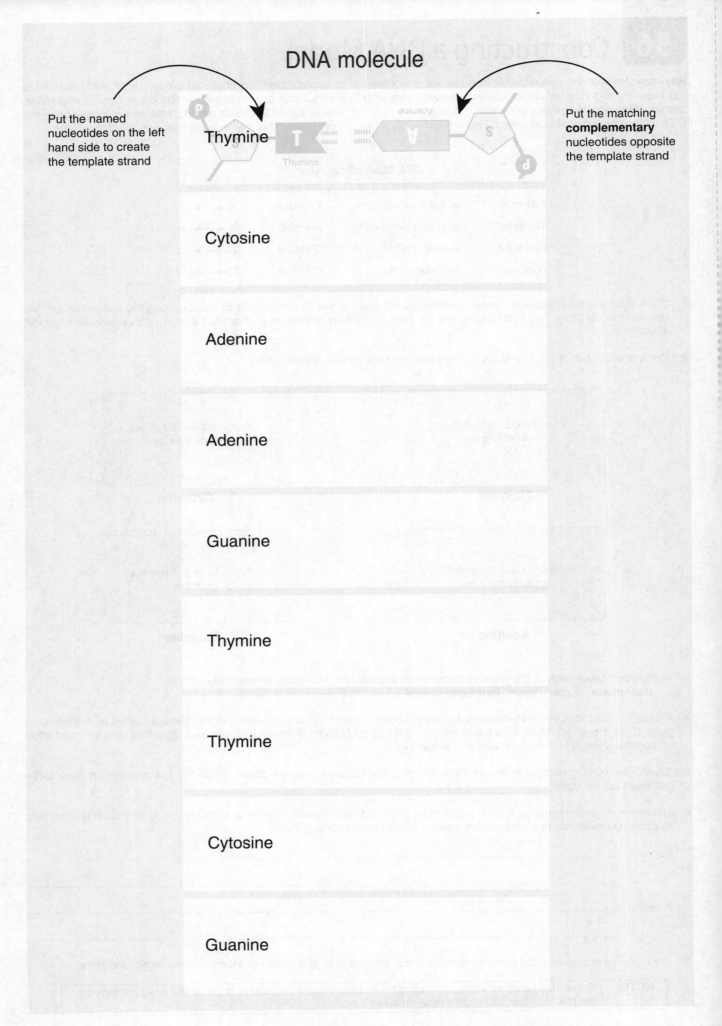

Nucleotides

Tear out this page along the perforation and separate each of the 24 nucleotides by cutting along the columns and rows (see arrows indicating the cutting points).

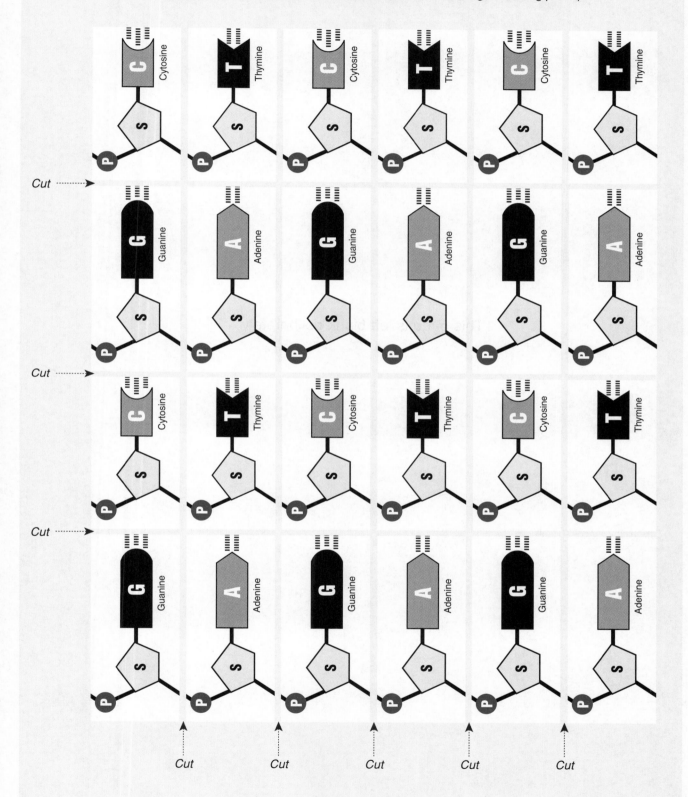

This page is left blank deliberately

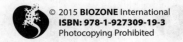

© 2015 **BIOZONE** International
ISBN: 978-1-927309-19-3

57 DNA Replication

Key Idea: Semi conservative DNA replication produces two identical copies of DNA, each containing half original material and half new material.

Before a cell can divide, it must double its DNA. It does this by a process called DNA replication. This process ensures that each resulting cell receives a complete set of genes from the original cell. After the DNA has replicated, each chromosome is made up of two chromatids, joined at the centromere. The two chromatids will become separated during cell division to form two separate chromosomes. During DNA replication, nucleotides are added at the replication fork. Enzymes are responsible for all of the key events.

Step 1
Unwinding the DNA molecule

A normal chromosome consists of an unreplicated DNA molecule. Before cell division, this long molecule of double stranded DNA must be replicated.

For this to happen, it is first untwisted and separated (unzipped) at high speed at its replication fork by an enzyme called **helicase**. Another enzyme relieves the strain that this generates by cutting, winding and rejoining the DNA strands.

Step 2
Making new DNA strands

The formation of new DNA is carried out mostly by an enzyme complex called **DNA polymerase**.

DNA polymerase catalyses the condensation reaction that joins adjacent nucleotides. The enzyme works in a 5' to 3' direction, so nucleotides are assembled in a continuous fashion on one strand but in short fragments on the other strand. These fragments are later joined by an enzyme to form one continuous length.

Step 3
Rewinding the DNA molecule

Each of the two new double-helix DNA molecules has one strand of the original DNA (dark grey and white) and one strand that is newly synthesised (blue). The two DNA molecules rewind into their double-helix shape again.

DNA replication is semi-conservative, with each new double helix containing one old (parent) strand and one newly synthesised (daughter) strand. The new chromosome has twice as much DNA as a non-replicated chromosome. The two chromatids will become separated in the cell division process to form two separate chromosomes.

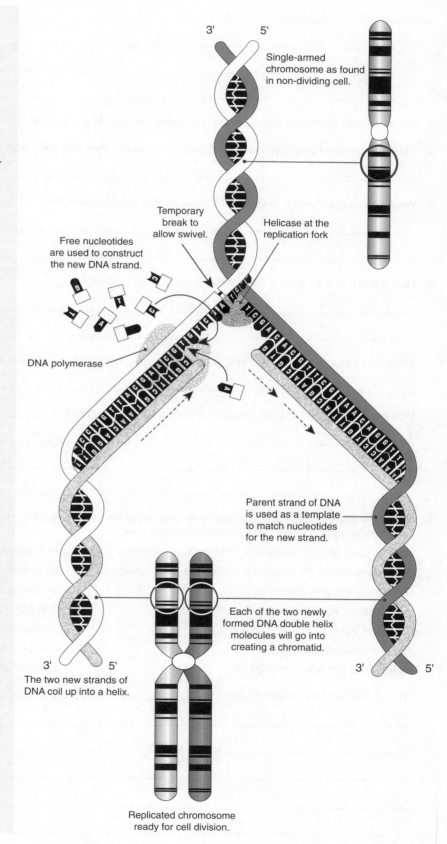

Single-armed chromosome as found in non-dividing cell.

Temporary break to allow swivel.

Free nucleotides are used to construct the new DNA strand.

Helicase at the replication fork

DNA polymerase

Parent strand of DNA is used as a template to match nucleotides for the new strand.

Each of the two newly formed DNA double helix molecules will go into creating a chromatid.

The two new strands of DNA coil up into a helix.

Replicated chromosome ready for cell division.

78

1. What is the purpose of DNA replication? _____

_____

2. Summarise the three main steps involved in DNA replication:

(a) _____

_____

(b) _____

_____

(c) _____

_____

3. For a cell with 22 chromosomes, state how many chromatids would exist following DNA replication: _____

4. State the percentage of DNA in each daughter cell that is new and the percentage that is original: _____

_____

5. What does it mean when we say DNA replication is semi-conservative? _____

_____

_____

6. How are the new strands of DNA lengthened during replication: _____

_____

_____

7. What rule ensures that the two new DNA strands are identical to the original strand? _____

_____

8. Why does one strand of DNA need to be copied in short fragments? _____

_____

_____

_____

9. Match the statements in the table below to form complete sentences, then put the sentences in order to make a coherent paragraph about DNA replication and its role:

The enzymes also proofread the DNA during replication...	...is required before mitosis or meiosis can occur.
DNA replication is the process by which the DNA molecule...	...by enzymes.
Replication is tightly controlled...	...to correct any mistakes.
After replication, the chromosome...	...and half new DNA.
DNA replication...	...during mitosis.
The chromatids separate...	...is copied to produce two identical DNA strands.
A chromatid contains half original ...	...is made up of two chromatids.

Write the complete paragraph here: _____

_____

_____

_____

_____

_____

58 Enzyme Control of DNA Replication

Key Idea: DNA replication is a directional process controlled by several different enzymes.

DNA replication involves many enzyme-controlled steps. They are shown below as separate, but many of the enzymes are clustered together as enzyme complexes. As the DNA is replicated, enzymes 'proof-read' it and correct mistakes. The polymerase enzyme can only work in one direction, so that one new strand is constructed as a continuous length (the leading strand) while the other new strand (the lagging strand) is made in short segments to be later joined together.

DNA replication occurs during interphase of the cell cycle at an astounding rate. As many as 4000 nucleotides per second are replicated. This explains how bacterial cells, with as many as 4 million nucleotides, can complete a cell cycle in about 20 minutes. Note that the nucleotides are present as deoxynucleoside triphosphates. When hydrolysed, these provide the energy for incorporating the nucleotide into the strand.

During the replication of the DNA, a mistake is made about once every 100 000 nucleotides replicated. These mistakes are corrected in two ways. A process called proof-reading occurs during replication. A second process called mis-match repair occurs after replication.

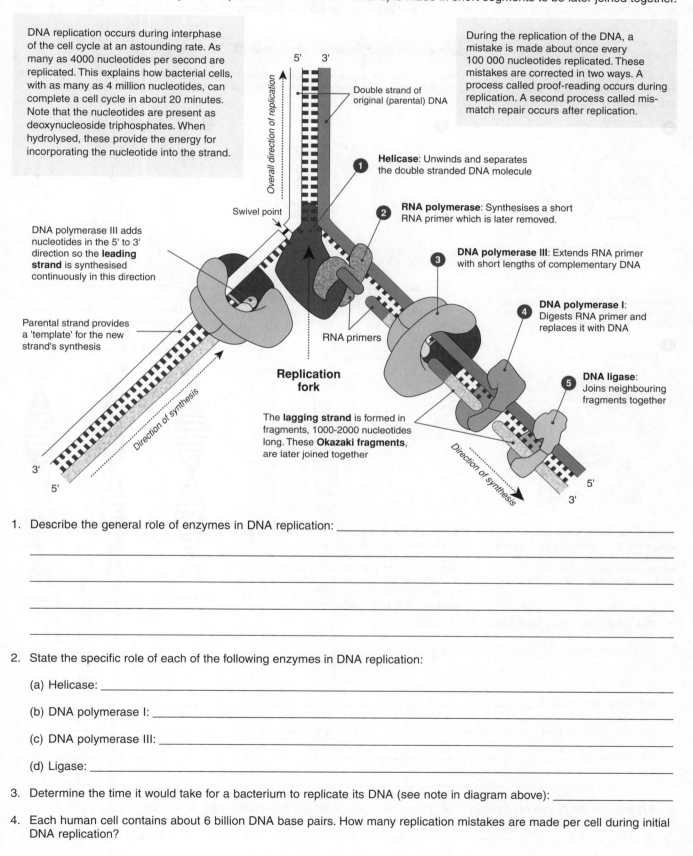

Overall direction of replication

5' 3'

Double strand of original (parental) DNA

Swivel point

Helicase: Unwinds and separates the double stranded DNA molecule ①

RNA polymerase: Synthesises a short RNA primer which is later removed. ②

DNA polymerase III: Extends RNA primer with short lengths of complementary DNA ③

DNA polymerase III adds nucleotides in the 5' to 3' direction so the **leading strand** is synthesised continuously in this direction

DNA polymerase I: Digests RNA primer and replaces it with DNA ④

Parental strand provides a 'template' for the new strand's synthesis

RNA primers

DNA ligase: Joins neighbouring fragments together ⑤

Replication fork

Direction of synthesis

The **lagging strand** is formed in fragments, 1000-2000 nucleotides long. These **Okazaki fragments**, are later joined together

3'

5'

Direction of synthesis

5'

3'

1. Describe the general role of enzymes in DNA replication: _____

_____

_____

_____

_____

2. State the specific role of each of the following enzymes in DNA replication:

(a) Helicase: _____

(b) DNA polymerase I: _____

(c) DNA polymerase III: _____

(d) Ligase: _____

3. Determine the time it would take for a bacterium to replicate its DNA (see note in diagram above): _____

4. Each human cell contains about 6 billion DNA base pairs. How many replication mistakes are made per cell during initial DNA replication?

_____

59 Meselson and Stahl's Experiment

Key Idea: Meselson and Stahl devised an experiment that showed DNA replication is semi-conservative. The anti-parallel, complementary structure of DNA suggested three possible mechanisms for its replication. The **semi-conservative model** proposed that each strand served as a template, forming new DNA molecules that were half old and half new DNA. The **conservative model** proposed that the original DNA served as a complete template so that the new DNA comprised two new strands. The **dispersive model** proposed that the two new DNA molecules had new and old DNA mixed throughout them. **Meselson and Stahl** devised a simple experiment to determine which model was correct.

Meselson and Stahl's experiment

E. coli were grown for several generations in a medium containing a **heavy nitrogen isotope** (^{15}N). Once all the bacterial DNA contained ^{15}N, they were transferred to a medium containing a **light nitrogen isotope** (^{14}N). After the transfer, newly synthesised DNA would contain ^{14}N and old DNA would contain ^{15}N.

1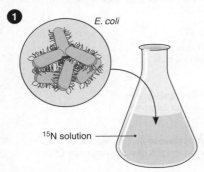

E. coli were grown in a nutrient solution containing ^{15}N. After 14 generations, all the bacterial DNA contained ^{15}N. A sample is removed. This is **generation 0**.

2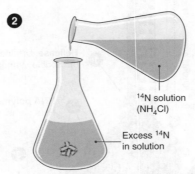

Generation 0 is added to a solution containing excess ^{14}N (as NH_4Cl). During replication, new DNA will incorporate ^{14}N and be 'lighter' than the original DNA (which contains only ^{15}N).

3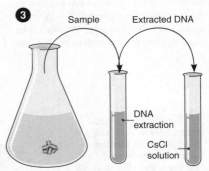

Every generation (~ 20 minutes), a sample is taken and treated to release the DNA. The DNA is placed in a CsCl solution which provides a density gradient for separation of the DNA.

4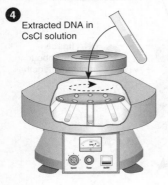

Samples are spun in a high speed ultracentrifuge at 140 000 *g* for 20 hours. Heavier ^{15}N DNA moves closer to the bottom of the test tube than light ^{14}N DNA or intermediate $^{14}N/^{15}N$ DNA.

5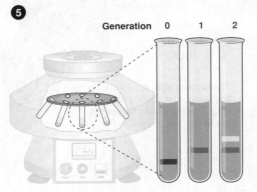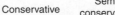

All the DNA in the generation 0 sample moved to the bottom of the test tube. All the DNA in the generation 1 sample moved to an intermediate position. At generation 2 half the DNA was at the intermediate position and half was near the top of the test tube. In subsequent generations, more DNA was near the top and less was in the intermediate position.

Models for DNA Replication

Conservative   Semi-conservative   Dispersive

1. Describe each of the DNA replication models:

   (a) Conservative: _____

   _____

   (b) Semi-conservative: _____

   _____

   (c) Dispersive: _____

   _____

2. Explain why the *E. coli* were grown in an ^{15}N solution before being transferred to an ^{14}N solution: _____

   _____

   _____

60 Modelling DNA Replication

Key Idea: Meselson and Stahl's experiment to determine the nature of DNA replication can be modelled.

There were three possible models proposed to explain how DNA replicated. Meselson and Stahl's experiment was able to determine which method was used by starting with parent DNA that was heavier than would normally be expected. They were then able to analyse the relative weight of the replicated DNA to work out the correct replication method.

Instructions:

1. Cut out the DNA shapes provided on this page.

2. Intertwine the first pair (labelled 0) of heavy ^{15}N (black) DNA. This forms Generation 0 (parental DNA).

3. Use the descriptions of the three possible models for DNA replication on the previous page to model DNA replication in semi-conservative, conservative, and dispersive DNA replication.

4. For each replication method, record in the spaces provided on page 175 the percentage of **heavy** ^{15}N-^{15}N (black-black), **intermediate** ^{15}N-^{14}N (black-grey), **light** ^{14}N-^{14}N (grey-grey), or other DNA molecules formed.

5. For the dispersive model you will need to cut the DNA along the dotted lines and then stick them back together in the dispersed sequence with tape. **Construct the dispersive model LAST.**

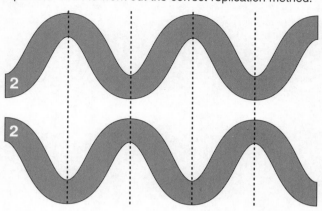

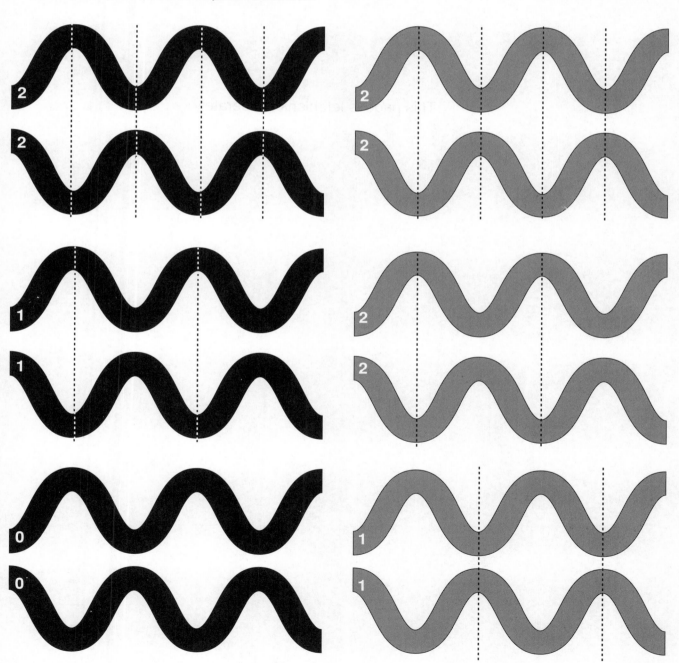

LINK
59

PRAC

This page is left blank deliberately

© 2015 BIOZONE International
ISBN: 978-1-927309-19-3
Photocopying Prohibited

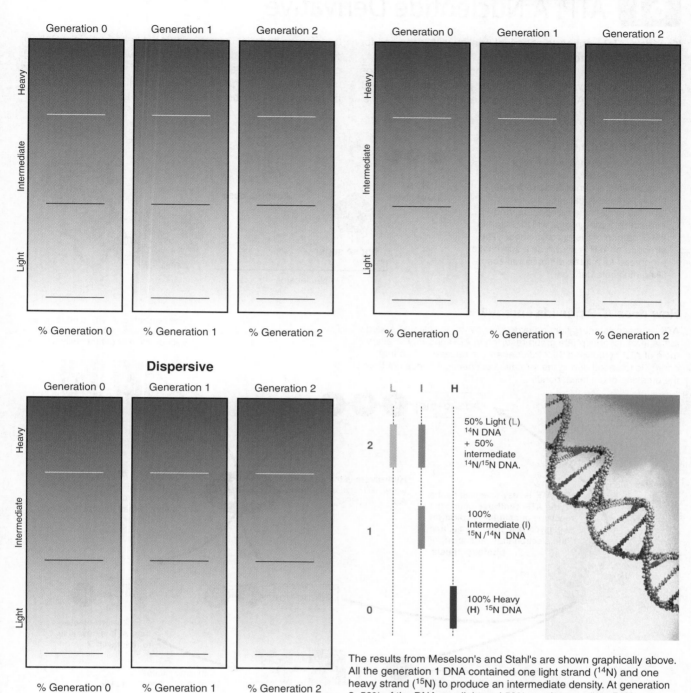

Conservative

Generation 0 | Generation 1 | Generation 2

Heavy — Intermediate — Light

% Generation 0 | % Generation 1 | % Generation 2

Semi-conservative

Generation 0 | Generation 1 | Generation 2

Heavy — Intermediate — Light

% Generation 0 | % Generation 1 | % Generation 2

Dispersive

Generation 0 | Generation 1 | Generation 2

Heavy — Intermediate — Light

% Generation 0 | % Generation 1 | % Generation 2

L   I   H

2   50% Light (L) ^{14}N DNA + 50% intermediate ^{14}N/^{15}N DNA.

1   100% Intermediate (I) ^{15}N /^{14}N DNA

0   100% Heavy (H) ^{15}N DNA

The results from Meselson's and Stahl's are shown graphically above. All the generation 1 DNA contained one light strand (^{14}N) and one heavy strand (^{15}N) to produce an intermediate density. At generation 2, 50% of the DNA was light and 50% was intermediate DNA.

1. (a) Compare your modelling results to the results gained by Meselson and Stahl to decide which of the three DNA replication models is supported by the data:

_____

_____

(b) Was Watson and Crick's proposal correct? _____

2. Identify the replication model that fits the following data:

(a) 100% of generation 0 is "heavy DNA", 50% of generation 1 is "heavy" and 50% is "light", and 25% of generation 2 is "heavy" and 75% is "light":

_____

(b) 100% of generation 0 is "heavy DNA", 100% of generation 1 is "intermediate DNA", and 100% generation 2 lies between the "intermediate" and "light" DNA regions:

_____

61 ATP: A Nucleotide Derivative

Key Idea: ATP transports chemical energy within the cell for use in metabolic processes.

ATP is one of a group of phosphorylated nucleosides that generally provide energy and a phosphate group for phosphorylations. ATP is the universal energy carrier in cells, transferring chemical energy within the cell for use in metabolic processes such as biosynthesis, cell division, cell signalling, cell mobility, and active transport of substances across membranes. ATP is produced during cellular respiration from the coupling of an inorganic phosphate to an ADP.

The structure of ATP

The ATP molecule is a nucleotide derivative. It consists of three components; a purine base (adenine) and a pentose sugar (ribose), which form the nucleoside component, and three phosphate groups, which attach to the 5' carbon of the pentose sugar. The structure of ATP is shown as a schematic (right) and as a three dimensional space filling molecule (far right).

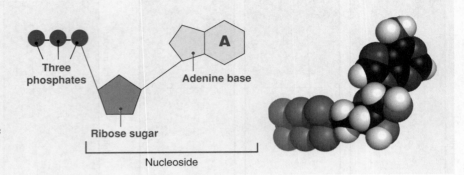

Three phosphates
Adenine base
Ribose sugar
Nucleoside

How does ATP provide energy?

ATP releases its energy during hydrolysis. Water is split and added to the terminal phosphate group resulting in ADP and Pi. For every mole of ATP hydrolysed **30.7 kJ** of energy is released. Note that energy is released during the formation of chemical bonds not from the breaking of chemical bonds.

The reaction of A + B is endergonic. It requires energy to proceed and will not occur spontaneously.

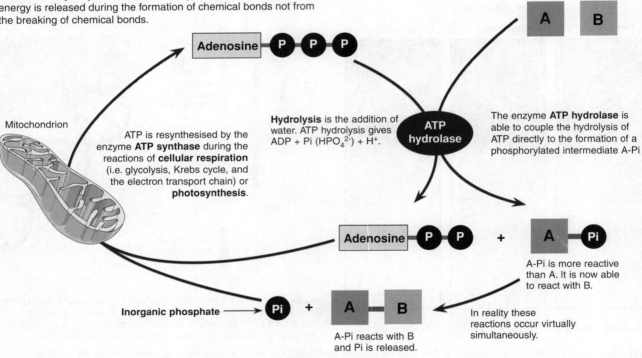

Adenosine P P P

Mitochondrion

ATP is resynthesised by the enzyme **ATP synthase** during the reactions of **cellular respiration** (i.e. glycolysis, Krebs cycle, and the electron transport chain) or **photosynthesis**.

Hydrolysis is the addition of water. ATP hydrolysis gives ADP + Pi (HPO_4^{2-}) + H^+.

ATP hydrolase

The enzyme **ATP hydrolase** is able to couple the hydrolysis of ATP directly to the formation of a phosphorylated intermediate A-Pi

A B

Adenosine P P + A — Pi

A-Pi is more reactive than A. It is now able to react with B.

Inorganic phosphate → Pi + A — B

A-Pi reacts with B and Pi is released.

In reality these reactions occur virtually simultaneously.

1. In which organelle is ATP produced in the cell? _____

2. Which enzyme catalyses the hydrolysis of ATP? _____

3. Which enzyme catalyses the synthesis of ATP? _____

4. On the space filling model of ATP at the top right of the page:

    (a) Label the three components of an ATP molecule:

    (b) Show which phosphate bond is hydrolysed to provide the energy for cellular work:

5. In what way is the ADP/ATP system like a rechargeable battery? _____

    _____

    _____

© 2015 **BIOZONE** International
ISBN: 978-1-927309-19-3
Photocopying Prohibited

62 Water

Key Idea: Water forms bonds between other water molecules and also with ions allowing water to act as a medium for transporting molecules and the biological reactions of life.
Water (H_2O) is the main component of living things, and typically makes up about 70% of any organism. Water is important in cell chemistry as it takes part in, and is a common product of, many reactions. Water can form bonds with other water molecules, and also with other ions (charged molecules). Because of this chemical ability, water is regarded as the universal solvent.

Water forms hydrogen bonds

A water molecule is polar, meaning it has a positively and a negatively charged region. In water, oxygen has a slight negative charge and each of the hydrogens have a slight positive charge. Water molecules have a weak attraction for each other, forming large numbers of weak hydrogen bonds with other water molecules (far right).

Intermolecular bonds between water and other polar molecules or ions are important for biological systems. Inorganic ions may have a positive or negative charge (e.g sodium ion is positive, chloride ion is negative). The charged water molecule is attracted to the charged ion and surrounds it (right). This formation of intermolecular bonds between water and the ions is what keeps the ions dissolved in water. Polar molecules such as amino acids and carbohydrates also dissolve readily in water.

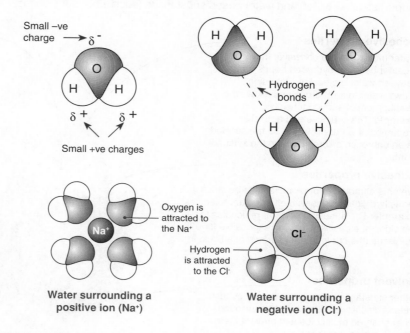

Water surrounding a positive ion (Na⁺)

Water surrounding a negative ion (Cl⁻)

The importance of water

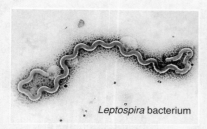

Leptospira bacterium

The metabolic reactions carried out by all organisms depend on dissolved reactants (solutes) coming into contact. Water provides the medium for metabolic reactions. Water can also act as an acid (donating H^+) or a base (receiving H^+) in chemical reactions.

Water provides an aquatic environment for organisms to live in. Ice is less dense than water and floats, insulating the underlying water and maintaining the aquatic habitat. A lot of energy is needed for water to change state, so water has a buffering effect on climate.

Water is colourless, with a high transmission of visible light. Light penetrates aquatic environments, allowing photosynthesis to continue at depth. Water also has a high heat capacity, absorbing and releasing energy slowly. This means large bodies of water are thermally stable.

1. The diagram at the top of the page shows a positive sodium ion and a negative chloride ion surrounded by water molecules. On the diagram, draw on the charge of the water molecules.

2. Explain the formation of hydrogen bonds between water and other polar molecules: _____

_____

_____

_____

_____

3. Explain the central role of water in metabolic processes: _____

_____

_____

63 The Properties of Water

Key Idea: Water's chemical properties influence its physical properties and its ability to transport molecules in solution. Water's cohesive, adhesive, thermal, and solvent properties come about because of its polarity and ability to form hydrogen bonds with other polar molecules. These physical properties allow water, and water based substances (such as blood), to transport polar molecules in solution. The ability of substances to dissolve in water varies. **Hydrophilic** (water-loving) substances dissolve readily in water (e.g. salts, sugars). **Hydrophobic** (water-hating) substances (e.g. oil) do not dissolve in water. Blood must transport many different substances, including hydrophobic ones.

Cohesive properties

Water molecules are cohesive, they stick together because hydrogen bonds form between water molecules. Cohesion allows water to form drops and allows the development of surface tension.
Example: The cohesive and adhesive properties of water allow it to be transported as an unbroken column through the xylem of plants.

Adhesive properties

Water is attracted to other molecules because it forms hydrogen bonds with other polar molecules.
Example: The adhesion of water molecules to the sides of a capillary tube is responsible for a meniscus (the curved upper surface of a liquid in a tube).

Solvent properties

Other substances dissolve in water because water's dipolar nature allows it to surround other charged molecules and prevent them from clumping together.
Example: Mineral transport through a plant.

Thermal properties

▶ Water has the highest heat capacity of all liquids, so it takes a lot of energy before it will change temperature. As a result, water heats up and cools down slowly, so large bodies of water maintain a relatively stable temperature.

▶ Water is liquid at room temperature and has a high boiling point because a lot of energy is needed to break the hydrogen bonds. The liquid environment supports life and metabolic processes.

▶ Water has a high latent heat of vaporisation, meaning it takes a lot of energy to transform it from the liquid to the gas phase. In sweating, the energy is provided by the body, so sweat has a cooling effect.

Transporting substances in blood

Protein
Cholesterol
Phospholipid
Triglyceride

Sodium chloride	Glucose	Amino acids	Oxygen	Fats and cholesterol
Sodium chloride (NaCl) is highly soluble. NaCl dissolves in blood plasma into the ions Na$^+$ and Cl$^-$.	Glucose is a polar molecule so readily dissolves into blood plasma for transport around the body.	All amino acids have both a positive or negative charge, and are highly soluble in blood. However, their variable R-chain can alter the solubility of amino acids slightly.	Oxygen has low solubility in water. In blood, it is bound to the protein haemoglobin in red blood cells so it can be transported around the body.	Fats are non-polar substances and are insoluble in water. Cholesterol has a slight charge, but is also water insoluble. Both are transported in blood within lipoprotein complexes, spheres of phospholipids arranged with the hydrophilic heads and proteins facing out and hydrophobic tails facing inside.

1. (a) Describe the difference between a **hydrophilic** and **hydrophobic** molecule: _____

_____

_____

(b) Use an example to describe how a hydrophilic and a hydrophobic molecule are transported in blood: _____

_____

_____

_____

2. How does water act as a coolant during sweating? _____

_____

© 2015 **BIOZONE** International
ISBN: 978-1-927309-19-3
Photocopying Prohibited

64 Inorganic Ions

Key Idea: Inorganic ions are charged molecules that do not contain carbon-hydrogen bonds. They are central to many biological structures and processes.

Inorganic compounds do not contain C-H bonds. An **inorganic ion** is an atom (or group of atoms) that has gained or lost one or more electrons and therefore has a positive or negative charge. Inorganic ions are central to the structure and metabolism of all living organisms, participating in metabolic reactions and combining with organic molecules to form complex molecules (e.g. iron and haemoglobin).

Cation: A positive ion; an atom or group of atoms that has lost one or more electrons.

Anion: A negative ion; an atom or group of atoms that has gained one or more electrons.

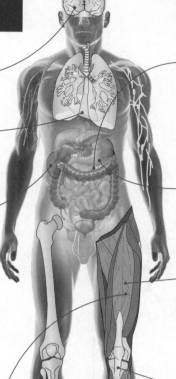

Sodium (Na^+)
Roles: The major extracellular cation in animal cells, involved in transmission of nerve impulses and in fluid and electrolyte balance. In plants, Na^+ is involved in maintaining cell turgor and in opening and closing stomata.

Potassium (K^+)
Roles: The main intracellular cation in all cell types. Involved in heart function and transmission of the nerve impulses. In plants, K^+ is involved in controlling stomatal opening via the guard cells.

Ammonium (NH_4^+)
Roles: An important source of nitrogen for many plants. Generated in the mammalian kidney as part of acid-base regulation.

Iron (Fe^{3+}/Fe^{2+})
Roles: Iron-bindng proteins are involved in redox reactions, electron transport, and in the transport of oxygen as a component of haemoglobin.

Hydrogen (H^+)
Roles: Important in acid-base chemistry. Establish trans-membrane electrochemical gradients which can be used to generate ATP.

Calcium (Ca^{2+})
Roles: In vertebrates, Ca^{2+} is a component of teeth and bone (as calcium phosphate) and is involved in muscle contraction, blood clotting, activation of some enzymes, and cell signalling. In plants, it is a component of the cell wall.

Hydrogen carbonate (HCO_3^-)
Also called bicarbonate ion.
Roles: Bicarbonate is alkaline and acts as a pH buffer in the human body to maintain acid-base homeostasis. A buffer is a molecule that can bind or release hydrogen ions in order to maintain a particular pH. Bicarbonate is released from the pancreas to neutralise the acidic chyme entering the small intestine from the stomach.

Chloride (Cl^-)
Roles: Essential electrolyte present in all body fluids. Involved in fluid balance, acid-base balance, and to form hydrochloric acid in gastric juice

Nitrate (NO_3^-)
An important source of nitrogen for plants (unlike animals, which obtain their nitrogen by eating other organisms). Nitrogen is a component of amino acids and nucleotides.

Phosphate (PO_4^{3-})
Roles: Component of phospholipids, nucleotides and ATP. Combines with calcium as calcium phosphate in bones and teeth

Hydroxide (OH^-)
Roles: Important in acid-base chemistry. Central to many biological reactions.

1. (a) Define a cation: _____

   (b) Define an anion: _____

2. (a) Describe the role of Ca^{2+} in organisms: _____

   (b) Predict the biological consequences of inadequate levels of calcium in the diet: _____

3. (a) Why is NO_3^- so important for plants? _____

   (b) Why is it not directly important to animals? _____

4. (a) Which inorganic ions are involved in acid-base regulation: _____

   (b) What feature of their structure enables this role: _____

© 2015 **BIOZONE** International
ISBN: 978-1-927309-19-3
Photocopying Prohibited

LINK 106　LINK 61　LINK 43　**KNOW**

65 Chapter Review

Summarise what you know about this topic under the headings provided. You can draw diagrams or mind maps, or write short notes to organise your thoughts. Use the images and hints to help you and refer back to the introduction to check the points covered:

Monomers and polymers
HINT: What is an organic molecule? Distinguish between monomers and polymers.

Carbohydrates
HINT: Relate carbohydrate structure to function.

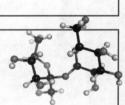

Proteins
HINT: Protein structure and relationship between structure and function.

Enzymes
HINT: How do enzymes work and what factors influence reaction rate?

REVISE

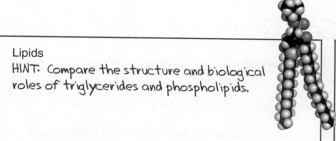

Lipids
HINT: Compare the structure and biological roles of triglycerides and phospholipids.

Water and inorganic ions
HINT: Properties of water and ions that are essential for life.

Nucleic acids and ATP
HINT: Structure of nucleic acids. Structure and replication of DNA. Function of ATP in a cell.

66 KEY TERMS: Did You Get It?

1. Test your vocabulary by matching each term to its correct definition, as identified by its preceding letter code.

activation energy

amino acids

base pairing rule

carbohydrates

condensation

denaturation

DNA

enzyme

fibrous proteins

globular proteins

hydrolysis

inhibition

inorganic ion

lipids

monomers

polymer

RNA

A   A globular protein that acts as catalyst to speed up a specific biological reaction.

B   A process whereby an enzyme activity is stopped, either permanently or temporarily.

C   Organic molecules consisting only of carbon, hydrogen and oxygen that serve as structural components in cells and as energy sources.

D   The building blocks of proteins

E   The splitting of a molecule into smaller components by addition of a water molecule.

F   Small units that can be join together to form larger, more complex molecules.

G   Proteins with a rod or wire-like structure that are important in structure or storage..

H   A large complex molecule consisting of many small units joined together.

I   The loss of a protein's three dimensional functional structure is called this.

J   A class of organic compounds with an oily, greasy, or waxy consistency. Important as energy storage molecules and as components of cellular membranes.

K   A general term for a reaction in which water is released.

L   Single stranded nucleic acid that consists of nucleotides containing ribose sugar.

M   The rule governing the pairing of complementary bases in DNA.

N   An atom (or group of atoms) with no C-H bonds and a positive or negative charge.

O   Water soluble proteins with a spherical tertiary structure. They are involved in many cellular functions including as catalysts and in transport and regulation.

P   Energy required to initiate a chemical reaction.

Q   Macromolecule consisting of many millions of units containing a phosphate group, sugar and a base (A,T, C or G). Stores the genetic information of the cell.

2. (a) On the diagram shown right, highlight the structure that indicates a DNA helix.

   (b) Circle the region that indicates there is a double helix.

   (c) What do the blank diamond shaped areas in the diagram indicate?

   _____

   _____

   _____

   _____

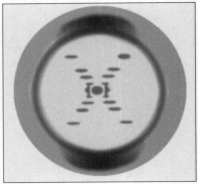

3. The graph (right) shows the effect of an enzyme inhibitor in enzyme reaction rate.

   (a) It show competitive inhibition/non-competitive inhibition (delete one).

   (b) Circle the diagram below that illustrates your choice in (a):

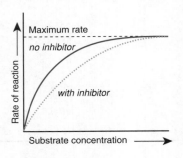

TEST

Cells

Key terms

active immunity
active transport
antibody
antigen
B cell (=B lymphocyte)
binary fission
cell cycle
cellular response
clonal selection
co-transport
concentration gradient
cytokinesis
diffusion
electron microscope
eukaryotic cell
facilitated diffusion
fluid mosaic model
humoral response
immunity
immunological memory
interphase
ion pump
light microscope
magnification
mitosis
mitotic index
monoclonal antibody
multicellular
organelle
osmosis
passive immunity
passive transport
pathogen
phagocyte
phospholipid
plasma membrane
primary response
prokaryotic cell
resolution
secondary response
T cell (=T lymphocyte)
vaccination
virus
water potential

2.1 Cell structure

Learning outcomes

		Activity number
☐	1 Appreciate that all life on Earth exists as cells. Appreciate the range of cell types and cell sizes. Outline the cell theory and the evidence supporting it.	67 68
☐	2 Describe the structure of eukaryotic cells, including the organelles and structures found in plant and animal cells and their functions.	67 70-74 76
☐	3 Using examples, describe how the cells of multicellular eukaryotes are specialised to perform specific roles.	77 78
☐	4 Describe the hierarchy of organisation in multicellular organisms, using examples to show how specialised cells are organised into tissues, tissues into organs, and organs into organ systems.	79 80 81
☐	5 Describe the structure and characteristic features of prokaryotic cells, including reference to the cell wall, ribosomes, and bacterial chromosome.	67 69
☐	6 Describe the structure of viruses as acellular, non-living particles.	82
☐	7 Describe the principles and limitations of optical microscopes, transmission electron microscopes, and scanning electron microscopes. Include reference to magnification, resolution, and features of the images produced.	83 88
☐	8 **PR-2** Prepare and stain a tissue sample for viewing with an optical microscope.	84 85
☐	9 **AT** Use a light microscope at high and low power, including use of a graticule. Produce an annotated scientific drawing from observation. Calculate the magnification of drawings and the size of cell structures in light and electron micrographs and in drawings (cross reference MS 1.8).	86 87
☐	10 Explain how cell fractionation and ultracentrifugation are used to separate cellular components.	75

2.2 All cells arise from other cells

Learning outcomes

		Activity number
☐	11 Understand that cells can only form by division of pre-existing cells but that, within multicellular organisms, not all cells retain the ability to divide. Describe the outcome of mitotic division and explain its role in eukaryotes.	67 89
☐	12 Describe the cell cycle including the events in interphase, mitosis, and cytokinesis. Describe the behaviour of chromosomes during prophase, metaphase, anaphase, and telophase of mitosis.	90
☐	13 **PR-2** Calculate mitotic index in a stained root tip squash.	91
☐	14 Describe the cell cycle as a controlled process and explain the consequences of uncontrolled cell division. Explain why many cancer treatments focus on controlling the rate of cell division.	92 93
☐	15 Describe the process and purpose of binary fission in prokaryotes.	94
☐	16 Describe replication in a virus, recognising the essential differences between viral replication and the division of cells.	95

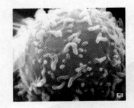

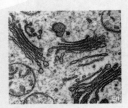

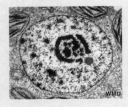

2.3 Transport across cell membranes

Learning outcomes

Activity number

☐ 17 Describe the roles of membranes in cells.

96

☐ 18 Describe the fluid mosaic model of the plasma membrane, including reference to the roles of cholesterol and embedded proteins.

97 98

☐ 19 **PR-4** Investigate the effect of a named variable (e.g. temperature) on the permeability of the cell surface membrane.

99

☐ 20 Explain how molecules move across membranes by diffusion, facilitated diffusion, and osmosis. Explain how surface area, number of channel or carrier proteins, and differences in water potential affects the rate at which molecules move across membranes by passive transport processes.

100-102

☐ 21 **PR-3** Produce and use a dilution series of a solute to produce a calibration curve to identify the water potential of plant tissue.

103 104

☐ 22 Describe and explain how molecules are transported across membranes by active transport. Include reference to ion pumps, co-transport, and cytosis.

105-107

2.4 Cell recognition and the immune system

Learning outcomes

Activity number

☐ 23 Describe the nature of self recognition, explaining how the immune system distinguishes the body's own cells from foreign cells and antigens.

108

☐ 24 Describe the effect of antigenic variability on disease and disease prevention.

110

☐ 25 Recognise non-specific (innate) defences against pathogens in animals. Describe the action of phagocytes in ingesting and destroying pathogens.

109 111

☐ 26 Describe the general structure and roles of B and T lymphocytes in specific immunity. Describe clonal selection and the basis of immunological memory.

112 113

☐ 27 Describe the cellular response to foreign antigens, including the role of antigen-presenting cells and the role of helper T cells in stimulating cells involved in specific immunity.

112

☐ 28 Describe the response of B lymphocytes to foreign antigens. Include reference to the structure and role of antibodies and the formation of an antigen-antibody complex and its result.

113 114

☐ 29 Distinguish the primary and secondary immune responses and the role of plasma cells and memory cells in these.

114 115

☐ 30 Using examples, distinguish between naturally acquired and artificially acquired immunity and between active and passive immunity.

115

☐ 31 Explain the basis of vaccination and the concept of herd immunity. Discuss the role of vaccination in public health programmes and the prevention of epidemics.

115 116

☐ 32 Discuss ethical issues and evaluate evidence and data relating to the development and use of vaccines.

117

☐ 33 Describe the structure of human immunodeficiency virus (HIV) and its impact on the immune system. Explain how HIV causes the symptoms of AIDS and explain why antibiotics cannot to be used to combat this disease.

118

☐ 34 Describe the use of monoclonal antibodies in diagnostic and therapeutic medicine. Discuss ethical issues and evaluate evidence and data relating to the use of monoclonal antibodies.

119 120

67 The Cell is the Unit of Life

Key Idea: All living organisms are composed of cells. Cells are broadly classified as prokaryotic or eukaryotic.

The cell theory is a fundamental idea of biology. This idea, that all living things are composed of cells, developed over many years and is strongly linked to the invention and refinement of the microscope in the 1600s.

The cell theory

The idea that cells are fundamental units of life is part of the cell theory. The basic principles of the theory are:

► All living things are composed of cells and cell products.

► New cells are formed only by the division of pre-existing cells.

► The cell contains inherited information (genes) that are used as instructions for growth, functioning, and development.

► The cell is the functioning unit of life; all chemical reactions of life take place within cells.

All cells show the functions of life

Cells use food (e.g. glucose) to maintain a stable internal environment, grow, reproduce, and produce wastes. The sum total of all the chemical reactions that sustain life is called metabolism.

Movement
Respiration
Sensitivity
Growth
Reproduction
Excretion
Nutrition

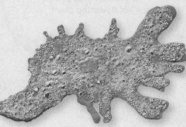

Viruses are non-cellular

- Non-cellular.
- Typical size range: 20-300 nm.
- Contain no cytoplasm or organelles.
- No chromosome, just RNA or DNA strands.
- Enclosed in a protein coat.
- Depend on cells for metabolism and reproduction (replication).

Influenzavirus

Living things → **Cells**

Prokaryotic (bacterial) cells

- Autotrophic or heterotrophic
- Single celled
- Lack a membrane-bound nucleus and membrane-bound organelles
- Cells 0.5-10 µm
- DNA a single, circular chromosome. There may be small accessory chromosomes called plasmids.
- Cell walls containing peptidoglycan.

Eukaryotic cells

- Cells 30-150 µm • Membrane-bound nucleus and membrane-bound organelles • Linear chromosomes

Plant cells

- Exist as part of multicellular organism with specialisation of cells into many types.
- Autotrophic (make their own food): photosynthetic cells with chloroplasts.
- Cell walls of cellulose.

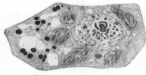

Generalised plant cell

Animal cells

- Exist as part of multicellular organism with specialisation of cells into many types.
- Lack cell walls.
- Heterotrophic (rely on other organisms for food).

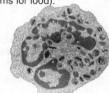

White blood cell

Protoctist cells

- Mainly single-celled or exist as cell colonies.
- Some are autotrophic and carry out photosynthesis.
- Some are heterotrophic.

Amoeba cell

Fungal cells

- Rarely exist as discrete cells, except for some unicellular forms (e.g. yeasts)
- Plant-like, but lack chlorophyll.
- Rigid cell walls containing chitin.
- Heterotrophic.

Yeast cell

---

1. What are the characteristic features of a prokaryotic cell? _____

_____

2. What are the characteristic features of a eukaryotic cell? _____

_____

3. Why are viruses considered to be non-cellular (non-living)? _____

LINK 72   LINK 70   LINK 69   WEB 67   **KNOW**

68 Cell Sizes

Key Idea: Cells vary in size (2-100 μm), with prokaryotic cells being approximately 10 times smaller than eukaryotic cells. Cells can only be seen properly when viewed through the magnifying lenses of a microscope. The images below show a variety of cell types, including a multicellular microscopic animal and a virus (non-cellular) for comparison. For each of these images, note the scale and relate this to the type of microscopy used.

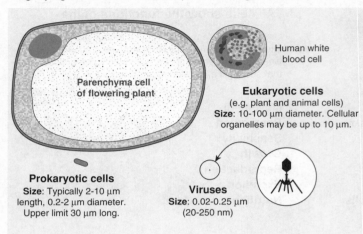

Parenchyma cell of flowering plant

Human white blood cell

Eukaryotic cells
(e.g. plant and animal cells)
Size: 10-100 μm diameter. Cellular organelles may be up to 10 μm.

Prokaryotic cells
Size: Typically 2-10 μm length, 0.2-2 μm diameter. Upper limit 30 μm long.

Viruses
Size: 0.02-0.25 μm (20-250 nm)

Unit of length (international system)

Unit	Metres	Equivalent
1 metre (m)	1 m	= 1000 millimetres
1 millimetre (mm)	10^{-3} m	= 1000 micrometres
1 micrometre (μm)	10^{-6} m	= 1000 nanometres
1 nanometre (nm)	10^{-9} m	= 1000 picometres

Micrometres are sometime referred to as microns. Smaller structures are usually measured in nanometres (nm) e.g. molecules (1 nm) and plasma membrane thickness (10 nm).

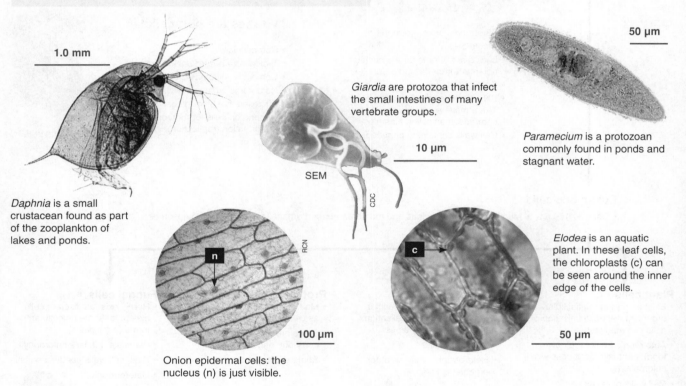

1.0 mm

50 μm

Giardia are protozoa that infect the small intestines of many vertebrate groups.

SEM

CDC

10 μm

Paramecium is a protozoan commonly found in ponds and stagnant water.

Daphnia is a small crustacean found as part of the zooplankton of lakes and ponds.

n

RCN

c

Elodea is an aquatic plant. In these leaf cells, the chloroplasts (c) can be seen around the inner edge of the cells.

100 μm

50 μm

Onion epidermal cells: the nucleus (n) is just visible.

1. Using the measurement scales provided on each of the photographs above, determine the longest dimension (length or diameter) of the cell/animal/organelle indicated in μm and mm. Attach your working:

   (a) *Daphnia*: —————— μm —————— mm   (d) *Elodea* leaf cell: —————— μm —————— mm

   (b) *Giardia*: —————— μm —————— mm   (e) Chloroplast: —————— μm —————— mm

   (c) Nucleus —————— μm —————— mm   (f) *Paramecium*: —————— μm —————— mm

2. (a) List a-f in question 1 in order of size, from the smallest to the largest:

   _____

   (b) Study your ruler. Which one of the above could you see with your unaided eye?_____

3. Calculate the equivalent length in millimetres (mm) of the following measurements:

   (a) 0.25 μm: _____   (b) 450 μm: _____   (c) 200 nm: _____

© 2015 **BIOZONE** International
ISBN: 978-1-927309-19-3
Photocopying Prohibited

69 Bacterial Cells

Key Idea: Prokaryotic cells lack many of the features of eukaryotic cells, including membrane-bound organelles. Bacterial (prokaryotic) cells are much smaller than eukaryotic cells and lack many eukaryotic features, such as a distinct nucleus and membrane-bound cellular organelles. The cell wall is an important feature. It is a complex, multi-layered structure and has a role in the organism's ability to cause disease. A generalised prokaryote, *E. coli*, is shown below.

E. coli structure

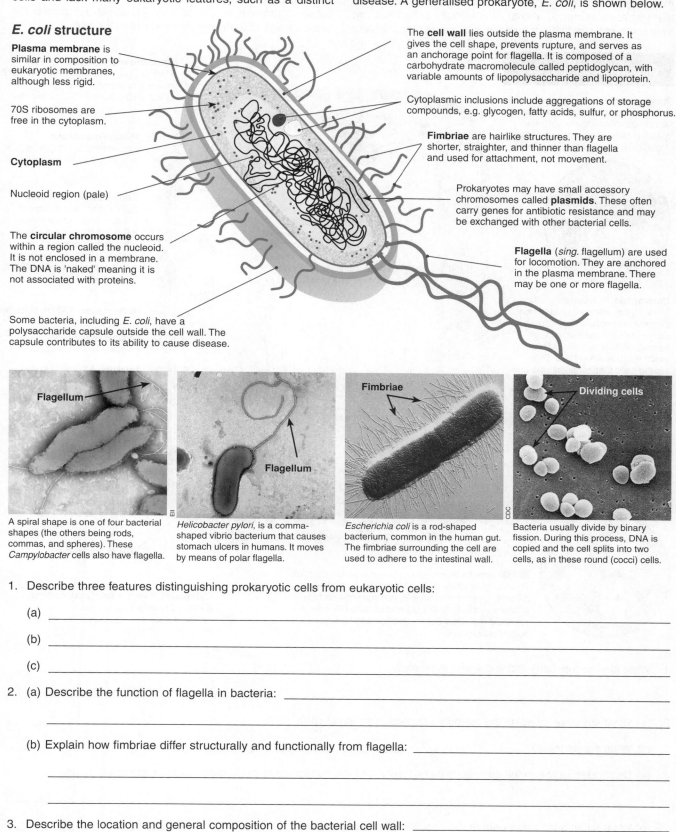

Plasma membrane is similar in composition to eukaryotic membranes, although less rigid.

70S ribosomes are free in the cytoplasm.

Cytoplasm

Nucleoid region (pale)

The **circular chromosome** occurs within a region called the nucleoid. It is not enclosed in a membrane. The DNA is 'naked' meaning it is not associated with proteins.

Some bacteria, including *E. coli*, have a polysaccharide capsule outside the cell wall. The capsule contributes to its ability to cause disease.

The **cell wall** lies outside the plasma membrane. It gives the cell shape, prevents rupture, and serves as an anchorage point for flagella. It is composed of a carbohydrate macromolecule called peptidoglycan, with variable amounts of lipopolysaccharide and lipoprotein.

Cytoplasmic inclusions include aggregations of storage compounds, e.g. glycogen, fatty acids, sulfur, or phosphorus.

Fimbriae are hairlike structures. They are shorter, straighter, and thinner than flagella and used for attachment, not movement.

Prokaryotes may have small accessory chromosomes called **plasmids**. These often carry genes for antibiotic resistance and may be exchanged with other bacterial cells.

Flagella (*sing*. flagellum) are used for locomotion. They are anchored in the plasma membrane. There may be one or more flagella.

Flagellum

A spiral shape is one of four bacterial shapes (the others being rods, commas, and spheres). These *Campylobacter* cells also have flagella.

Flagellum

Helicobacter pylori, is a comma-shaped vibrio bacterium that causes stomach ulcers in humans. It moves by means of polar flagella.

Fimbriae

Escherichia coli is a rod-shaped bacterium, common in the human gut. The fimbriae surrounding the cell are used to adhere to the intestinal wall.

Dividing cells

Bacteria usually divide by binary fission. During this process, DNA is copied and the cell splits into two cells, as in these round (cocci) cells.

1. Describe three features distinguishing prokaryotic cells from eukaryotic cells:

   (a) _____

   (b) _____

   (c) _____

2. (a) Describe the function of flagella in bacteria: _____

   _____

   (b) Explain how fimbriae differ structurally and functionally from flagella: _____

   _____

   _____

3. Describe the location and general composition of the bacterial cell wall: _____

   _____

   _____

70 Plant Cells

Key Idea: Plant cells are eukaryotic cells. They have features in common with animal cells, but also several unique features. Eukaryotic cells have a similar basic structure, although they may vary tremendously in size, shape, and function. Certain features are common to almost all eukaryotic cells, including their three main regions: a nucleus, surrounded by a watery cytoplasm, which is itself enclosed by the plasma membrane. Plant cells are enclosed in a cellulose cell wall, which gives them a regular, uniform appearance. The cell wall protects the cell, maintains its shape, and prevents excessive water uptake. It provides rigidity to plant structures but permits the free passage of materials into and out of the cell.

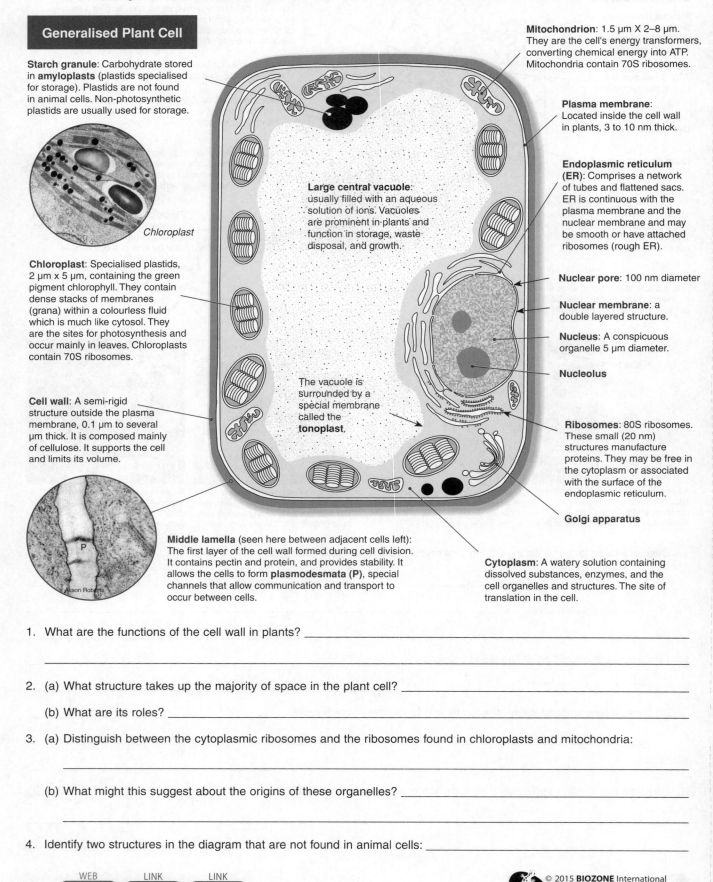

Generalised Plant Cell

Starch granule: Carbohydrate stored in **amyloplasts** (plastids specialised for storage). Plastids are not found in animal cells. Non-photosynthetic plastids are usually used for storage.

Chloroplast

Chloroplast: Specialised plastids, 2 μm x 5 μm, containing the green pigment chlorophyll. They contain dense stacks of membranes (grana) within a colourless fluid which is much like cytosol. They are the sites for photosynthesis and occur mainly in leaves. Chloroplasts contain 70S ribosomes.

Cell wall: A semi-rigid structure outside the plasma membrane, 0.1 μm to several μm thick. It is composed mainly of cellulose. It supports the cell and limits its volume.

P

Alison Roberts

Large central vacuole: usually filled with an aqueous solution of ions. Vacuoles are prominent in plants and function in storage, waste disposal, and growth.

The vacuole is surrounded by a special membrane called the **tonoplast**.

Mitochondrion: 1.5 μm X 2–8 μm. They are the cell's energy transformers, converting chemical energy into ATP. Mitochondria contain 70S ribosomes.

Plasma membrane: Located inside the cell wall in plants, 3 to 10 nm thick.

Endoplasmic reticulum (ER): Comprises a network of tubes and flattened sacs. ER is continuous with the plasma membrane and the nuclear membrane and may be smooth or have attached ribosomes (rough ER).

Nuclear pore: 100 nm diameter

Nuclear membrane: a double layered structure.

Nucleus: A conspicuous organelle 5 μm diameter.

Nucleolus

Ribosomes: 80S ribosomes. These small (20 nm) structures manufacture proteins. They may be free in the cytoplasm or associated with the surface of the endoplasmic reticulum.

Golgi apparatus

Middle lamella (seen here between adjacent cells left): The first layer of the cell wall formed during cell division. It contains pectin and protein, and provides stability. It allows the cells to form **plasmodesmata (P)**, special channels that allow communication and transport to occur between cells.

Cytoplasm: A watery solution containing dissolved substances, enzymes, and the cell organelles and structures. The site of translation in the cell.

1. What are the functions of the cell wall in plants? _____

_____

2. (a) What structure takes up the majority of space in the plant cell? _____

(b) What are its roles? _____

3. (a) Distinguish between the cytoplasmic ribosomes and the ribosomes found in chloroplasts and mitochondria:

_____

(b) What might this suggest about the origins of these organelles? _____

_____

4. Identify two structures in the diagram that are not found in animal cells: _____

© 2015 **BIOZONE** International
ISBN: 978-1-927309-19-3
Photocopying Prohibited

71 Identifying Structures in a Plant Cell

Key Idea: The position and appearance of the organelles in an electron micrograph can be used to identify them.

1. Study the diagrams on the other pages in this chapter to familiarise yourself with the structures found in eukaryotic cells. Identify the 11 structures in the cell below using the following word list: *cytoplasm, smooth endoplasmic reticulum, mitochondrion, starch granule, chromosome, nucleus, vacuole, plasma membrane, cell wall, chloroplast, nuclear membrane*

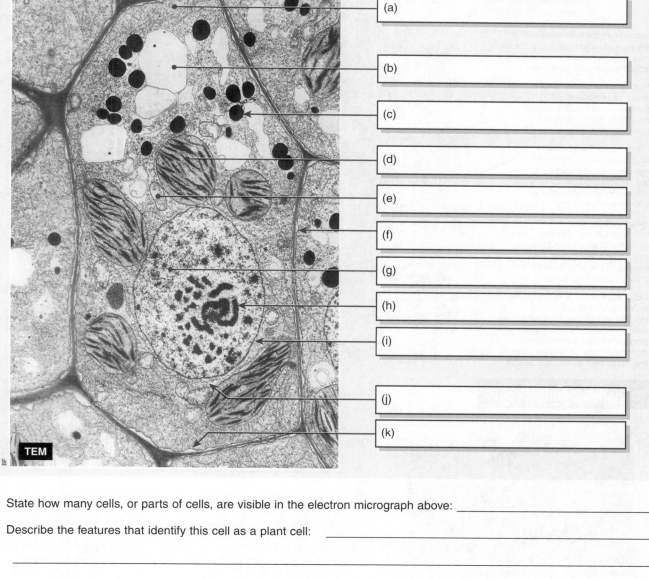

(a)

(b)

(c)

(d)

(e)

(f)

(g)

(h)

(i)

(j)

(k)

TEM

BF

2. State how many cells, or parts of cells, are visible in the electron micrograph above: _____

3. Describe the features that identify this cell as a plant cell: _____

_____

_____

4. (a) Explain where cytoplasm is found in the cell: _____

_____

(b) Describe what cytoplasm is made up of: _____

_____

5. Describe two structures, pictured in the cell above, that are associated with storage:

(a) _____

_____

(b) _____

_____

LINK   WEB

74   71   **KNOW**

72 Animal Cells

Key Idea: Animal cells are eukaryotic cells. They have many features in common with plant cells, but also have a number of unique features.

Animal cells, unlike plant cells, do not have a regular shape. In fact, some animal cells (such as phagocytes) are able to alter their shape for various purposes (e.g. engulfing foreign material). The diagram below shows the structure and organelles of a liver cell. It contains organelles common to most relatively unspecialised human cells. Note the differences between this cell and the generalised plant cell. The plant cells activity provides further information on the organelles listed here but not described.

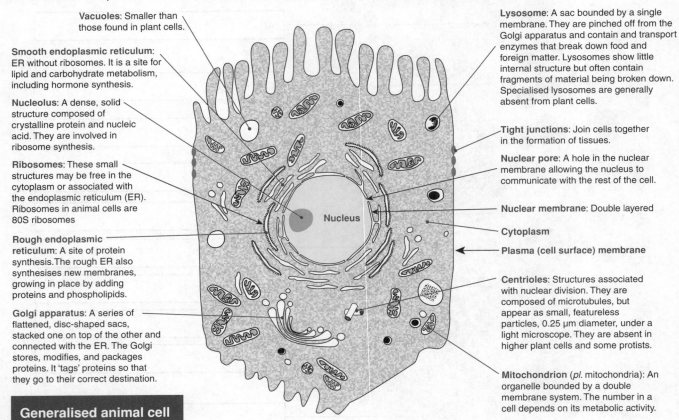

Vacuoles: Smaller than those found in plant cells.

Smooth endoplasmic reticulum: ER without ribosomes. It is a site for lipid and carbohydrate metabolism, including hormone synthesis.

Nucleolus: A dense, solid structure composed of crystalline protein and nucleic acid. They are involved in ribosome synthesis.

Ribosomes: These small structures may be free in the cytoplasm or associated with the endoplasmic reticulum (ER). Ribosomes in animal cells are 80S ribosomes

Rough endoplasmic reticulum: A site of protein synthesis.The rough ER also synthesises new membranes, growing in place by adding proteins and phospholipids.

Golgi apparatus: A series of flattened, disc-shaped sacs, stacked one on top of the other and connected with the ER. The Golgi stores, modifies, and packages proteins. It 'tags' proteins so that they go to their correct destination.

Lysosome: A sac bounded by a single membrane. They are pinched off from the Golgi apparatus and contain and transport enzymes that break down food and foreign matter. Lysosomes show little internal structure but often contain fragments of material being broken down. Specialised lysosomes are generally absent from plant cells.

Tight junctions: Join cells together in the formation of tissues.

Nuclear pore: A hole in the nuclear membrane allowing the nucleus to communicate with the rest of the cell.

Nuclear membrane: Double layered

Cytoplasm

Plasma (cell surface) membrane

Centrioles: Structures associated with nuclear division. They are composed of microtubules, but appear as small, featureless particles, 0.25 µm diameter, under a light microscope. They are absent in higher plant cells and some protists.

Mitochondrion (*pl.* mitochondria): An organelle bounded by a double membrane system. The number in a cell depends on its metabolic activity.

Nucleus

Generalised animal cell

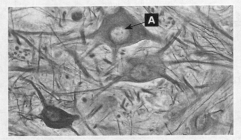

Neurones (nerve cells) in the spinal cord

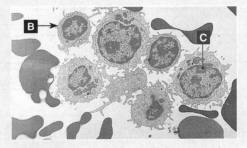

White blood cells and red blood cells (blood smear)

Photos: Ell

1. The two photomicrographs (left) show several types of animal cells. Identify the features indicated by the letters **A-C**:

   A: _____

   B: _____

   C: _____

2. White blood cells are mobile, phagocytic cells, whereas red blood cells are smaller than white blood cells and, in humans, lack a nucleus.

   (a) In the photomicrograph (lower, left), circle a white blood cell and a red blood cell:

   (b) With respect to the features that you can see, explain how you made your decision.

   _____

   _____

   _____

   _____

3. Name one structure or organelle present in generalised animal cells but absent from plant cells and describe its function:

   _____

   _____

WEB 72   LINK 73   LINK 78

KNOW

© 2015 **BIOZONE** International
ISBN: 978-1-927309-19-3
Photocopying Prohibited

73 Identifying Structures in an Animal Cell

Key Idea: The position of the organelles in an electron micrograph can result in variations in their appearance. Transmission electron microscopy (TEM) is the most frequently used technique for viewing cellular organelles.

When viewing TEMs, the cellular organelles may have quite different appearances depending on whether they are in transverse or longitudinal section.

1. Identify and label the structures in the animal cell below using the following list of terms: *cytoplasm, plasma membrane, rough endoplasmic reticulum, mitochondrion, nucleus, centriole, Golgi apparatus, lysosome*

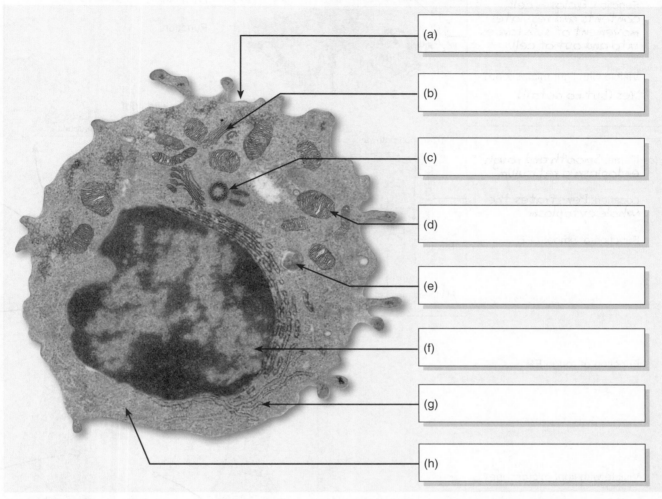

(a)

(b)

(c)

(d)

(e)

(f)

(g)

(h)

2. Which of the organelles in the EM above are obviously shown in both transverse and longitudinal section?

_____

3. Why do plants lack any of the mobile phagocytic cells typical of animal cells? _____

_____

_____

4. The animal cell pictured above is a lymphocyte. Describe the features that suggest to you that:

(a) It has a role in producing and secreting proteins: _____

_____

(b) It is metabolically very active: _____

_____

5. What features of the lymphocyte cell above identify it as eukaryotic? _____

_____

_____

© 2015 **BIOZONE** International
ISBN: 978-1-927309-19-3
Photocopying Prohibited

74 Cell Structures and Organelles

Key Idea: Each type of organelle in a cell has a specific role. Not all cell types contain every type of organelle. The diagram below provides spaces for you to summarise

information about the organelles found in eukaryotic cells. The log scale of measurements (top of next page) illustrates the relative sizes of some cellular structures.

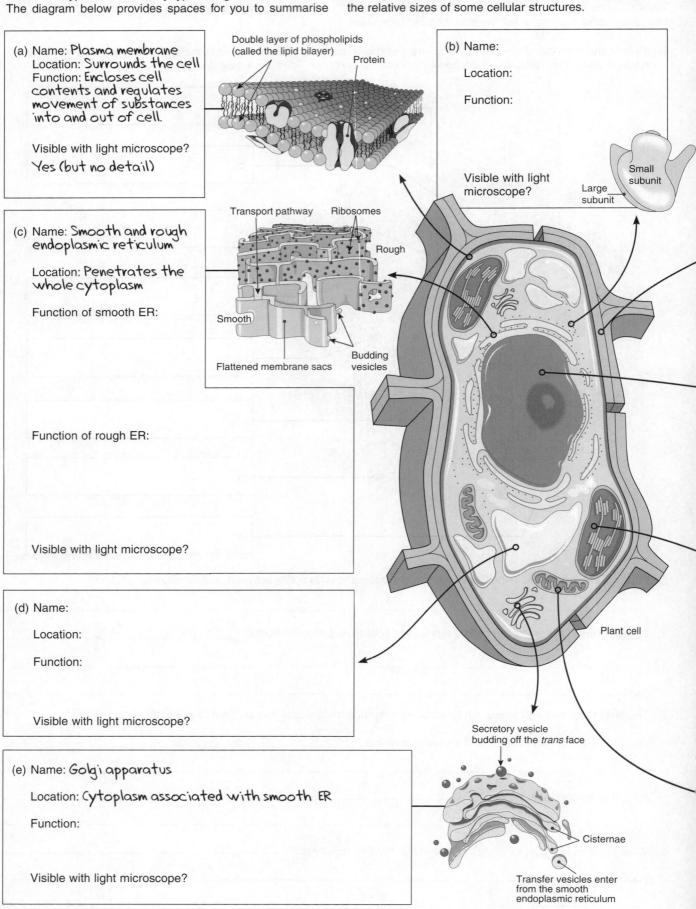

(a) Name: Plasma membrane
Location: Surrounds the cell
Function: Encloses cell contents and regulates movement of substances into and out of cell.

Visible with light microscope?
Yes (but no detail)

Double layer of phospholipids (called the lipid bilayer)

Protein

(b) Name:

Location:

Function:

Visible with light microscope?

Small subunit
Large subunit

(c) Name: Smooth and rough endoplasmic reticulum

Location: Penetrates the whole cytoplasm

Function of smooth ER:

Function of rough ER:

Visible with light microscope?

Transport pathway   Ribosomes

Rough

Smooth

Flattened membrane sacs

Budding vesicles

(d) Name:

Location:

Function:

Visible with light microscope?

Plant cell

(e) Name: Golgi apparatus

Location: Cytoplasm associated with smooth ER

Function:

Visible with light microscope?

Secretory vesicle budding off the *trans* face

Cisternae

Transfer vesicles enter from the smooth endoplasmic reticulum

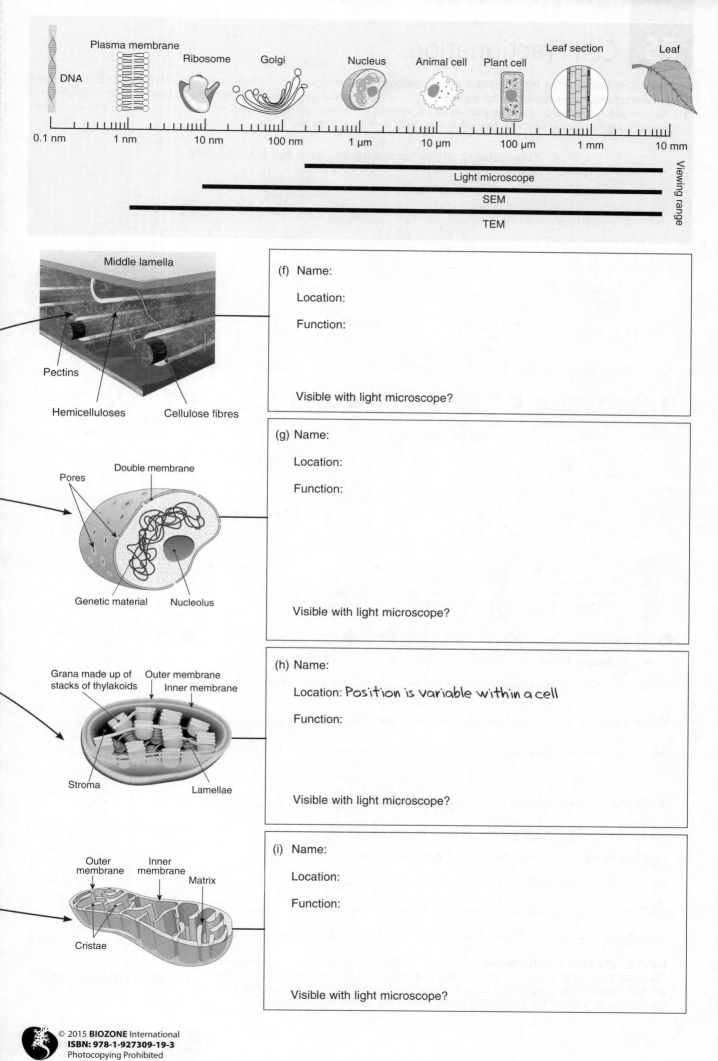

DNA — Plasma membrane — Ribosome — Golgi — Nucleus — Animal cell — Plant cell — Leaf section — Leaf

0.1 nm   1 nm   10 nm   100 nm   1 µm   10 µm   100 µm   1 mm   10 mm

Light microscope
SEM
TEM

Viewing range

Middle lamella
Pectins
Hemicelluloses   Cellulose fibres

(f) Name:

     Location:

     Function:

     Visible with light microscope?

Pores   Double membrane
Genetic material   Nucleolus

(g) Name:

     Location:

     Function:

     Visible with light microscope?

Grana made up of stacks of thylakoids   Outer membrane   Inner membrane
Stroma   Lamellae

(h) Name:

     Location: Position is variable within a cell

     Function:

     Visible with light microscope?

Outer membrane   Inner membrane   Matrix
Cristae

(i) Name:

     Location:

     Function:

     Visible with light microscope?

75 Cell Fractionation

Key Idea: Cell fractionation (or differential centrifugation) is used to extract organelles from cells for study.

The aim of cell fractionation is to extract intact organelles. Samples are kept very cool so that metabolism is slowed and self digestion of the organelles is prevented. The samples are also kept in a buffered, isotonic solution so that the organelles do not change volume and the enzymes are not denatured by changes in pH.

Separating cellular components using cell fractionation

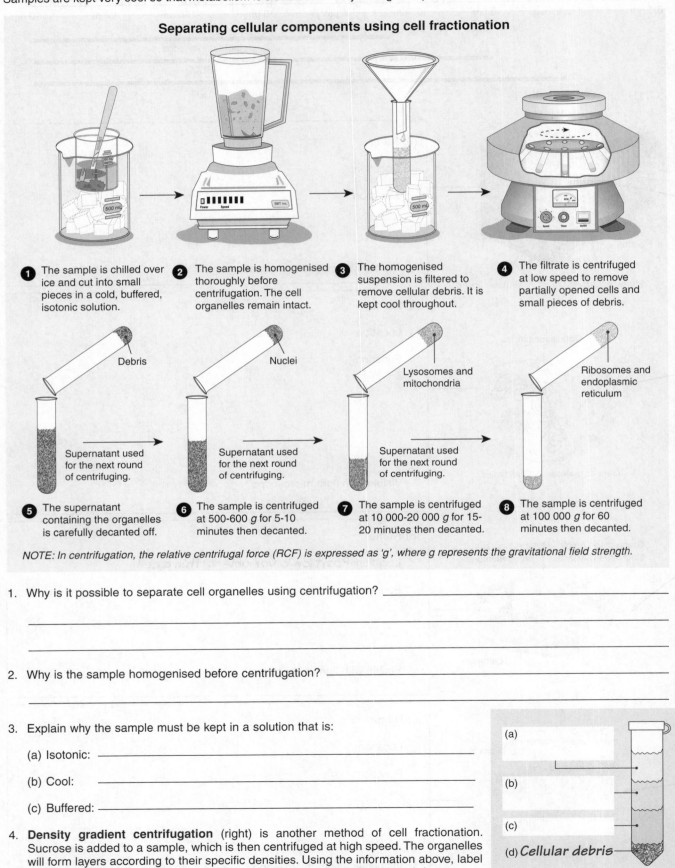

1. The sample is chilled over ice and cut into small pieces in a cold, buffered, isotonic solution.

2. The sample is homogenised thoroughly before centrifugation. The cell organelles remain intact.

3. The homogenised suspension is filtered to remove cellular debris. It is kept cool throughout.

4. The filtrate is centrifuged at low speed to remove partially opened cells and small pieces of debris.

Debris — Supernatant used for the next round of centrifuging.

Nuclei — Supernatant used for the next round of centrifuging.

Lysosomes and mitochondria — Supernatant used for the next round of centrifuging.

Ribosomes and endoplasmic reticulum

5. The supernatant containing the organelles is carefully decanted off.

6. The sample is centrifuged at 500-600 *g* for 5-10 minutes then decanted.

7. The sample is centrifuged at 10 000-20 000 *g* for 15-20 minutes then decanted.

8. The sample is centrifuged at 100 000 *g* for 60 minutes then decanted.

NOTE: In centrifugation, the relative centrifugal force (RCF) is expressed as '*g*', where *g* represents the gravitational field strength.

1. Why is it possible to separate cell organelles using centrifugation? _____

_____

_____

2. Why is the sample homogenised before centrifugation? _____

_____

3. Explain why the sample must be kept in a solution that is:

   (a) Isotonic: _____

   (b) Cool: _____

   (c) Buffered: _____

4. **Density gradient centrifugation** (right) is another method of cell fractionation. Sucrose is added to a sample, which is then centrifuged at high speed. The organelles will form layers according to their specific densities. Using the information above, label the centrifuge tube on the right with the organelles you would find in each layer.

(a)

(b)

(c)

(d) *Cellular debris*

© 2015 **BIOZONE** International
ISBN: 978-1-927309-19-3
Photocopying Prohibited

KNOW

76 Identifying Organelles

Key Idea: Cellular organelles can be identified in electron micrographs by their specific features.

Electron microscopes produce a magnified image at high resolution (distinguish between close together but separate objects). The transmission electron microscope (TEM) images below show the ultrastructure of some organelles.

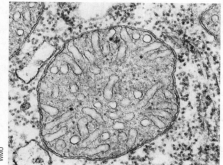

1. (a) Name the circled organelle: _____

   (b) Which kind of cell(s) would this organelle be found in?

   _____

   (c) Describe the function of this organelle: _____

   _____

   _____

   _____

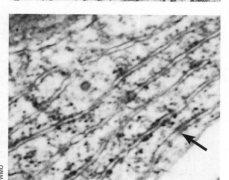

2. (a) Name this organelle (arrowed): _____

   (b) State which kind of cell(s) this organelle would be found in:

   _____

   (c) Describe the function of this organelle: _____

   _____

   _____

3. (a) Name the large, circular organelle: _____

   (b) State which kind of cell(s) this organelle would be found in:

   _____

   (c) Describe the function of this organelle: _____

   _____

   _____

   (d) Label **two** regions that can be seen **inside** this organelle.

4. (a) Name and label the ribbon-like organelle in this photograph (arrowed):

   _____

   (b) State which kind of cell(s) this organelle is found in:

   _____

   (c) Describe the function of this organelle: _____

   _____

   (d) Name the dark 'blobs' attached to the organelle you have labelled:

   _____

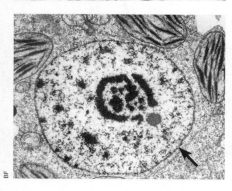

5. (a) Name this large circular organelle (arrowed): _____

   (b) State which kind of cell(s) this organelle would be found in: _____

   _____

   (c) Describe the function of this organelle: _____

   _____

   (d) Label three features relating to this organelle in the photograph.

TEST

77 Specialisation in Plant Cells

Key Idea: The specialised cells in a plant have specific features associated with their particular roles. The differentiation of cells gives rise to specialised cell types that fulfil specific roles in the plant, e.g. support, transport, or photosynthesis. Each of the cell types illustrated below has features that set it apart from other cell types.

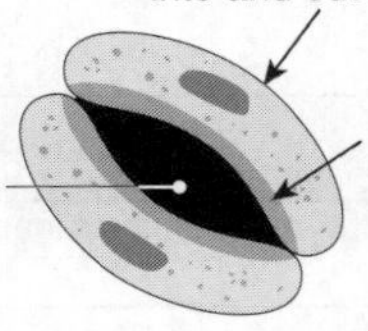

Changes its shape depending on water fluxes into and out of the cell.

Uneven thickening of the cell wall makes this side more rigid.

Open pore

A pair of guard cells forming a stoma

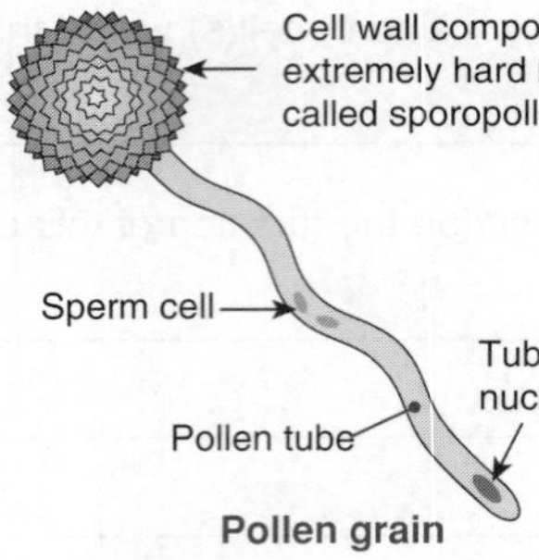

Cell wall composed of extremely hard material called sporopollenin.

Sperm cell

Tube nucleus

Pollen tube

Pollen grain

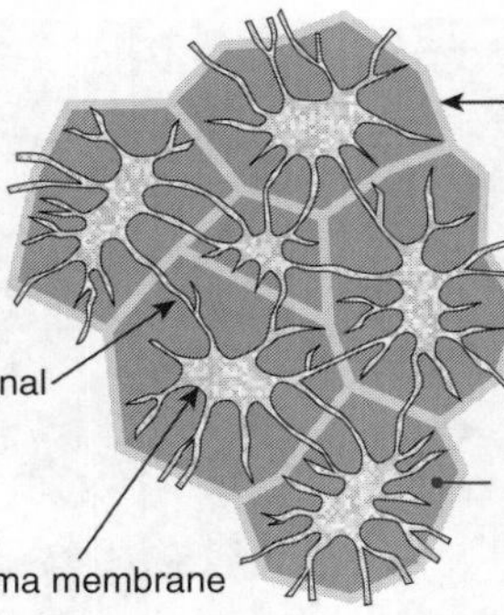

Primary cell wall

Canal

Lignified cell wall

Plasma membrane

Stone cells (sclereids) covering the seed in stone fruit

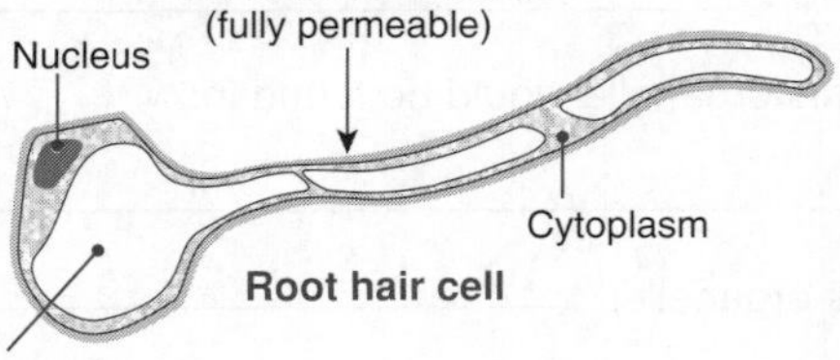

Thin cellulose cell wall (fully permeable)

Nucleus

Cytoplasm

Root hair cell

Vacuole

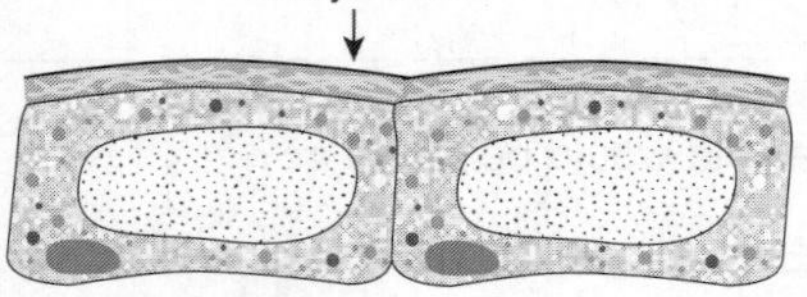

Waxy cuticle

Epidermal cells

Phloem cells

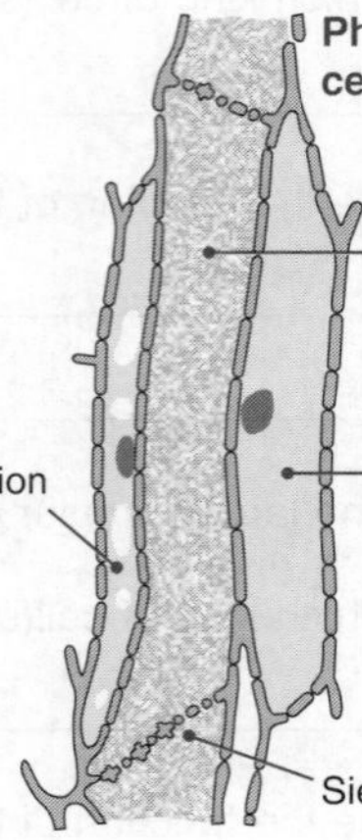

Sieve tube member

Companion cell

Phloem parenchyma cell

Sieve plate

Walls are lignified to add strength

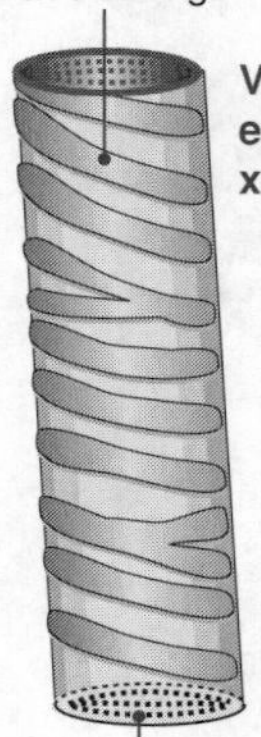

Vessel element of xylem

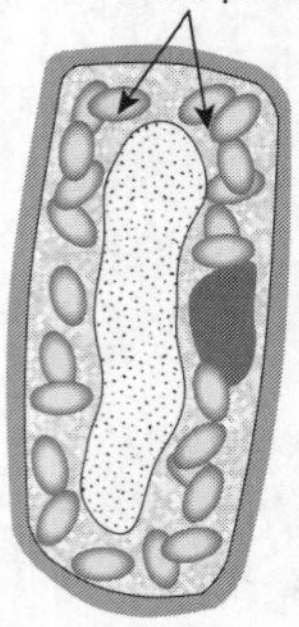

The end walls perforated cuticle

Large number of chloroplasts

Palisade parenchyma cell of the mesophyll

1. Using the information given above, describe the **specialised features** and **role** of each of the cell types (b)-(h) below:

   (a) **Guard cell**: Features: _Curved, sausage shaped cell, unevenly thickened._

   Role in plant: _Turgor changes alter the cell shape to open or close the stoma._

   (b) **Pollen grain**: Features: _____

   Role in plant: _____

   (c) **Palisade parenchyma cell**: Features: _____

   Role in plant: _____

   (d) **Epidermal cell**: Features: _____

   Role in plant: _____

   (e) **Vessel element**: Features: _____

   Role in plant: _____

   (f) **Stone cell**: Features: _____

   Role in plant: _____

   (g) **Sieve tube member** (of phloem): Features: _____

   Role in plant: _____

   (h) **Root hair cell**: Features: _____

   Role in plant: _____

© 2015 **BIOZONE** International
ISBN: 978-1-927309-19-3
Photocopying Prohibited

78 Specialisation in Human Cells

Key Idea: Specialised cells carry out specific roles in animals. Humans have at least 230 specialised cell types, each with features that enable it to perform its designated role. The eight cell types below are a representative sample of these.

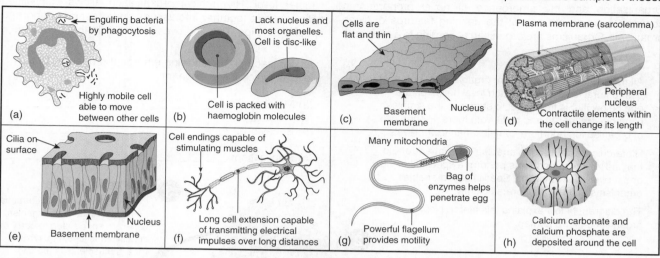

(a) Engulfing bacteria by phagocytosis. Highly mobile cell able to move between other cells

(b) Lack nucleus and most organelles. Cell is disc-like. Cell is packed with haemoglobin molecules

(c) Cells are flat and thin. Basement membrane. Nucleus

(d) Plasma membrane (sarcolemma). Peripheral nucleus. Contractile elements within the cell change its length

(e) Cilia on surface. Nucleus. Basement membrane

(f) Cell endings capable of stimulating muscles. Long cell extension capable of transmitting electrical impulses over long distances

(g) Many mitochondria. Bag of enzymes helps penetrate egg. Powerful flagellum provides motility

(h) Calcium carbonate and calcium phosphate are deposited around the cell

1. For each cell type pictured above, describe its **specialised features** and **role** in the body:

   (a) **Phagocytic white blood cell (neutrophil).** Specialised features: _____

   _____

   Role of cell within body: _____

   (b) **Red blood cell (erythrocyte).** Specialised features: _____

   _____

   Role of cell within body: _____

   (c) **Squamous epithelial cell.** Specialised features: _____

   _____

   Role of cell within body: _____

   (d) **Skeletal muscle cell.** Specialised features: _____

   _____

   Role of cell within body: _____

   (e) **Ciliated epithelial cell.** Specialised features: _____

   _____

   Role of cell within body: _____

   (f) **Motor neurone.** Specialised features: _____

   _____

   Role of cell within body: _____

   (g) **Sperm cell.** Specialised features: _____

   _____

   Role of cell within body: _____

   (h) **Bone cell (osteocyte).** Specialised features: _____

   _____

   Role of cell within body: _____

© 2015 **BIOZONE** International
ISBN: 978-1-927309-19-3
Photocopying Prohibited

LINK 80   WEB 78   **KNOW**

79 Levels of Organisation

Key Idea: Structural organisation in multicellular organisms is hierarchical, with new properties arising at each level. Organisation and the emergence of novel properties in complex systems are two of the defining features of living organisms. Organisms are organised according to a hierarchy of structural levels, each level building on the one before it. At each level, new properties arise that were absent at the simpler level. Hierarchical organisation allows specialised cells to group together into tissues and organs to perform a specific function. This improves efficiency in the organism.

All multicellular organisms are organised in a hierarchy of structural levels, where each level builds on the one below it. It is traditional to start with the simplest components (parts) and build from there. Higher levels of organisation are more complex than lower levels.

Hierarchical organisation enables **specialisation** so that individual components perform a specific function or set of related functions. Specialisation enables organisms to function more efficiently.

The diagram below explains this hierarchical organisation for a human.

1. Assign each of the following emergent properties to the level at which it first appears:

   (a) Metabolism: _____

   (b) Behaviour: _____

   (c) Replication: _____

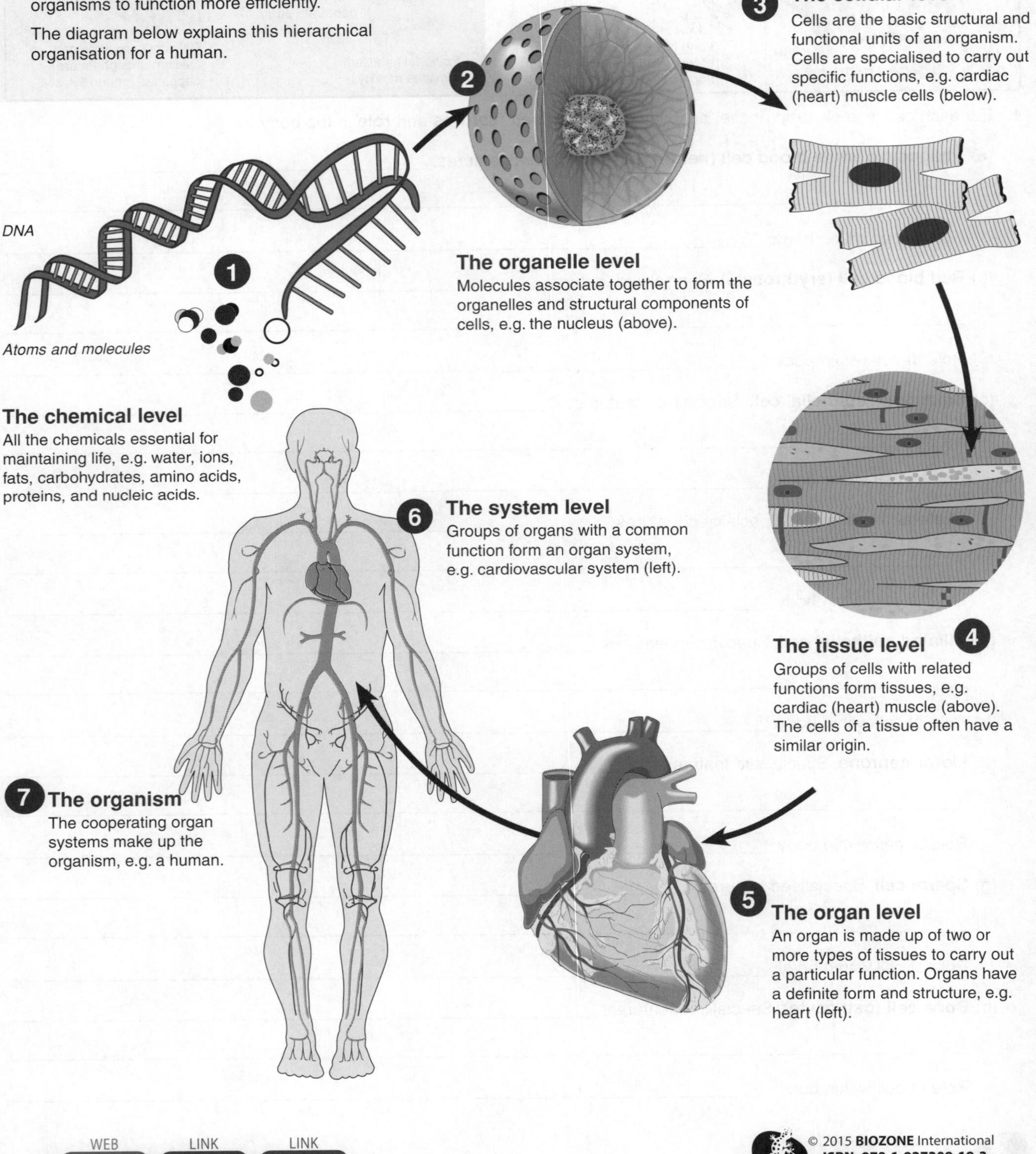

The chemical level
All the chemicals essential for maintaining life, e.g. water, ions, fats, carbohydrates, amino acids, proteins, and nucleic acids.

DNA

Atoms and molecules

1

2

The organelle level
Molecules associate together to form the organelles and structural components of cells, e.g. the nucleus (above).

3 **The cellular level**
Cells are the basic structural and functional units of an organism. Cells are specialised to carry out specific functions, e.g. cardiac (heart) muscle cells (below).

4 **The tissue level**
Groups of cells with related functions form tissues, e.g. cardiac (heart) muscle (above). The cells of a tissue often have a similar origin.

5 **The organ level**
An organ is made up of two or more types of tissues to carry out a particular function. Organs have a definite form and structure, e.g. heart (left).

6 **The system level**
Groups of organs with a common function form an organ system, e.g. cardiovascular system (left).

7 **The organism**
The cooperating organ systems make up the organism, e.g. a human.

© 2015 **BIOZONE** International
ISBN: 978-1-927309-19-3
Photocopying Prohibited

80 Animal Tissues

Key Idea: A tissue is a collection of related cell types that work together to carry out a specific function. Four main tissue types make up the animal body.

Tissues are formed from related cell types that carry out a specific function. They improve functional efficiency because tasks can be shared amongst specialised cells. Animal tissues fall into four broad groups: epithelial, connective, muscle, and nervous tissues. Different tissues come together to form organs. For example, the heart consists of cardiac muscle tissue, but also has epithelial tissue, which lines the heart chambers, connective tissue for strength and elasticity, and nervous tissue, which directs muscle contraction.

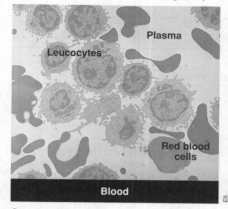

Blood

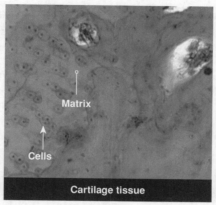

Cartilage tissue

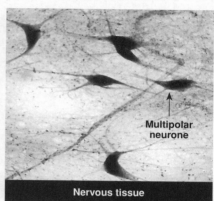

Nervous tissue

Connective tissues form the major supporting tissue of the body made up of cells within a semi-fluid matrix. Connective tissues bind structures together and provide support and protection. They include dentine (teeth), adipose (fat) tissue, bone, and cartilage (above centre), and the tissues around the organs and blood vessels. Blood is a specialised liquid tissue, made up of cells floating in a liquid matrix.

Nervous tissue contains densely packed nerve cells (neurones) which transmit information in the form of nerve impulses. There may also be supporting connective tissue and blood vessels.

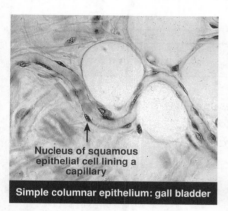

Simple columnar epithelium: gall bladder

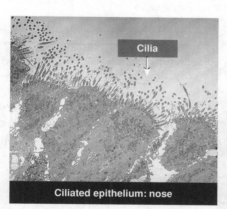

Ciliated epithelium: nose

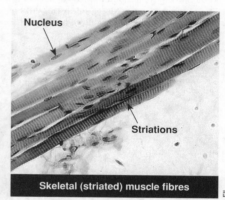

Skeletal (striated) muscle fibres

Epithelial tissue is organised into single or layered sheets. It lines internal and external surfaces (e.g. blood vessels, ducts, gut lining) and protects the structures underneath from wear, infection, or pressure. The cells may be specialised for absorption, secretion, or excretion. Examples: stratified epithelium of vagina, ciliated epithelium of respiratory tract, cuboidal epithelium of kidney ducts, columnar epithelium of the intestine, and the squamous epithelium found in capillaries, alveoli, and the glomeruli of the kidney.

Muscle tissue consists of specialised cells called fibres, held together by connective tissue. The three muscle types are cardiac, skeletal, and smooth muscle. Muscles bring about movement of body parts by contracting.

1. Explain how the development of tissues improves functional efficiency: _____

_____

_____

2. Describe the general function of each of the following broad tissue types:

   (a) Epithelial tissue: _____ (c) Muscle tissue: _____

   (b) Nervous tissue: _____ (d) Connective tissue: _____

3. Identify the particular features that contribute to the particular functional role of each of the following tissue types:

   (a) Muscle tissue: _____

   _____

   (b) Nervous tissue: _____

   _____

LINK
78

WEB
80

KNOW

81 Plant Tissues

Key Idea: Plant tissues are either simple or complex tissues. Plant tissues are divided into simple and complex tissues. **Simple tissues** contain only one cell type and form packing and support tissues. **Complex tissues** contain more than one cell type and form the conducting and support tissues of plants. Tissues are grouped into tissue systems which make up the plant body. Vascular plants have dermal, vascular, and ground tissue systems. The dermal system covers the plant providing protection and reducing water loss. Vascular tissue provides the water and nutrient transport system of the plant. The ground tissue system carries out a variety of roles within the plant (e.g. photosynthesis, storage, and support).

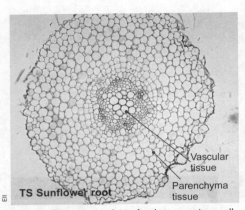

TS Sunflower root — Vascular tissue, Parenchyma tissue

Simple tissues consists of only one or two cell types. **Parenchyma tissue** is the most common and involved in storage, photosynthesis, and secretion. **Collenchyma tissue** comprises thick-walled collenchyma cells alternating with layers of intracellular substances to provide flexible support. The fibres and sclereids of **sclerenchyma** tissue have rigid cell walls which provide support.

Xylem

Phloem

Complex tissues comprise more than two cell types. **Xylem** and **phloem**, which make up the plant **vascular tissue** system, are complex tissues. Each is made up of several cell types: tracheids, vessels, parenchyma, and fibres in xylem, and sieve tube members, companion cells, parenchyma and sclerenchyma in phloem.

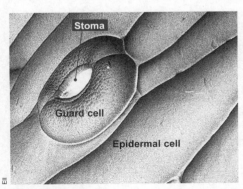

Stoma

Guard cell

Epidermal cell

Dermal tissue covers the outside of the plant. Its composition varies depending on its location. The leaf epidermis has a waxy cuticle to reduce water loss and guard cells to regulate water loss and gas exchange via pores in the leaf (stomata).

Simple tissue	Cell type(s)	Role within the plant
Parenchyma	Parenchyma cells	Photosynthesis, storage and secretion.
Collenchyma		
Sclerenchyma		
Root endodermis	Endodermal cells	
Pericycle		

Complex tissue	Cell type(s)	Role within the plant
Leaf mesophyll	Spongy mesophyll cells, palisade mesophyll cells	
Xylem		
Phloem		
Epidermis		

1. Identify the three tissue systems of plants: _____

2. The tables above list the major types of simple and complex plant tissues. Complete the tables by filling in the cell types that make up the tissue and the role that each tissue has within the plant. The first example has been completed for you. Use the weblinks sites to help you.

© 2015 **BIOZONE** International
ISBN: 978-1-927309-19-3
Photocopying Prohibited

82 Viruses

Key Idea: A virus is an infectious, highly specialised intracellular parasite. They are acellular and non-living.

A **virus** is an infectious agent that replicates only inside the living cells of other organisms. Although they are often identified as microorganisms, viruses are acellular, meaning they are not made up of cells, so they do not conform to the existing criteria upon which a five or six kingdom classification system is based. A typical virus contains genetic material (DNA or RNA) encased in a protein coat (capsid). Some viruses have an additional membrane, called an envelope, surrounding the capsid. Many viruses have glycoprotein receptor spikes on their envelopes that help them to attach to surface of the host cell they are infecting. Viruses vary greatly in their appearance and the type of host they infect (below).

> **Viruses are not organisms!** Viruses are metabolically inert until they are inside the host cell and hijacking its metabolic machinery to make new viral particles. However, they are often called microorganisms.

Glycoprotein spikes mediate attachment to the host cells' receptors.

Two copies of single stranded RNA

Viral envelope (lipoprotein)

Reverse transcriptase forms viral DNA from viral RNA

Capsid

Structure of HIV, an enveloped retrovirus.

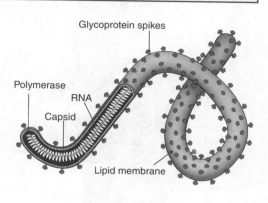

Glycoprotein spikes

Polymerase

RNA

Capsid

Lipid membrane

Structure of Ebola virus, an RNA filovirus that causes Ebola haemorrhagic fever.

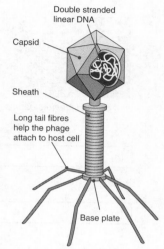

Double stranded linear DNA

Capsid

Sheath

Long tail fibres help the phage attach to host cell

Base plate

Structure of Lambda phage, a bacteriophage that infects E.coli.

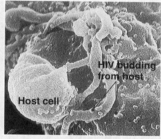

Host cell

HIV budding from host

When viral replication is complete, the new viral particles leave the host cell to infect more cells. In enveloped viruses, this is achieved by budding from the host cell. Each viral particle takes some of the host's cell membrane to create the viral envelope. This also helps the virus (e.g. HIV and *Influenzavirus*) avoid detection by the host's immune system.

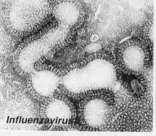

Influenzavirus

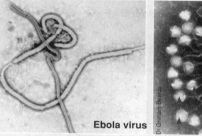

Ebola virus

Viruses cause a wide variety of common human diseases, e.g. colds, influenza, and life-threatening diseases such as AIDS and Ebola (above).

Bacteriophages (arrowed) infect bacterial cells. They use tail fibres to attach to the host and a contractile region below the capsid to inject their DNA into the cell.

1. What is the significance of viruses being non-living? _____

_____

_____

2. Describe the basic structure of a generalised virus, identifying the features they all have in common: _____

_____

_____

3. Describe the purpose of the following:

(a) Glycoprotein spikes: _____

(b) A bacteriophage's tail fibres: _____

(c) Protein capsid: _____

83 Optical Microscopes

Key Idea: Optical microscopes use light focussed through a series of lenses to magnify objects up to several 100 times. The light (or optical) microscope is an important tool in biology and using it correctly is an essential skill. High power compound light microscopes use visible light and a combination of lenses to magnify objects up to several 100 times. The resolution of light microscopes is limited by the wavelength of light and specimens must be thin and mostly transparent so that light can pass through. No detail will be seen in specimens that are thick or opaque.

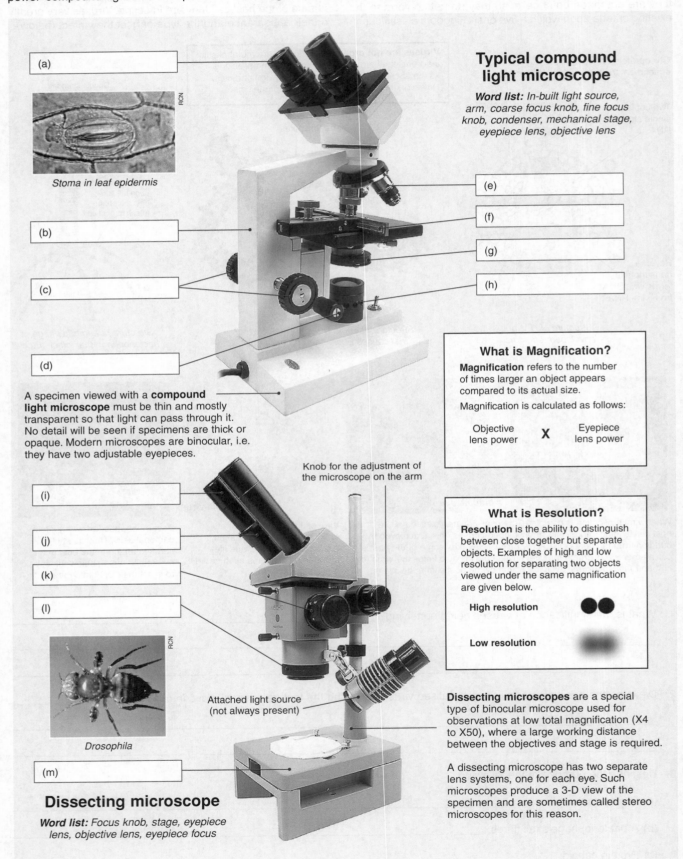

(a)

Stoma in leaf epidermis

(b)

(c)

(d)

Typical compound light microscope

Word list: In-built light source, arm, coarse focus knob, fine focus knob, condenser, mechanical stage, eyepiece lens, objective lens

(e)

(f)

(g)

(h)

A specimen viewed with a **compound light microscope** must be thin and mostly transparent so that light can pass through it. No detail will be seen if specimens are thick or opaque. Modern microscopes are binocular, i.e. they have two adjustable eyepieces.

What is Magnification?

Magnification refers to the number of times larger an object appears compared to its actual size.

Magnification is calculated as follows:

Objective lens power **X** Eyepiece lens power

Knob for the adjustment of the microscope on the arm

(i)

(j)

(k)

(l)

Drosophila

(m)

What is Resolution?

Resolution is the ability to distinguish between close together but separate objects. Examples of high and low resolution for separating two objects viewed under the same magnification are given below.

High resolution

Low resolution

Attached light source (not always present)

Dissecting microscopes are a special type of binocular microscope used for observations at low total magnification (X4 to X50), where a large working distance between the objectives and stage is required.

A dissecting microscope has two separate lens systems, one for each eye. Such microscopes produce a 3-D view of the specimen and are sometimes called stereo microscopes for this reason.

Dissecting microscope

Word list: Focus knob, stage, eyepiece lens, objective lens, eyepiece focus

© 2015 **BIOZONE** International
ISBN: 978-1-927309-19-3
Photocopying Prohibited

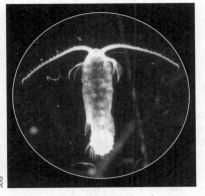

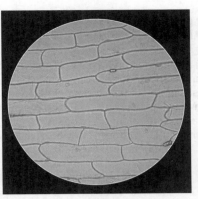

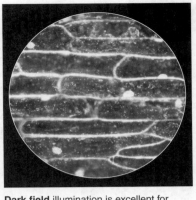

Dissecting microscopes are used for identifying and sorting organisms, observing microbial cultures, and dissections.

These onion epidermal cells are viewed with standard **bright field** lighting. Very little detail can be seen (only cell walls) and the cell nuclei are barely visible.

Dark field illumination is excellent for viewing specimens that are almost transparent. The nuclei of these onion epidermal cells are clearly visible.

1. Label the two photographs on the previous page, the compound light microscope (a) to (h) and the dissecting microscope (i) to (m). Use words from the lists supplied for each image.

2. Determine the magnification of a microscope using:

   (a) 15 X eyepiece and 40 X objective lens: _____   (b) 10 X eyepiece and 60 X objective lens: _____

3. Describe the main difference between a compound light microscope and a dissecting microscope: _____
   _____
   _____

4. What type of microscope would you use to:

   (a) Count stream invertebrates in a sample: _____   (b) Observe cells in mitosis: _____

5. (a) Distinguish between **magnification** and **resolution**: _____
   _____

   (b) Explain the benefits of a higher resolution: _____
   _____
   _____

6. Below is a list of ten key steps taken to set up a microscope and optimally view a sample. The steps have been mixed up. Put them in their **correct order** by numbering each step:

   ☐ Focus and centre the specimen using the high objective lens. Adjust focus using the fine focus knob only.

   ☐ Adjust the illumination to an appropriate level by adjusting the iris diaphragm and the condenser. The light should appear on the slide directly below the objective lens, and give an even amount of illumination.

   ☐ Rotate the objective lenses until the shortest lens is in place (pointing down towards the stage).
   This is the lowest / highest power objective lens (delete one).

   ☐ Place the slide on the microscope stage. Secure with the sample clips.

   ☐ Fine tune the illumination so you can view maximum detail on your sample.

   ☐ Focus and centre the specimen using the medium objective lens. Focus firstly with the coarse focus knob, then with the fine focus knob (if needed).

   ☐ Turn on the light source.

   ☐ Focus and centre the specimen using the low objective lens. Focus firstly with the coarse focus knob, then with the fine focus knob.

   ☐ Focus the eyepieces to adjust your view.

   ☐ Adjust the distance between the eyepieces so that they are comfortable for your eyes.

84 Preparing a Slide

Key Idea: Correctly preparing and mounting a specimen on a slide is important if structures are to be seen clearly under a microscope. A wet mount is suitable for most slides.

Specimens are often prepared in some way before viewing in order to highlight features and reveal details. A wet mount is a temporary preparation in which a specimen and a drop of fluid are trapped under a thin coverslip. Wet mounts are used to view thin tissue sections, live microscopic organisms, and suspensions such as blood. A wet mount improves a sample's appearance and enhances visible detail. Sections must be made very thin for two main reasons. A thick section stops light shining through making it appear dark when viewed. It also ends up with too many layers of cells, making it difficult to make out detail.

Preparing a specimen

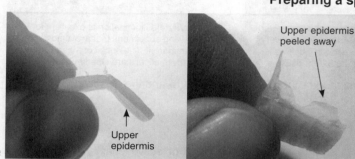

Onions make good subjects for preparing a simple wet mount. A square segment is cut from a thick leaf from the bulb. The segment is then bent towards the upper epidermis and snapped so that just the epidermis is left attached. The epidermis can then be peeled off to provide a thin layer of cells for viewing.

Sections through stems or other soft objects need to be made with a razor blade or scalpel, and must be very thin. Cutting at a slight angle to produce a wedge shape creates a thin edge. Ideally specimens should be set in wax first, to prevent crushing and make it easier to cut the specimen accurately.

Mounting a specimen

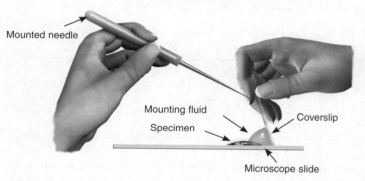

Mounting: The thin layer is placed in the centre of a clean glass microscope slide and covered with a drop of mounting liquid (e.g. water, glycerol, or stain). A coverslip is placed on top using a mounted needle to support and lower it gently over the specimen. This avoids including air in the mount.

Viewing

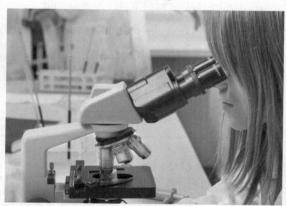

Locate the specimen or region of interest at the lowest magnification. Focus using the lowest magnification first, before switching to the higher magnifications.

1. Why must sections viewed under a microscope be very thin? _____

_____

2. What is the purpose of the coverslip? _____

_____

_____

3. Why would no chloroplasts be visible in an onion epidermis cell slide? _____

_____

4. Why is it necessary to focus on the lowest magnification first, before switching to higher magnifications? _____

_____

_____

© 2015 **BIOZONE** International
ISBN: 978-1-927309-19-3
Photocopying Prohibited

85 Staining a Slide

Key Idea: Staining material to be viewed under a microscope can make it easier to distinguish particular cell structures. **Stains** and dyes can be used to highlight specific components or structures. Most stains are **non-viable**, and are used on dead specimens, but harmless viable stains can be applied to living material. Stains contain chemicals that interact with molecules in the cell. Some stains bind to a particular molecule making it easier to see where those molecules are. Others cause a change in a target molecule, which changes their colour, making them more visible.

Some commonly used stains		
Stain	Final colour	Used for
Iodine solution	blue-black	Starch
Crystal violet	purple	Gram staining
Aniline sulfate	yellow	lignin
Methylene blue	blue	Nuclei
Hematoxylin and eosin (H&E)	H=dark blue/violet E=red/pink	H=Nuclei E=Proteins

Iodine stain

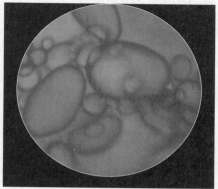

Iodine stains starch-containing organelles, such as **potato amyloplasts**, blue-black.

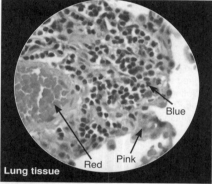

Lung tissue   Red   Pink   Blue

H&E stain is one of the most common histological stains. Nuclei stain dark blue, whereas proteins, extracellular material, and red blood cells stain pink or red.

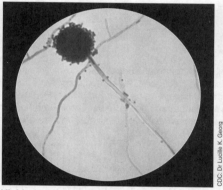

Viable (or vital) **stains** do not immediately harm living cells. **Trypan blue** is a vital stain that stains dead cells blue but is excluded by live cells. It is also used to study fungal hyphae.

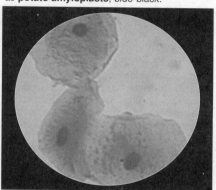

Methylene blue is a common temporary stain for animal cells, such as these **cheek cells**. It stains DNA and so makes the **nuclei** more visible. It is distinct from methyl blue, a histological stain.

How to apply a simple stain

If a specimen is already mounted, a drop of stain can be placed at one end of the coverslip and drawn through using filter paper (below). Water can be drawn through in the same way to remove excess stain.

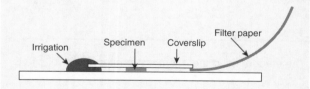

Irrigation   Specimen   Coverslip   Filter paper

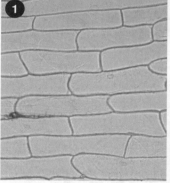

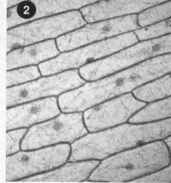

The light micrographs 1 and 2 (above) illustrate how the use of a stain can enhance certain structures. The left image (1) is unstained and only the cell wall is easily visible. Adding iodine (2) makes the cell wall and nuclei stand out.

1. What is the main purpose of using a stain? _____
_____

2. What is the difference between a viable and non-viable stain? _____
_____

3. Identify a stain that would be appropriate for distinguishing each of the following:

   (a) Live vs dead cells: _____ (c) Lignin in a plant root section: _____

   (b) Red blood cells in a tissue preparation: _____ (d) Nuclei in cheek cells: _____

WEB

KNOW

86 Measuring and Counting Using a Microscope

Key Idea: Graticules make it possible to measure cell size. Haemocytometers are used to count the number of cells. Measuring and counting objects to be viewed under a microscope requires precisely marked measuring equipment.

Two common pieces of equipment are the graticule and the haemocytometer. A graticule can be used to measure the size of an object whereas a haemocytometer is used to count the number of cells in a set area or volume.

Measuring cell size

A graticule is a scale placed in the eyepiece of a microscope. It is usually about 1 mm long and divided into 100 equal units. A graticule is used in combination with a stage micrometer to work out the size of an object being viewed. The stage micrometer is a slide with a scale that is exactly 1 mm long and also divided into 100 divisions (so that each division is 0.01 mm) and is placed on the microscope stage. The stage micrometer allows the graticule to be calibrated so that a precise scale can be calculated at each magnification.

The scale on the graticule is lined up with the stage micrometer. The number of graticule divisions between the divisions of the stage micrometer can then be read off. In the example right, each division of the stage micrometer is equal to four large divisions of the graticule. Each large division of the graticule is therefore 2.5×10^{-3} mm at 400x magnification.

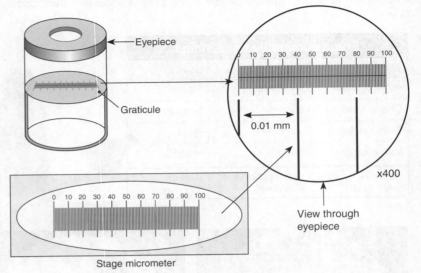

0.01 mm

x400

View through eyepiece

Stage micrometer

Counting cells

Microscopes can be used as a tool to count cells or other small objects (e.g pollen grains). By counting the number of cells in a known area, the total number of cells in a larger area can be calculated. A haemocytometer is commonly used to count cells viewed with a light microscope. It is a simple slide with precisely etched lines forming a grid and was developed for counting blood cells. There are a number of types of haemocytometer, including the Improved Neubauer, shown below. The slide holds a coverslip 0.1 mm above the surface of the grid, allowing volume to be calculated. The central counting grid is divided into 25 large squares, each of which is further divided into 16 squares.

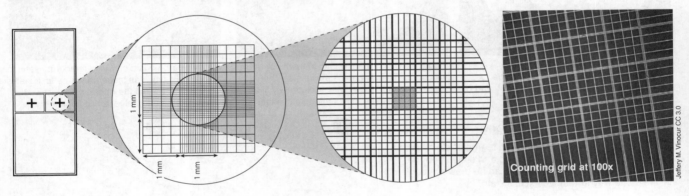

Counting grid at 100x

Jeffery M. Vinocur CC 3.0

1. A student using the graticule scale shown at the top of this page found a cell to be 56 divisions wide. Calculate the width of the cell in mm and in m:

2. A second student grew yeast cells in 5 cm³ of nutrient solution. The student used the haemocytometer shown above to count the number of yeast cells each day for 3 days.

   (a) Calculate the area and volume of the grid shown in blue: Area: _____ Volume: _____

   (b) The student counted yeast cells in the central blue grid. Complete the table below based on the counts obtained:

	Day 1	Day 2	Day 3
Number of cells counted	4	9	17
Cells in 5 cm³			

3. A botanist wished to know the number of pollen grains produced per anther by a flower with eight anthers. She cut the anthers and placed them in 3 cm³ of distilled water, shaking the mix vigorously. Using a haemocytometer she counted 6 grains in the large central counting grid (1 x 1 mm). Calculate the total number of pollen grains produced **per anther**:

LINK 12   LINK 83

© 2015 **BIOZONE** International
ISBN: 978-1-927309-19-3
Photocopying Prohibited

87 Calculating Linear Magnification

Key Idea: Magnification is how much larger an object appears compared to its actual size. Magnification can be calculated from the ratio of image size to object size.

Microscopes produce an enlarged (magnified) image of an object allowing it to be observed in greater detail than is possible with the naked eye. **Magnification** refers to the number of times larger an object appears compared to its actual size. Linear magnification is calculated by taking a ratio of the image height to the object's actual height. If this ratio is greater than one, the image is enlarged. If it is less than one, it is reduced. To calculate magnification, all measurements are converted to the same units. Often, you will be asked to calculate an object's actual size, in which case you will be told the size of the object and the magnification.

Calculating linear magnification: a worked example

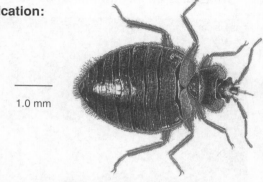
1.0 mm

1 Measure the body length of the bed bug image (right). Your measurement should be 40 mm (*not* including the body hairs and antennae).

2 Measure the length of the scale line marked 1.0 mm. You will find it is 10 mm long. The magnification of the scale line can be calculated using equation 1 (below right).

The magnification of the scale line is **10** (10 mm / 1 mm)

NB: The magnification of the bed bug image will also be 10x because the scale line and image are magnified to the same degree.

3 Calculate the actual (real) size of the bed bug using equation 2 (right):

The actual size of the bed bug is **4 mm** (40 mm / 10 x magnification)

Microscopy equations

1. $\text{Magnification} = \dfrac{\text{measured size of the object}}{\text{actual size of the object}}$

2. $\text{Actual object size} = \dfrac{\text{size of the image}}{\text{magnification}}$

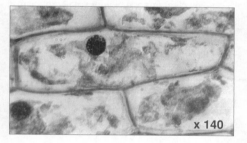
x 140

1. The bright field microscopy image on the left is of onion epidermal cells. The measured length of the onion cell in the centre of the photograph is 52 000 μm (52 mm). The image has been magnified 140 x. Calculate the actual size of the cell:

_____

_____

_____

2. The image of the flea (left) has been captured using light microscopy.

(a) Calculate the magnification using the scale line on the image:

_____

_____

_____

0.5 mm

(b) The body length of the flea is indicated by a line. Measure along the line and calculate the actual length of the flea:

_____

_____

_____

3. The image size of the *E.coli* cell (left) is 43 mm, and its actual size is 2 μm. Using this information, calculate the magnification of the image:

_____

_____

_____

DATA

88 Electron Microscopes

Key Idea: Electron microscopes use the short wavelengths of electrons to produce high resolution images of extremely small objects.

Electron microscopes (EMs) use a beam of electrons, instead of light, to produce an image. The higher resolution of EMs is due to the shorter wavelengths of electrons. There are two basic types of electron microscope: **scanning electron microscopes** (SEM) and **transmission electron microscopes** (TEM). In SEMs, the electrons are bounced off the surface of an object to produce detailed images of the external appearance. TEMs produce very clear images of specially prepared thin sections.

Transmission electron microscope (TEM)

The transmission electron microscope is used to view extremely thin sections of material. Electrons pass through the specimen and are scattered. Magnetic lenses focus the image onto a fluorescent screen or photographic plate. The sections are so thin that they have to be prepared with a special machine, called an ultramicrotome, which can cut wafers to just 30 thousandths of a millimetre thick. It can magnify several hundred thousand times.

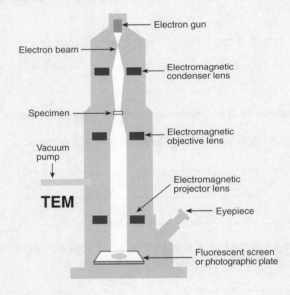

TEM diagram labels:
- Electron gun
- Electron beam
- Electromagnetic condenser lens
- Specimen
- Electromagnetic objective lens
- Vacuum pump
- Electromagnetic projector lens
- Eyepiece
- **TEM**
- Fluorescent screen or photographic plate

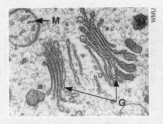

TEM photo showing the Golgi (**G**) and a mitochondrion (**M**).

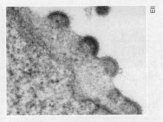

Three HIV viruses budding out of a human lymphocyte (TEM).

Scanning electron microscope (SEM)

The scanning electron microscope scans a sample with a beam of primary electrons, which knocks electrons from the sample's surface. These secondary electrons are picked up by a collector, amplified, and transmitted onto a viewing screen or photographic plate, producing a 3-D image. A microscope of this power easily obtains clear images of very small organisms such as bacteria, and small particles such as viruses. The image produced is of the outside surface only.

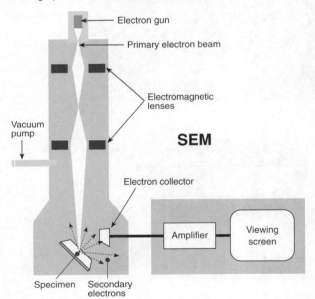

SEM diagram labels:
- Electron gun
- Primary electron beam
- Electromagnetic lenses
- Vacuum pump
- **SEM**
- Electron collector
- Amplifier
- Viewing screen
- Specimen
- Secondary electrons

SEM photo of stoma and epidermal cells on the upper surface of a leaf.

Image of hair louse clinging to two hairs on a Hooker's sealion (SEM).

© 2015 **BIOZONE** International
ISBN: 978-1-927309-19-3

	Light microscope	Transmission electron microscope (TEM)	Scanning electron microscope (SEM)
Radiation source:	light	electrons	electrons
Wavelength:	400-700 nm	0.005 nm	0.005 nm
Lenses:	glass	electromagnetic	electromagnetic
Specimen:	living or non-living supported on glass slide	non-living supported on a small copper grid in a vacuum	non-living supported on a metal disc in a vacuum
Maximum resolution:	200 nm	1 nm	10 nm
Maximum magnification:	1500 x	250 000 x	100 000 x
Stains:	coloured dyes	impregnated with heavy metals	coated with carbon or gold
Type of image:	coloured, surface or section	monochrome, section	monochrome, surface only

1. Explain why electron microscopes are able to resolve much greater detail than a light microscope:

   _____

   _____

   _____

2. Which type of microscope [TEM, SEM, compound light microscope, or dissecting microscope] would you use for each of the following scenarios. Explain your choice in each case:

   (a) Distinguishing extinct plant species on the basis of pollen surface features: _____

   _____

   (b) Resolving the ultrastructure of a chloroplast: _____

   _____

   (c) Performing a count of white blood cells from the blood of a person with an infection: _____

   _____

   (d) Counting the heart rate and rate of limb beating in a water flea (*Daphnia*): _____

   _____

3. Identify which type of electron microscope (SEM or TEM) or optical microscope (compound light microscope or dissecting) was used to produce each of the images in the photos below (A-H):

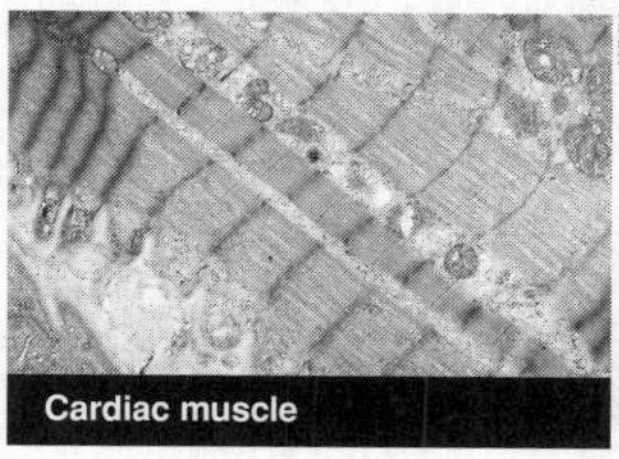

   Cardiac muscle

   A _____

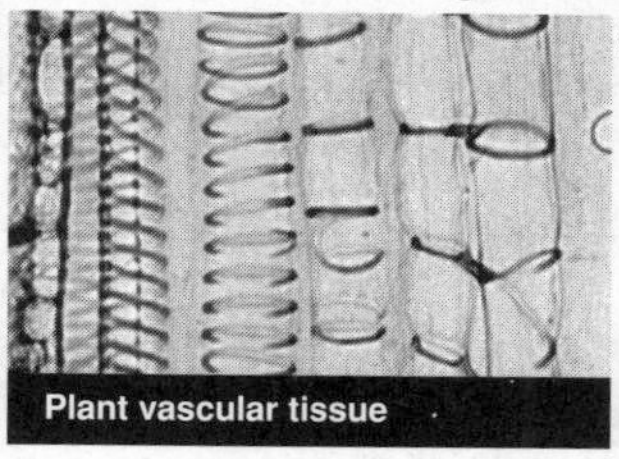

   Plant vascular tissue

   B _____

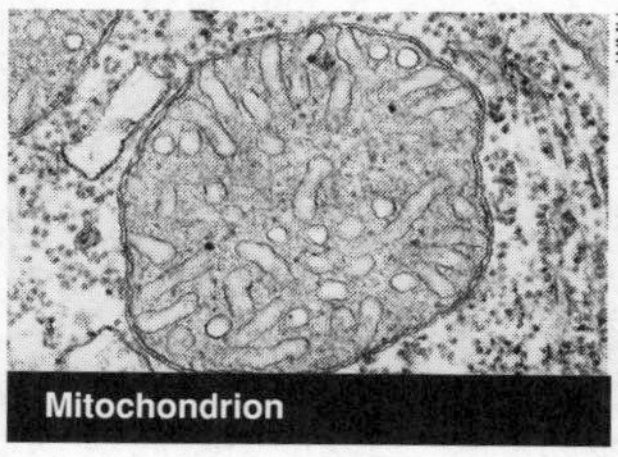

   Mitochondrion

   C _____

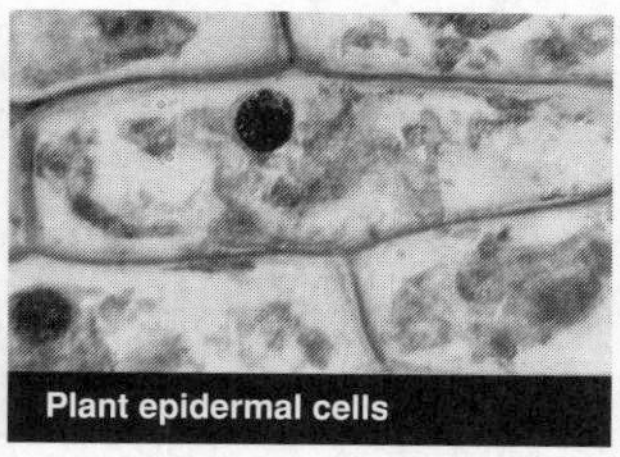

   Plant epidermal cells

   D _____

   Head louse

   E _____

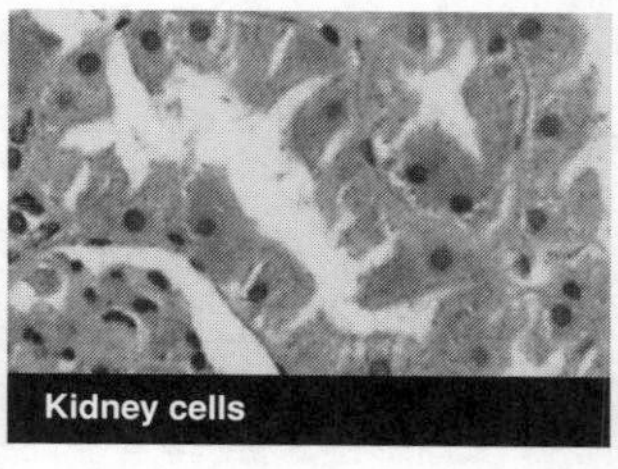

   Kidney cells

   F _____

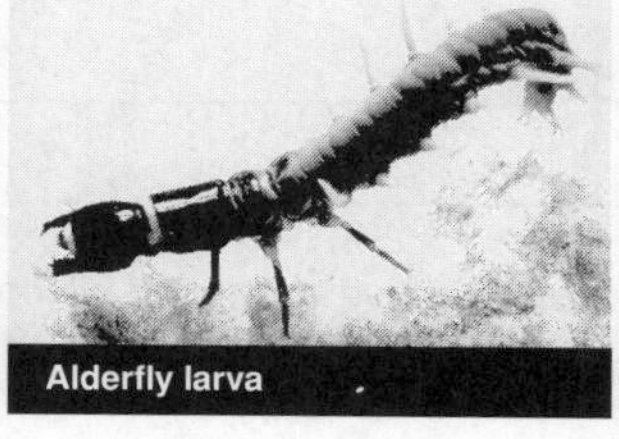

   Alderfly larva

   G _____

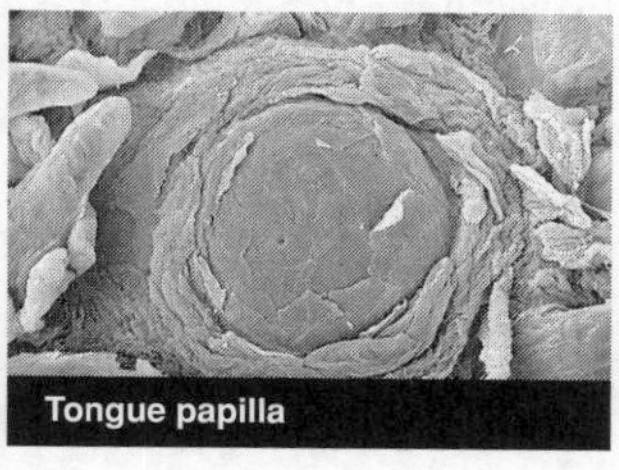

   Tongue papilla

   H _____

© 2015 **BIOZONE** International
ISBN: 978-1-927309-19-3

89 Cell Division

Key Idea: New cells arise from the division of existing cells. There are two types of cell division, mitosis and meiosis.

New cells are formed when existing cells divide. In eukaryotes, cell division begins with the replication of a cell's DNA followed by division of the nucleus. There are two forms of cell division. **Mitosis** produces two identical daughter cells from each parent cell. Mitosis is responsible for growth and repair processes in multicellular organisms, and asexual reproduction in some eukaryotes, e.g. yeasts. **Meiosis** is a special type of cell division concerned with producing sex cells (gametes or haploid spores) for sexual reproduction. It occurs in the sex organs of plants and animals.

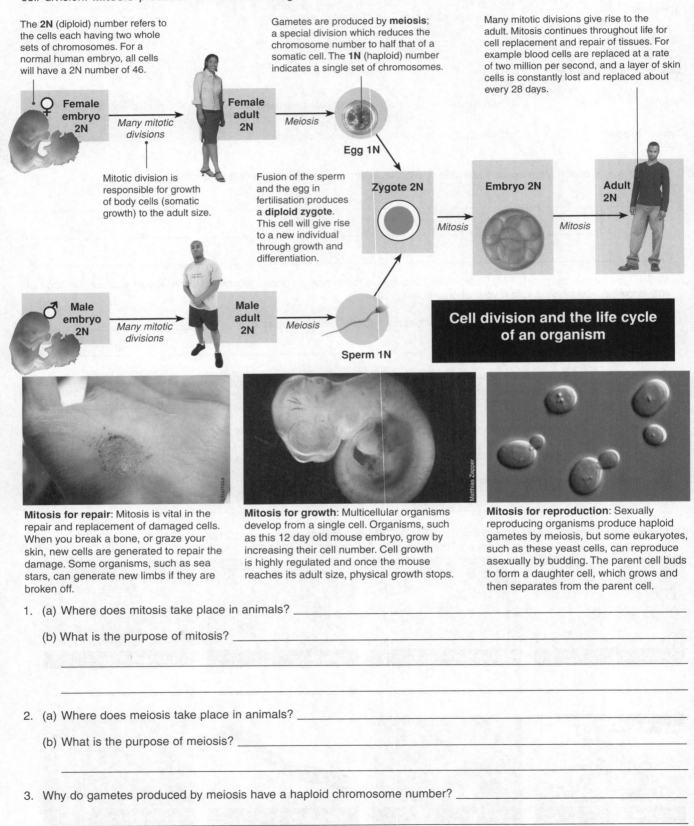

The **2N** (diploid) number refers to the cells each having two whole sets of chromosomes. For a normal human embryo, all cells will have a 2N number of 46.

Gametes are produced by **meiosis**; a special division which reduces the chromosome number to half that of a somatic cell. The **1N** (haploid) number indicates a single set of chromosomes.

Many mitotic divisions give rise to the adult. Mitosis continues throughout life for cell replacement and repair of tissues. For example blood cells are replaced at a rate of two million per second, and a layer of skin cells is constantly lost and replaced about every 28 days.

Female embryo 2N → *Many mitotic divisions* → **Female adult 2N** → *Meiosis* → **Egg 1N**

Mitotic division is responsible for growth of body cells (somatic growth) to the adult size.

Fusion of the sperm and the egg in fertilisation produces a **diploid zygote**. This cell will give rise to a new individual through growth and differentiation.

Male embryo 2N → *Many mitotic divisions* → **Male adult 2N** → *Meiosis* → **Sperm 1N**

Zygote 2N → *Mitosis* → **Embryo 2N** → *Mitosis* → **Adult 2N**

Cell division and the life cycle of an organism

Mitosis for repair: Mitosis is vital in the repair and replacement of damaged cells. When you break a bone, or graze your skin, new cells are generated to repair the damage. Some organisms, such as sea stars, can generate new limbs if they are broken off.

Mitosis for growth: Multicellular organisms develop from a single cell. Organisms, such as this 12 day old mouse embryo, grow by increasing their cell number. Cell growth is highly regulated and once the mouse reaches its adult size, physical growth stops.

Mitosis for reproduction: Sexually reproducing organisms produce haploid gametes by meiosis, but some eukaryotes, such as these yeast cells, can reproduce asexually by budding. The parent cell buds to form a daughter cell, which grows and then separates from the parent cell.

1. (a) Where does mitosis take place in animals? _____

   (b) What is the purpose of mitosis? _____

   _____

   _____

2. (a) Where does meiosis take place in animals? _____

   (b) What is the purpose of meiosis? _____

   _____

3. Why do gametes produced by meiosis have a haploid chromosome number? _____

   _____

   _____

© 2015 **BIOZONE** International
ISBN: 978-1-927309-19-3
Photocopying Prohibited

KNOW   LINK 90   LINK 179

90 Mitosis and the Cell Cycle

Key Idea: Mitosis is an important part of the cell cycle in which the replicated chromosomes are separated and the cell divides, producing two new identical cells.

Mitosis (or M-phase) is part of the **cell cycle** in which an existing cell (the parent cell) divides into two daughter cells. Unlike meiosis, mitosis does not result in a change of chromosome numbers and the daughter cells are identical to

the parent cell. Although mitosis is part of a continuous cell cycle, it is often divided into stages to help differentiate the processes occurring. Mitosis is one of the shortest stages of the cell cycle. When a cell is not undergoing mitosis, it is said to be in interphase. Interphase accounts for 90% of the cell cycle. Cytokinesis (the division of the newly formed cells) is distinct from nuclear division.

Interphase

Cells spend most of their time in interphase. Interphase is divided into three stages (right):

▸ The first gap phase (G1).
▸ The S-phase.
▸ The second gap phase (G2).

During interphase the cell grows, carries out its normal activities, and replicates its DNA in preparation for cell division.
Interphase is not a stage in mitosis.

Mitosis and cytokinesis (M-phase)

Mitosis and cytokinesis occur during M-phase. During mitosis, the cell nucleus (containing the replicated DNA) divides in two equal parts. Cytokinesis occurs at the end of M-phase. During cytokinesis the cell cytoplasm divides, and two new daughter cells are produced.

The cell cycle

S phase: Chromosome replication (DNA synthesis).

Second gap phase: Rapid cell growth and protein synthesis. Cell prepares for mitosis.

Mitosis: Nuclear division

First gap phase: Cell growth and development.

Cytokinesis: The cytoplasm divides and the two cells separate. Cytokinesis is part of M phase but distinct from nuclear division.

An overview of mitosis

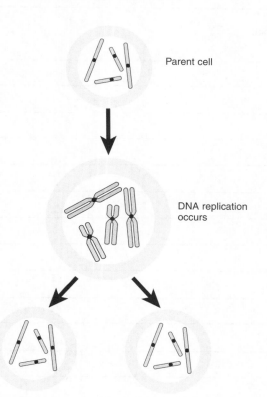

Parent cell

DNA replication occurs

The cell divides forming two identical daughter cells. The chromosome number remains the same as the parent cell.

Cytokinesis

In plant cells (below top), cytokinesis (division of the cytoplasm) involves construction of a cell plate (a precursor the new cell wall) in the middle of the cell. The cell wall materials are delivered by vesicles derived from the Golgi. The vesicles coalesce to become the plasma membranes of the new cell surfaces.

Animal cell cytokinesis (below bottom) begins shortly after the sister chromatids have separated in anaphase of mitosis. A contractile ring of microtubular elements assembles in the middle of the cell, next to the plasma membrane, constricting it to form a cleavage furrow. In an energy-using process, the cleavage furrow moves inwards, forming a region of abscission (separation) where the two cells will separate.

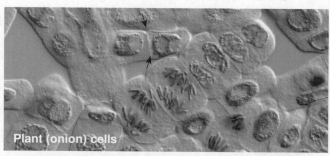

Plant (onion) cells

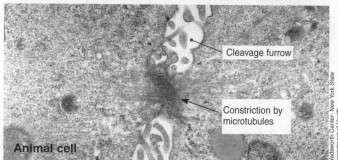

Cleavage furrow

Constriction by microtubules

Animal cell

Wadsworth Center- New York State Department of Health

LINK **92** LINK **91** WEB **90** **KNOW**

The cell cycle and stages of mitosis in a plant cell

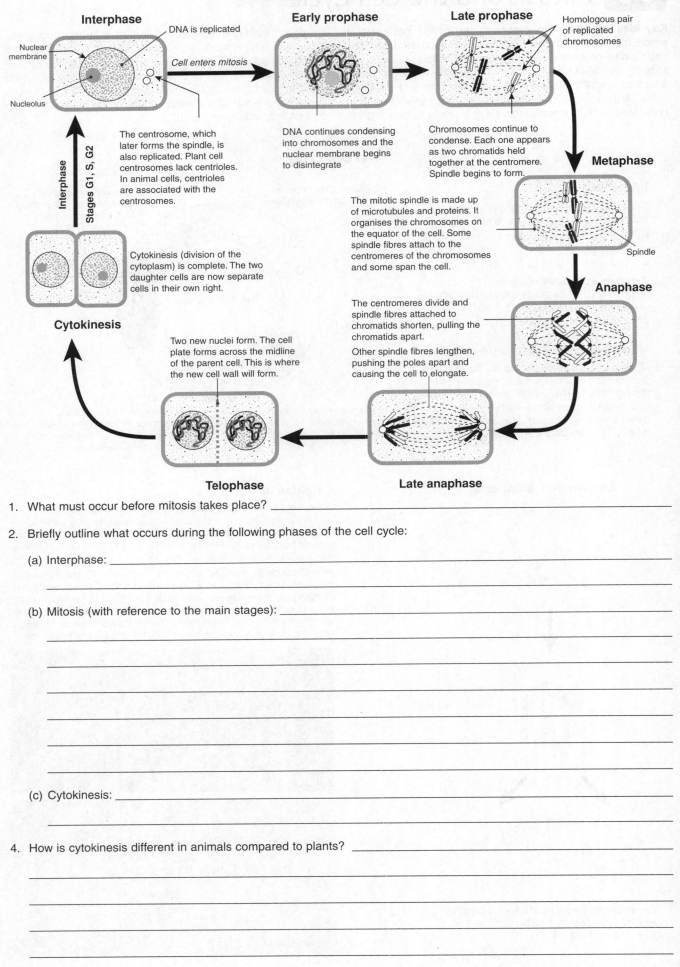

Interphase

Nuclear membrane

DNA is replicated

Nucleolus

Cell enters mitosis

Interphase

Stages G1, S, G2

The centrosome, which later forms the spindle, is also replicated. Plant cell centrosomes lack centrioles. In animal cells, centrioles are associated with the centrosomes.

Early prophase

DNA continues condensing into chromosomes and the nuclear membrane begins to disintegrate

Late prophase

Homologous pair of replicated chromosomes

Chromosomes continue to condense. Each one appears as two chromatids held together at the centromere. Spindle begins to form.

Metaphase

The mitotic spindle is made up of microtubules and proteins. It organises the chromosomes on the equator of the cell. Some spindle fibres attach to the centromeres of the chromosomes and some span the cell.

Spindle

Cytokinesis

Cytokinesis (division of the cytoplasm) is complete. The two daughter cells are now separate cells in their own right.

Two new nuclei form. The cell plate forms across the midline of the parent cell. This is where the new cell wall will form.

Anaphase

The centromeres divide and spindle fibres attached to chromatids shorten, pulling the chromatids apart.

Other spindle fibres lengthen, pushing the poles apart and causing the cell to elongate.

Telophase

Late anaphase

1. What must occur before mitosis takes place? _____

2. Briefly outline what occurs during the following phases of the cell cycle:

   (a) Interphase: _____

   _____

   (b) Mitosis (with reference to the main stages): _____

   _____

   _____

   _____

   _____

   _____

   _____

   _____

   (c) Cytokinesis: _____

   _____

4. How is cytokinesis different in animals compared to plants? _____

   _____

   _____

   _____

   _____

91 Recognising Stages in Mitosis

Key Idea: The stages of mitosis can be recognised by the organisation of the cell and chromosomes.

Although mitosis is a continuous process, it is divided into four stages (prophase, anaphase, metaphase, and telophase) to more easily describe the processes occurring during its progression.

The mitotic index

The mitotic index measures the ratio of cells in mitosis to the number of cells counted. It is a measure of cell proliferation and can be used to diagnose cancer. In areas of high cell growth the mitotic index is high such as in plant apical meristems or the growing tips of plant roots. The mitotic index can be calculated using the formula:

$$\text{Mitotic index} = \frac{\text{Number of cells in mitosis}}{\text{Total number of cells}}$$

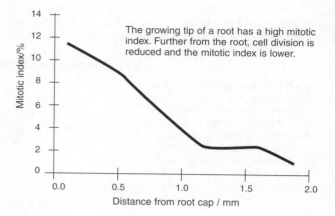

The growing tip of a root has a high mitotic index. Further from the root, cell division is reduced and the mitotic index is lower.

1. Use the information on the previous page to identify which stage of mitosis is shown in each of the photographs below:

 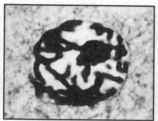  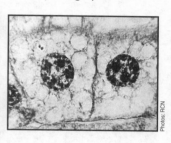

(a) _____ (b) _____ (c) _____ (d) _____

2. (a) The light micrograph (right) shows a section of cells in an onion root tip. These cells have a cell cycle of approximately 24 hours. The cells can be seen to be in various stages of the cell cycle. By counting the number of cells in the various stages it is possible to calculate how long the cell spends in each stage of the cycle. Count and record the number of cells in the image that are in mitosis and those that are in interphase. Cells in cytokinesis can be recorded as in interphase. Estimate the amount of time a cell spends in each phase.

Onion root tip cells

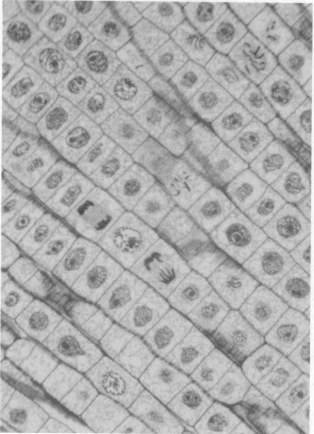

Stage	No. of cells	% of total cells	Estimated time in stage
Interphase			
Mitosis			
Total		100	

(b) Use your counts from 2(a) to calculate the mitotic index for this section of cells.

_____

_____

3. What would you expect to happen to the mitotic index of a population of cells that loses the ability to divide as they mature?

_____

_____

LINK

90

DATA

92 Regulation of the Cell Cycle

Key Idea: The cell cycle is regulated by checkpoints, which ensure the cell has met certain conditions before it continues to the next phase of the cell cycle.

The cell cycle is an orderly sequence of events, but its duration varies enormously between cells of different species and between cell types in one organism. For example, human intestinal cells normally divide around twice a day, whereas cells in the liver typically divide once a year. However, if these tissues are damaged, cell division increases to repair the damage. Some cells, such as neurones in the central nervous system, are unable to divide, and cannot be repaired if damaged. Progression through the cell cycle is controlled by regulatory checkpoints, which ensure the cell has met the conditions required to successfully complete the next phase.

Checkpoints during the cell cycle

There are three **checkpoints** during the cell cycle. A checkpoint is a critical regulatory point in the cell cycle. At each checkpoint, a set of conditions determines whether or not the cell will continue into the next phase. For example, cell size is important in regulating whether or not the cell can pass through the G_1 checkpoint.

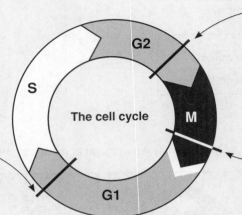

G_2 checkpoint:
Pass this checkpoint if:
▶ Cell size is large enough.
▶ Replication of chromosomes has been successfully completed.
▶ Proteins required for mitosis have been synthesised.

G_1 checkpoint
Pass this checkpoint if:
▶ Cell size is large enough.
▶ Sufficient nutrients are available.
▶ Signals from other cells have been received.

Metaphase checkpoint
Pass this checkpoint if:
▶ All chromosomes are attached to the mitotic spindle.

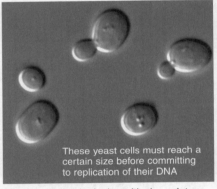
These yeast cells must reach a certain size before committing to replication of their DNA

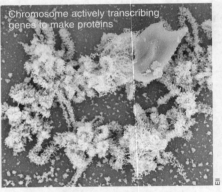
Chromosome actively transcribing genes to make proteins

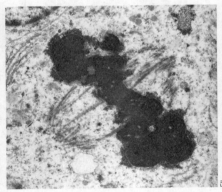

The G_1 checkpoint is the critical regulatory point in cells. At this checkpoint, the cell decides whether to commit to the cell cycle or to enter an arrested phase called G_0. Once sufficient nutrients or cell size is reached and the checkpoint is passed the cell is committed to replication of the nuclear material. Most cells that pass G_1 complete the cell cycle.

The G_2 checkpoint determines if DNA synthesis was completed correctly, that the necessary proteins for mitosis have been synthesised, and that the cell has reached a size suitable for cell division. Damage to the DNA prevents entry to M phase. The entry into M phase is controlled by a protein called cyclin B, which reaches a concentration peak at the G_2-M phase boundary.

The metaphase checkpoint, or spindle checkpoint, checks that all the chromatids are attached to the spindle fibres and under the correct tension. At this point, cyclin B is degraded, ultimately resulting in the sister chromatids separating and the cell entering anaphase, pulling the chromatids apart. The cell then begins cytokinesis and produces two new daughter cells.

1. What is the general purpose of cell cycle checkpoints? _____

_____

_____

2. (a) What is the purpose of the metaphase checkpoint? _____

_____

(b) Why is this checkpoint important? _____

_____

3. What would happen if the cell cycle was not regulated? _____

_____

© 2015 **BIOZONE** International
ISBN: 978-1-927309-19-3
Photocopying Prohibited

93 Cancer: Cells out of Control

Key Idea: Cancerous cells have lost their normal cellular control mechanisms, and grow uncontrollably.

Cells that become damaged beyond repair will normally undergo a programmed cell death (apoptosis), which is part of the cell's normal control system. Some cells evade the control system and become immortal, continuing to divide without any regulation. Such cells are called **cancer cells**. They form tissue masses called tumours, and spread through blood and lymph to invade other tissues, eventually causing damage to the affected tissue. Treating cancer involves a multi-pronged approach, but many cancer treatments work by preventing cell division in cancerous cells.

How cancer cells form

Changes to DNA (mutations) can be caused by external agents called mutagens. Carcinogens are mutagens that cause cancer. Cancerous cells form when the genes controlling cell growth and multiplication are changed by carcinogens into oncogenes (genes that can cause cancer). Damaged cells usually fail to meet the checkpoints required for cell division to continue and are destroyed. However, cancerous cells evade the cell cycle checkpoints and divide rapidly, forming a tumour. A cancerous cell no longer carries out its designated role and instead takes on a parasitic 'lifestyle', taking from the body what it needs in the way of nutrients and contributing nothing in return. The rate of cell division is greater than in normal cells in the same tissue because there is no resting phase between divisions.

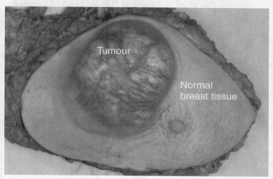

Emmanuelm cc3.0

The photo above shows a large tumour in the breast of a patient with breast cancer. The breast was surgically removed as part of treatment. Changes to the cell chemistry of cancerous cells encourage capillary formation. New capillaries grow into the tumour, providing it with nutrients so it can grow rapidly. Note how the cancerous tissue has grown rapidly compared to the normal breast tissue surrounding it.

Treating cancer by targeting rapidly dividing cells

Surgery, radiotherapy, and chemotherapy (toxic, cell-killing drugs) are often used in combination to treat cancer. While surgery and radiotherapy are localised treatments, chemotherapy has widespread effects because the drugs target and destroy rapidly dividing cells throughout the body (including cancer cells). Any healthy cells with a naturally high rate of cell division (e.g. hair cells, bone marrow stem cells, and cells lining the gastrointestinal tract) are damaged along with the cancerous cells. Hence chemotherapy patients suffer hair loss (right), feel nauseous, and have poor immunity because of loss of white blood cells.

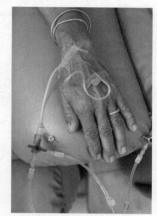

Chemotherapy drugs stop cells dividing by preventing them from completing the cell cycle. Some are non-specific and can act on any phase of the cell cycle, while others target only specific stages.

M-phase disruption
Mitosis inhibitor drugs disrupt mitosis, often by stopping the formation of the mitotic spindles. This stops the chromosomes migrating to the poles of the cell.

S phase disruption
Cell division can be halted by interfering with the synthesis of the precursor molecules needed for DNA replication or damaging the cell's DNA directly.

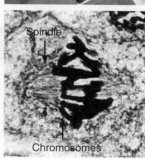

1. (a) What distinguishes a cancerous cell from a normal cell? _____

_____

_____

(b) Why can cancer cells grow rapidly? _____

_____

_____

2. (a) How do chemotherapy drugs kill cancer cells? _____

_____

_____

(b) Why are some healthy cells also killed during chemotherapy? _____

_____

LINK 178   LINK 108   WEB 93   **KNOW**

94 Binary Fission

Key Idea: Binary fission involves division of the parent body into two, fairly equal, parts to produce two identical cells. Binary fission is a form of asexual reproduction carried out by most prokaryotes, some eukaryotic organelles, such as chloroplasts, and some unicellular eukaryotes (although the process is somewhat different in eukaryotic cells). The time required for a bacterial cell to divide, or for a population of bacterial cells to double, is called the generation time. Generation times may be quite short (20 minutes) in some species and as long as several days in others.

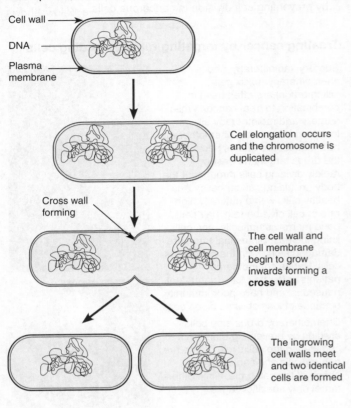

Cell wall
DNA
Plasma membrane

Cell elongation occurs and the chromosome is duplicated

Cross wall forming

The cell wall and cell membrane begin to grow inwards forming a **cross wall**

The ingrowing cell walls meet and two identical cells are formed

Most bacteria reproduce asexually by binary fission (left). The cell's DNA is replicated and each copy attaches to a different part of the plasma membrane. When the cell begins to pull apart, the replicate and original chromosomes are separated. Binary fission in bacteria does not involve mitosis or cytokinesis.

This gram positive coccus (right) is in the process of binary fission. A cross wall (arrow) has formed.

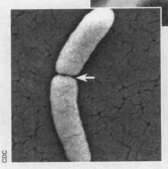

This *Salmonella typhimurium* bacterium (left) has completed cell division. The separation between the two cells can be clearly seen (arrow).

Generation time (minutes)	Population size
0	1
20	2
40	4
60	8
80	
100	
120	
140	
160	
180	
200	
220	
240	
260	
280	
300	
320	
340	
360	

1. What is **binary fission**? _____

_____

_____

_____

2. Explain why the formation of the **cross wall** is important in binary fission: _____

_____

_____

_____

3. Explain the term **generation time**: _____

_____

_____

4. A species of bacteria reproduces every 20 minutes. Complete the table (left) by calculating the number of bacteria present at 20 minute intervals.

5. State how many bacteria were present after:

(a) 1 hour: _____

(b) 3 hours: _____

(c) 6 hours: _____

© 2015 **BIOZONE** International
ISBN: 978-1-927309-19-3
Photocopying Prohibited

95 Replication in Viruses

Key Idea: Viruses infect living cells, and use the metabolism of the host cell to produce new viral particles.

Viruses are not living organisms, so they do not reproduce by cell division. Viruses must infect a living cell and use its cellular machinery to replicate. Viruses can replicate very quickly because viral replication produces many new viruses at once, unlike cell division, which produces two cells per division.

All viruses use the host's cellular machinery to replicate their genetic material and synthesise the viral enzymes and components needed to make new viral particles. Once assembled, the viruses leave the host cell to infect other cells. The precise nature of viral replication and exit from the host depend on the particular virus. The example below shows replication in a typical enveloped DNA virus.

Entry of an enveloped virus into a cell

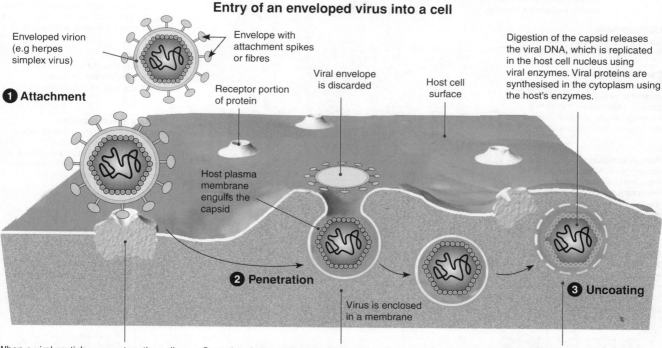

Enveloped virion (e.g herpes simplex virus)

Envelope with attachment spikes or fibres

Receptor portion of protein

Viral envelope is discarded

Host cell surface

Digestion of the capsid releases the viral DNA, which is replicated in the host cell nucleus using viral enzymes. Viral proteins are synthesised in the cytoplasm using the host's enzymes.

1 Attachment

Host plasma membrane engulfs the capsid

2 Penetration

Virus is enclosed in a membrane

3 Uncoating

When a viral particle encounters the cell surface, it attaches to the **receptor sites** of proteins on the cell's plasma membrane.

Once the viral particle is attached, the host cell begins to engulf the virus by endocytosis. This is the cell's usual response to foreign particles.

The nucleic acid core is uncoated and the biosynthesis of new viruses begins. Mature virions are released by budding from the host cell.

How viruses exit the host cell

Once replication is complete, the viral particles leave the host to infect new cells. This process, called **shedding**, can occur in three ways:

1. Budding (enveloped viruses)

The new viral particle adheres to the cell's plasma membrane and becomes engulfed by it. The virus then breaks away from the host cell surrounded by the cell's plasma membrane, which contributes to the viral envelope. The host cell is not destroyed. Many enveloped viruses such as HIV, SARS, smallpox, and the rubella virus (right) use this exit strategy.

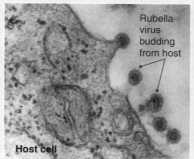

Rubella virus budding from host

Host cell

2. Cell lysis (bacteriophages)

Once enough new viruses have been replicated, the host cell membrane ruptures, and the viruses are released. Cell rupture may be triggered by the pressure of the viral load on the plasma membrane or by chemicals released by the viruses that lead to rupture of the cell. All bacteriophages exit the cell by cell lysis.

3. Apoptosis (non-enveloped viruses)

Some viruses trigger a programmed cell death of the cell. This process results in clumps of dead cell material, which are cleaned up by the body's macrophages, which then become infected. Primarily used by non-enveloped viruses, e.g. HPV.

1. (a) Where does an enveloped virus replicate its viral DNA? _____ Its proteins? _____

 (b) How does an enveloped virus exploit the host cell's capability for endo- and exocytosis? _____

 _____

 _____

2. Contrast shedding in enveloped and non-enveloped viruses and relate the method used to viral structure in each case:

 _____

 _____

 _____

LINK **110** LINK **108** LINK **82** WEB **95** **KNOW**

96 The Role of Membranes in Cells

Key Idea: Membranes create compartments, control entry and exit of substances from the cell and organelles, and enable cell communication.
Many cell organelles are composed of membranes.

Membranes within eukaryotic cells share the same basic structure as the plasma membrane that encloses the entire cell. Membranes have many functions (below) and create compartments within the cell where reactions can be localised.

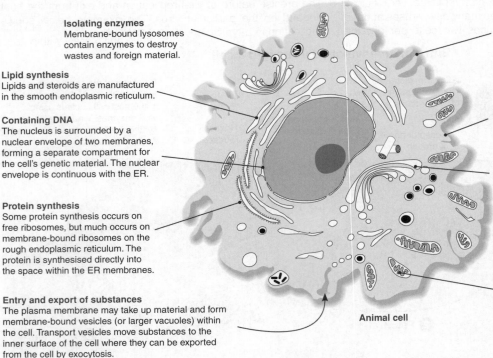

Isolating enzymes
Membrane-bound lysosomes contain enzymes to destroy wastes and foreign material.

Lipid synthesis
Lipids and steroids are manufactured in the smooth endoplasmic reticulum.

Containing DNA
The nucleus is surrounded by a nuclear envelope of two membranes, forming a separate compartment for the cell's genetic material. The nuclear envelope is continuous with the ER.

Protein synthesis
Some protein synthesis occurs on free ribosomes, but much occurs on membrane-bound ribosomes on the rough endoplasmic reticulum. The protein is synthesised directly into the space within the ER membranes.

Entry and export of substances
The plasma membrane may take up material and form membrane-bound vesicles (or larger vacuoles) within the cell. Transport vesicles move substances to the inner surface of the cell where they can be exported from the cell by exocytosis.

Cell communication and recognition
Proteins in the membrane act as receptors for signal molecules like hormones. Glycoproteins and glycolipids act as cell identity markers, helping cells to organise themselves into tissues.

Transport
Channel and carrier proteins are involved in selective transport across the plasma membrane.

Packaging and secretion
The Golgi apparatus is a specialised membrane-bound organelle, producing lysosomes and modifying, packaging, and secreting substances such as proteins and hormones.

Energy transfer
The reactions of cellular respiration take place in the membrane-bound mitochondria. In plant cells, the reactions of photosynthesis are located in specialised membranous organelles called chloroplasts.

Animal cell

The **nuclear membrane** around the nucleus helps to control the passage of genetic information to the cytoplasm. It may also serve to protect the DNA.

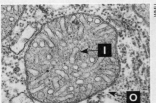

Mitochondria have an outer membrane (**O**) which controls the movement of materials involved in respiration. Inner membranes (**I**) provide attachment sites for enzyme activity.

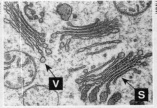

The **Golgi apparatus** comprises stacks of membrane-bound sacs (**S**). It is involved in packaging materials for transport or export from the cell as secretory vesicles (**V**).

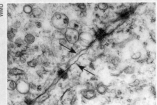

The cell's **plasma membrane** controls the movement of most substances into and out of the cell. This photo shows the plasma membranes of two neighbouring cells (arrows).

1. Explain the crucial role of membrane systems and organelles in the following:

    (a) Providing compartments within the cell: _____

    _____

    _____

    (b) Increasing the total membrane surface area within the cell: _____

    _____

    _____

2. (a) Name a membrane-bound cellular organelle: _____

    (b) What is the function of the organelle? _____

    (c) What is the membrane's role in this organelle? _____

    _____

    _____

© 2015 **BIOZONE** International
ISBN: 978-1-927309-19-3
Photocopying Prohibited

97 The Structure of Membranes

Key Idea: The plasma membrane is composed of a lipid bilayer with proteins moving freely within it.

All cells have a plasma membrane, which forms the outer limit of the cell and regulates the passage of materials into and out of the cell. A cell wall, if present, lies outside this, and it is quite distinct from it. Membranes are also found inside eukaryotic cells as part of membranous organelles. The original model of membrane structure was as a lipid bilayer coated with protein. This model was modified after the discovery that the protein molecules were embedded within the bilayer rather than coating the outside. The now-accepted **fluid-mosaic model** of membrane structure (below) satisfies the observed properties of membranes. The self-orientating properties of the phospholipids allows cellular membranes to reseal themselves when disrupted. The double layer of lipids is also quite fluid, and proteins move quite freely within it.

The fluid mosaic model of membrane structure

Glycolipids in membranes are phospholipids with attached carbohydrate. Like glycoproteins, they are involved in cell signalling and cell-cell recognition. They also help to stabilise membrane structure.

Cholesterol is a packing molecule and interacts with the phospholipids to regulate membrane consistency, keeping it firm but fluid.

Water molecules pass between the phospholipid molecules by osmosis.

Glycoproteins are proteins with attached carbohydrate. They are important in membrane stability, in cell-cell recognition, and in cell signalling, acting as receptors for hormones and neurotransmitters.

Attached carbohydrate

CO_2

Phospholipids naturally form a bilayer.

Some integral proteins do not span the lipid bilayer.

Phosphate head is hydrophilic

Fatty acid tail is hydrophobic

Carrier proteins permit the passage of specific molecules by facilitated diffusion or active transport. Transport capacity increases as the number of carrier proteins increases.

α-helical transmembrane glycoprotein

Phospholipid

A molecule's solubility, size, and charge affects how it is transported across a plasma membrane. In general, the smaller the molecule and the more hydrophobic it is, the more rapidly it will diffuse. Charged molecules, such as ions, are unable to diffuse through a phospholipid bilayer regardless of size. They must cross the lipid bilayer via membrane proteins.

Channel proteins form a pore through the hydrophobic interior of the membrane to enable water soluble molecules to pass by facilitated diffusion. Transport capacity increases as the number of channel proteins increases.

Lipid soluble molecules, e.g. gases and steroids, can move through the membrane by diffusion, down their concentration gradient.

Intracellular environment

Based on a diagram in Biol. Sci. Review, Nov. 2009, pp. 20-21

1. Identify the component(s) of the plasma membrane involved in:

   (a) Facilitated diffusion: _____   (c) Cell signalling: _____

   (b) Active transport: _____   (d) Regulating membrane fluidity: _____

2. How do the properties of phospholipids contribute to their role in forming the structural framework of membranes?

   _____

   _____

3. (a) Describe the modern fluid mosaic model of membrane structure: _____

   _____

   _____

LINK 98 WEB 97 KNOW

(b) Explain how the fluid mosaic model accounts for the observed properties of cellular membranes:

_____

_____

_____

_____

_____

_____

4. Explain the importance of each of the following to cellular function:

(a) Carrier proteins in the plasma membrane: _____

_____

(b) Channel proteins in the plasma membrane: _____

_____

5. Non-polar (lipid-soluble) molecules diffuse more rapidly through membranes than polar (lipid-insoluble) molecules:

(a) Explain the reason for this: _____

_____

(b) Discuss the implications of this to the transport of substances into the cell through the plasma membrane:

_____

_____

6. Describe the purpose of cholesterol in plasma membranes: _____

_____

7. List three substances that need to be transported **into** all kinds of animal cells, in order for them to survive:

(a) _____ (b) _____ (c) _____

8. List two substances that need to be transported **out** of all kinds of animal cells, in order for them to survive:

(a) _____ (b) _____

9. Use the symbol for a phospholipid molecule (below) to draw a **simple labelled diagram** to show the structure of a plasma membrane (include features such as lipid bilayer and various kinds of proteins):

Symbol for phospholipid

98 How Do We Know? Membrane Structure

Key Idea: The freeze-fracture technique for preparing and viewing cellular membranes has provided evidence to support the fluid mosaic model of the plasma membrane.

Cellular membranes play many extremely important roles in cells and understanding their structure is central to understanding cellular function. Moreover, understanding the structure and function of membrane proteins is essential to understanding cellular transport processes, and cell recognition and signalling. Cellular membranes are far too small to be seen clearly using light microscopy, and certainly any detail is impossible to resolve. Since early last century, scientists have known that membranes were composed of a lipid bilayer with associated proteins. The original model of membrane structure, proposed by Davson and Danielli, was the unit membrane (a lipid bilayer coated with protein). This model was later modified by Singer and Nicolson after the discovery that the protein molecules were embedded *within* the bilayer rather than coating the outside. But how did they find out just how these molecules were organised?

The answers were provided with electron microscopy, and one technique in particular – **freeze fracture**. As the name implies, freeze fracture, at its very simplest level, is the freezing of a cell and then fracturing it so the inner surface of the membrane can be seen using electron microscopy. Membranes are composed of two layers of phospholipids held together by weak intermolecular bonds. These split apart during fracture.

The procedure involves several steps:

▶ Cells are immersed in chemicals that alter the strength of the internal and external regions of the plasma membrane and immobilise any mobile macromolecules.

▶ The cells are passed through a series of glycerol solutions of increasing concentration. This protects the cells from bursting when they are frozen.

▶ The cells are mounted on gold supports and frozen using liquid propane.

▶ The cells are fractured in a helium-vented vacuum at -150°C. A razor blade cooled to -170° C acts as both a cold trap for water and the fracturing instrument.

▶ The surface of the fractured cells may be evaporated a little to produce some relief on the surface (known as etching) so that a three-dimensional effect occurs.

▶ For viewing under an electron microscope (EM), a replica of the cells is made by coating them with gold or platinum to ~3 nm thick. A layer of carbon around 30 nm thick is used to provide contrast and stability for the replica.

▶ The samples are then raised to room temperature and placed into distilled water or digestive enzymes, which separates the replica from the sample. The replica is then rinsed in distilled water before it is ready for viewing.

The freeze fracture technique provided the necessary supporting evidence for the current fluid mosaic model of membrane structure. When cleaved, proteins in the membrane left impressions that showed they were embedded into the membrane and not a continuous layer on the outside as earlier models proposed.

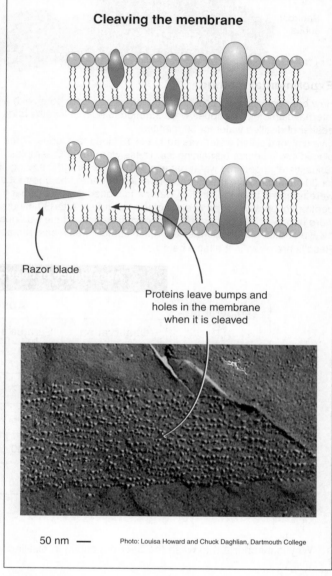

Cleaving the membrane

Razor blade

Proteins leave bumps and holes in the membrane when it is cleaved

50 nm ——   Photo: Louisa Howard and Chuck Daghlian, Dartmouth College

1. Explain how freeze-fracture studies provided evidence for our current model of membrane structure:

_____

_____

_____

2. The Davson and Danielli model of membrane structure was the unit membrane; a phospholipid bilayer with a protein coat. Explain how the freeze-fracture studies showed this model to be flawed:

_____

_____

_____

99 Factors Altering Membrane Permeability

Key Idea: Temperature and solvents can disrupt the structure of cellular membranes and alter their permeability.

Membrane permeability can be disrupted if membranes are subjected to high temperatures or solvents. At temperatures above the optimum, the membrane proteins become denatured. Alcohols, e.g. ethanol, can also denature proteins. In both instances, the denatured proteins no longer function properly and the membrane loses its selective permeability and becomes leaky. In addition, the combination of alcohol and high temperature can also dissolve lipids.

Beetroot cubes

Experimental method

Raw beetroot was cut into uniform cubes using a cork borer with a 4 mm internal diameter. The cubes were trimmed to 20 mm lengths and placed in a beaker of distilled water for 30 minutes.

Five cm³ of distilled water was added to 15 clean test tubes. Three were placed into a beaker containing ice. These were the 0°C samples. Three test tubes were placed into water baths at 20, 40, 60, or 90°C and equilibrated for 30 minutes. Once the tubes were at temperature, the beetroot cubes were removed from the distilled water and blotted dry on a paper towel. One beetroot cube was added to each of the test tubes. After 30 minutes, they were removed. The colour of the solution in each test tube was observed by eye and then the absorbance of each sample was measured at 530 nm. Results are given in the table below.

The aim and hypothesis

To investigate the effect of temperature on membrane permeability. The students hypothesised that the amount of pigment leaking from the beetroot cubes would increase with increasing temperature.

Background

Plant cells often contain a large central vacuole surrounded by a membrane called a **tonoplast**. In beetroot plants, the vacuole contains a water-soluble red pigment called betacyanin, which gives beetroot its colour. If the tonoplast is damaged, the red pigment leaks out into the surrounding environment. The amount of leaked pigment relates to the amount of damage to the tonoplast.

Absorbance of beetroot samples at varying temperatures					
Temperature / °C		Absorbance at 530 nm			Mean
	Observation	Sample 1	Sample 2	Sample 3	
0	No colour	0	0.007	0.004	
20	Very pale pink	0.027	0.022	0.018	
40	Very pale pink	0.096	0.114	0.114	
60	Pink	0.580	0.524	0.509	
90	Red	3	3	3	

1. Why is it important to wash the beetroot cubes in distilled water prior to carrying out the experiment? _____

_____

2. (a) Complete the table above by calculating the mean absorbance for each temperature:

   (b) Based on the results in the table above, describe the effect of temperature on membrane permeability: _____

   _____

   _____

   _____

   (c) Explain how temperature affects the permeability of the tonoplast: _____

   _____

   _____

   _____

© 2015 **BIOZONE** International
ISBN: 978-1-927309-19-3
Photocopying Prohibited

DATA

Method for determining effect of ethanol concentration on membrane permeability

Beetroot cubes were prepared the same way as described on the previous page. The following ethanol concentrations were prepared using serial dilution: 0, 6.25, 12.5, 25, 50, and 100%. Eighteen clean test tubes were divided into six groups of three and labelled with one of the six ethanol concentrations. Three cm^3 of the appropriate ethanol solution was placed into each test tube. A dried beetroot cube was added to each test tube. The test tubes were covered with parafilm (plastic paraffin film with a paper backing) and left at room temperature. After one hour the beetroot cubes were removed and the absorbance measured at 477 nm.
Results are given in the table, right.

Ethanol concentration / %	Absorbance at 477 nm			Mean
	Sample 1	Sample 2	Sample 3	
0	0.014	0.038	0.038	
6.25	0.009	0.015	0.023	
12.5	0.010	0.041	0.018	
25	0.067	0.064	0.116	
50	0.945	1.100	0.731	
100	1.269	1.376	0.907	

Absorbance of beetroot samples at varying ethanol concentrations

3. What was the purpose of the 0% ethanol solution in the experiment described above?

_____

_____

_____

4. (a) Why do you think the tubes were covered in parafilm?

_____

_____

_____

_____

(b) How could the results have been affected if the test tubes were not covered with parafilm?

_____

_____

_____

_____

5. (a) Complete the table above by calculating the mean absorbance for each ethanol concentration:

(b) Plot a line graph of ethanol concentration against mean absorbance on the grid (above):

(c) Describe the effect of ethanol concentration on the membrane permeability of beetroot: _____

_____

_____

_____

_____

6. How does ethanol affect membrane permeability? _____

_____

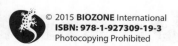

100 Diffusion

Key Idea: Diffusion is the movement of molecules from higher concentration to a lower concentration (i.e. down a concentration gradient).

The molecules that make up substances are constantly moving about in a random way. This random motion causes molecules to disperse from areas of high to low concentration. This dispersal is called **diffusion** and it requires no energy. Each type of molecule moves down its own concentration gradient. Diffusion is important in allowing exchanges with the environment and in the regulation of cell water content.

What is diffusion?

Diffusion is the movement of particles from regions of high concentration to regions of low concentration (down a concentration gradient). Diffusion is a **passive process**, meaning it needs no input of energy to occur. During diffusion, molecules move randomly about, becoming evenly dispersed.

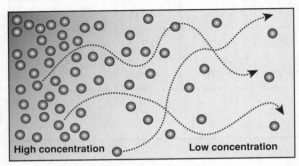

High concentration .... **Low concentration**

Concentration gradient

If molecules can move freely, they move from high to low concentration (down a concentration gradient) until evenly dispersed.

Factors affecting the rate of diffusion

Concentration gradient	The rate of diffusion is higher when there is a greater difference between the concentrations of two regions.
The distance moved	Diffusion over shorter distance occurs at a greater rate than over a larger distance.
The surface area involved	The larger the area across which diffusion occurs, the greater the rate of diffusion.
Barriers to diffusion	Thick barriers have a slower rate of diffusion than thin barriers.
Temperature	Particles at a high temperature diffuse at a greater rate than at a low temperature.

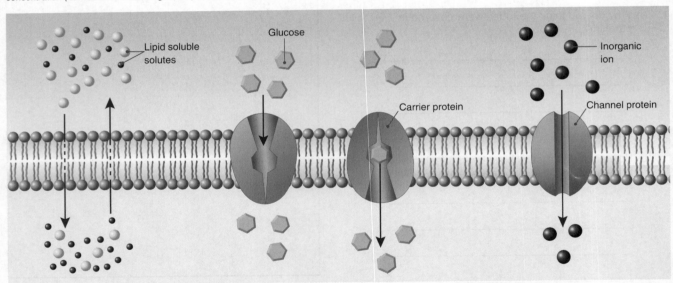

Simple diffusion
Molecules move directly through the membrane without assistance.
Example: O_2 diffuses into the blood and CO_2 diffuses out.

Carrier-mediated facilitated diffusion
Carrier proteins allow large lipid-insoluble molecules that cannot cross the membrane by simple diffusion to be transported into the cell.
Example: the transport of glucose into red blood cells.

Channel-mediated facilitated diffusion
Channels (hydrophilic pores) in the membrane allow inorganic ions to pass through the membrane.
Example: K^+ ions exiting nerve cells to restore resting potential.

1. What is diffusion? _____

_____

2. What do the three types of diffusion described above all have in common? _____

_____

3. How does facilitated diffusion differ from simple diffusion? _____

_____

101 Osmosis

Key Idea: Osmosis is the term describing the diffusion of water molecules down their concentration gradient across a partially permeable membrane.

The diffusion of water down its concentration gradient across a partially permeable membrane is called **osmosis** and it is the principal mechanism by which water moves in and out of living cells. A partially permeable membrane, such

as the plasma membrane, allows some molecules, but not others, to pass through. Water molecules can diffuse directly through the lipid bilayer, but movement is aided by specific protein channels called aquaporins. There is a net movement of water molecules until an equilibrium is reached and net movement is then zero. Osmosis is a passive process and does not require any energy input.

Demonstrating osmosis

Osmosis can be demonstrated using dialysis tubing in a simple experiment (described below). Dialysis tubing, like all cellular membranes, is a partially permeable membrane.

A sucrose solution (high solute concentration) is placed into dialysis tubing, and the tubing is placed into a beaker of water (low solute concentration). The difference in concentration of sucrose (solute) between the two solutions creates an osmotic gradient. Water moves by osmosis into the sucrose solution and the volume of the sucrose solution inside the dialysis tubing increases.

The dialysis tubing acts as a partially permeable membrane, allowing water to pass freely, while keeping the sucrose inside the dialysis tubing.

Glass capillary tube

Dialysis tubing containing sucrose solution

Water

Dialysis tubing (partially permeable membrane)

Sucrose molecule

Water molecule

Net water movement

Osmotic potential

Osmotic potential is a term often used when studying animal cells. The presence of solutes (dissolved substances) in a solution increases the tendency of water to move into that solution. This tendency is called the osmotic potential or osmotic pressure. The greater a solution's concentration (i.e. the more total dissolved solutes it contains) the greater the osmotic potential.

Describing solutions

Water movements in cells, particularly plant cells, are often explained in terms of water potential (see next activity). But you will often see other terms used to compare solutions of different solute concentration, especially in animal biology:

Isotonic solution: Having the same solute concentration relative to another solution (e.g. the cell's contents).

Hypotonic solution: Having a lower solute concentration relative to another solution.

Hypertonic solution: Having a higher solute concentration relative to another solution.

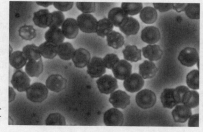

Zephyris

The red blood cells above were placed into a hypertonic solution. As a result, the cells have lost water and have begun to shrink, losing their usual discoid shape.

1. What is osmosis? _____

_____

_____

2. (a) In the blue box on the diagram above, draw an arrow to show the direction of net water movement.

   (b) Why did water move in this direction? _____

   _____

   _____

3. What would happen to the height of the water in the capillary tube if the sucrose concentration was increased?

_____

102 Water Movement in Plant Cells

Key Idea: Water potential explains the tendency of water to move from one region to another by osmosis. Water molecules moves to regions of lower water potential.

The water potential of a solution (denoted by ψ) is the term given to the tendency for water molecules to enter or leave a solution by osmosis. The tendency for water to move in any particular direction can be calculated on the basis of the water potential of the cell sap relative to its surrounding environment. The use of water potential to express the water relations of plant cells is used in preference to osmotic potential and osmotic pressure although these terms are still frequently used in areas of animal physiology and medicine.

Water potential and water movement

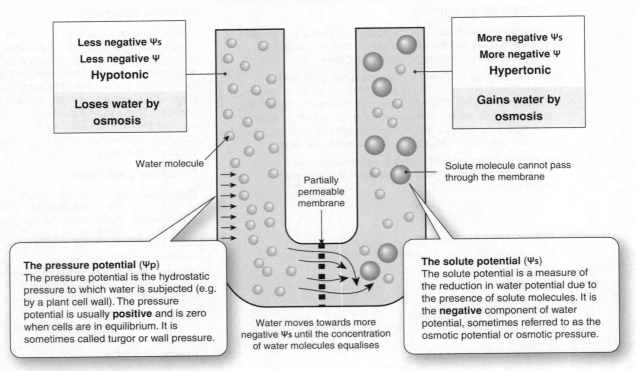

Less negative Ψs
Less negative Ψ
Hypotonic

Loses water by osmosis

Water molecule

More negative Ψs
More negative Ψ
Hypertonic

Gains water by osmosis

Solute molecule cannot pass through the membrane

Partially permeable membrane

The pressure potential (Ψp)
The pressure potential is the hydrostatic pressure to which water is subjected (e.g. by a plant cell wall). The pressure potential is usually **positive** and is zero when cells are in equilibrium. It is sometimes called turgor or wall pressure.

Water moves towards more negative Ψs until the concentration of water molecules equalises

The solute potential (Ψs)
The solute potential is a measure of the reduction in water potential due to the presence of solute molecules. It is the **negative** component of water potential, sometimes referred to as the osmotic potential or osmotic pressure.

As water molecules move around some collide with the plasma membrane and create pressure on the membrane called **water potential** (ψ).The greater the movement of water molecules, the higher their water potential. The presence of solutes (e.g. sucrose) lowers water potential because the solutes restrict the movement of water molecules. Pure water has the highest water potential (zero). Dissolving any solute in water lowers the water potential (makes it more negative).

Water always diffuses from regions of less negative to more negative water potential. Water potential is determined by two components: the **solute potential**, ψs (of the cell sap) and the **pressure potential**, ψp, expressed by:

$$\psi cell = \psi s + \psi p$$

The closer a value is to zero, the higher its water potential.

1. What is the water potential of pure water? _____

2. The diagrams below show three hypothetical situations where adjacent cells have different water potentials. Draw arrows on each pair of cells (a)-(c) to indicate the net direction of water movement and calculate ψ for each side:

(a)

A	B
ψs = −400 kPa	ψs = −500 kPa
ψp = 300 kPa	ψp = 300 kPa

(b)

A	B
ψs = −500 kPa	ψs = −600 kPa
ψp = 100 kPa	ψp = 100 kPa

(c)

A	B
ψs = −600 kPa	ψs = −500 kPa
ψp = 200 kPa	ψp = 300 kPa

ψ for side A: _____ _____ _____

ψ for side B: _____ _____ _____

© 2015 **BIOZONE** International
ISBN: 978-1-927309-19-3
Photocopying Prohibited

When the contents of a plant cell push against the cell wall they create **turgor** (tightness) which provides support for the plant body. When cells lose water, there is a loss of turgor and the plant wilts. Complete loss of turgor from a cell is called plasmolysis and is irreversible. The diagram below shows two situations: when the external water potential is less negative than the cell and when it is more negative than the cell. When the external water potential is the same as that of the cell, there is no net movement of water.

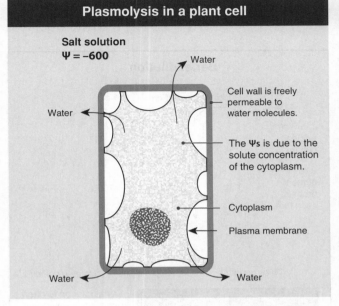

Plasmolysis in a plant cell

Salt solution
$\Psi = -600$

Water

Cell wall is freely permeable to water molecules.

The Ψ_s is due to the solute concentration of the cytoplasm.

Cytoplasm

Plasma membrane

Water

Turgor in a plant cell

Pure water
$\Psi = 0$

Water

Cell wall bulges outward

Water

Cytoplasm takes on water, putting pressure on the plasma membrane and cell wall. Ψ_p rises, offsetting Ψ_s at full turgor.

Water

Water

When external water potential is more negative than the water potential of the cell ($\Psi_{cell} = \Psi_s + \Psi_p$), water leaves the cell and, because the cell wall is rigid, the plasma membrane shrinks away from the cell wall. This process is termed **plasmolysis** and the cell becomes flaccid ($\Psi_p = 0$). Full plasmolysis is irreversible; the cell cannot recover by taking up water.

When the external water potential is less negative than the Ψ_{cell}, water enters the cell. A pressure potential is generated when sufficient water has been taken up to cause the cell contents to press against the cell wall. Ψ_p rises progressively until it offsets Ψ_s. Water uptake stops when the $\Psi_{cell} = 0$. The rigid cell wall prevents cell rupture. Cells in this state are **turgid**.

3. What is the effect of dissolved solutes on water potential? _____

_____

_____

4. Why don't plant cells burst when water enters them? _____

_____

_____

5. (a) Distinguish between plasmolysis and turgor: _____

_____

_____

(b) Describe the state of the plant in the photo on the right and explain your reasoning:

_____

_____

6. (a) Explain the role of pressure potential in generating cell turgor in plants: _____

_____

_____

(b) Explain the purpose of cell turgor to plants: _____

_____

_____

103 Making Dilutions

Key Idea: Dilution reduces the concentration of a stock solution by a known factor.

A dilution reduces the concentration of a solution by a known value. **Simple dilutions** are based on ratios, and involve taking a volume of stock solution and adding it to an appropriate volume of solvent to achieve the desired dilution.

Simple dilutions are often used to produce calibration curves. A **serial dilution** is a stepwise dilution that quickly amplifies the dilution factor. Serial dilutions are useful when you require a volume or amount that is too small to measure accurately, or when you need to quickly dilute a solution that is very concentrated to begin with (e.g. bacterial cells in a solution).

Simple dilution

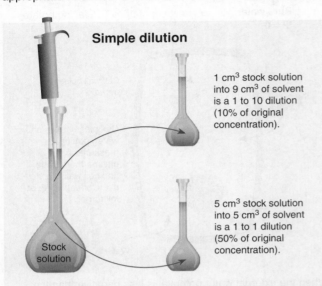

1 cm³ stock solution into 9 cm³ of solvent is a 1 to 10 dilution (10% of original concentration).

5 cm³ stock solution into 5 cm³ of solvent is a 1 to 1 dilution (50% of original concentration).

The following equation is used to calculate the volume needed to make a simple dilution:

$$C1 \times V1 = C2 \times V2$$

C1 = initial concentration of stock solution

V1 = initial volume of stock solution

C2 = final concentration required

V2 = final volume required

You will always know three of the values, so by rearranging the equation you can determine what volume of stock solution is needed to achieve the desired final concentration.

$$V1 = (C2 \times V2) / C1$$

Serial dilution

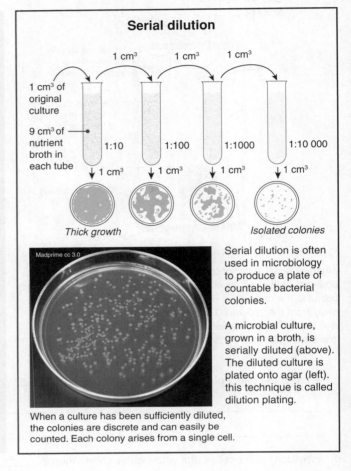

1 cm³ of original culture

9 cm³ of nutrient broth in each tube

1:10   1:100   1:1000   1:10 000

Thick growth   *Isolated colonies*

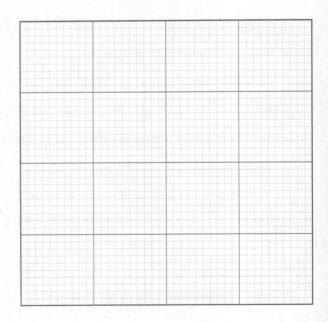

Madprime cc 3.0

Serial dilution is often used in microbiology to produce a plate of countable bacterial colonies.

A microbial culture, grown in a broth, is serially diluted (above). The diluted culture is plated onto agar (left). this technique is called dilution plating.

When a culture has been sufficiently diluted, the colonies are discrete and can easily be counted. Each colony arises from a single cell.

---

1. A student had a 1.00 mol dm⁻³ stock solution of sucrose. Calculate the dilutions required to produce 5 cm³ of sucrose solution at the following concentrations:

   (a) 0.75 mol dm⁻³: _____

   (b) 0.50 mol dm⁻³: _____

   (c) 0.25 mol dm⁻³: _____

2. (a) Use the equation below to calculate the solute potential (ψ_s) of the solutions in (1) and also of the 1.00 mol dm⁻³ solution (the solutions were at 22°C):

   0.75 mol dm⁻³: _____   0.50 mol dm⁻³: _____

   0.25 mol dm⁻³: _____   1.00 mol dm⁻³: _____

$$\psi_s = -iCRT$$

   i = ionisation constant (for sucrose, this is 1)
   C = molar concentration
   R = pressure constant = 8.31 dm³ kPa K⁻¹mol⁻¹
   T = temperature (°K) = 273 + °C of solution.

   (b) Plot sucrose concentration vs solute potential on the grid.

© 2015 **BIOZONE** International
ISBN: 978-1-927309-19-3
Photocopying Prohibited

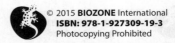

104 Estimating Osmolarity

Key Idea: A cell placed in a hypotonic solution will gain water while a cell placed in a hypertonic solution will lose water. The osmolarity (which is directly proportional to the solute potential) of a cell or tissue can be estimated by placing the tissue into a series of solutions of known concentration and observing if the tissue loses (hypertonic solution) or gains (hypotonic solution) water. The solution in which the tissue remains unchanged indicates the osmolarity of the tissue.

Potato cubes

The aim

To determine the solute potential of potatoes by placing potato cubes in varying solutions of sucrose, $C_{12}H_{22}O_{11}$ (table sugar).

The method

Fifteen identical 1.5 cm³ cubes of potato where cut and weighed in grams to two decimal places. Five solutions of sucrose were prepared in the following range (in mol dm⁻³): 0.00, 0.25, 0.50, 0.75, 1.00. Three potato cubes were placed in each solution, at 22°C, for two hours, stirring every 15 minutes. The cubes were then retrieved, patted dry on blotting paper and weighed again.

1. Complete the table (right) by calculating the total mass of the potato cubes, the total change in mass, and the total % change in mass for all the sucrose concentrations:

2. Use the grid below to draw a line graph of the sucrose concentration vs total percentage change in mass:

The results

	Potato sample	Initial mass (I) / g	Final mass (F) / g
[Sucrose] 0.00 mol dm⁻³	1	5.11	6.00
	2	5.15	6.07
	3	5.20	5.15
Total			
Change (C) (F-I) / g			
% Change (C/I x 100)			
[Sucrose] 0.25 mol dm⁻³	1	6.01	4.98
	2	6.07	5.95
	3	7.10	7.00
Total			
Change (C) (F-I) / g			
% Change (C/I x 100)			
[Sucrose] 0.50 mol dm⁻³	1	6.12	5.10
	2	7.03	6.01
	3	5.11	5.03
Total			
Change (C) (F-I) / g			
% Change (C/I x 100)			
[Sucrose] 0.75 mol dm⁻³	1	5.03	3.96
	2	7.10	4.90
	3	7.03	5.13
Total			
Change (C) (F-I) / g			
% Change (C/I x 100)			
[Sucrose] 1.00 mol dm⁻³	1	5.00	4.03
	2	5.04	3.95
	3	6.10	5.02
Total			
Change (C) (F-I) / g			
% Change (C/I x 100)			

3. (a) Use this graph to estimate the osmolarity of the potato (the point where there is no change in mass):

_____

(b) Use the calibration curve (opposite) to determine the solute potential (ψs) of your potato (in kPa):

_____

(c) What is the pressure potential (ψp) of the potato cells at equilibrium?

_____

(d) Use the equation $\psi = \psi s + \psi p$ to determine the water potential of the potato cells at equilibrium:

_____

KP

105 Active Transport

Key Idea: Active transport uses energy to transport molecules against their concentration gradient across a partially permeable membrane.

Active transport is the movement of molecules (or ions) from regions of low concentration to regions of high concentration across a cellular membrane by a transport protein. Active transport needs energy to proceed because molecules are being moved against their concentration gradient.

▶ The energy for active transport comes from **ATP** (adenosine triphosphate). Energy is released when ATP is hydrolysed (water is added) forming ADP (adenosine diphosphate) and inorganic phosphate (Pi).

▶ Transport (carrier) proteins in the membrane are used to actively transport molecules from one side of the membrane to the other (below).

▶ Active transport can be used to move molecules into and out of a cell.

▶ Active transport can be either primary or secondary. Primary active transport directly uses ATP for the energy to transport molecules. In secondary active transport, energy is stored in a concentration gradient. The transport of one molecule is coupled to the movement of another down its concentration gradient, ATP is not directly involved in the transport process.

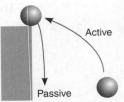

A ball falling is a passive process (it requires no energy input). Replacing the ball requires active energy input.

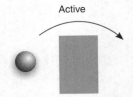

It requires energy to actively move an object across a physical barrier.

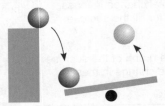

Sometimes the energy of a passively moving object can be used to actively move another. For example, a falling ball can be used to catapult another (left).

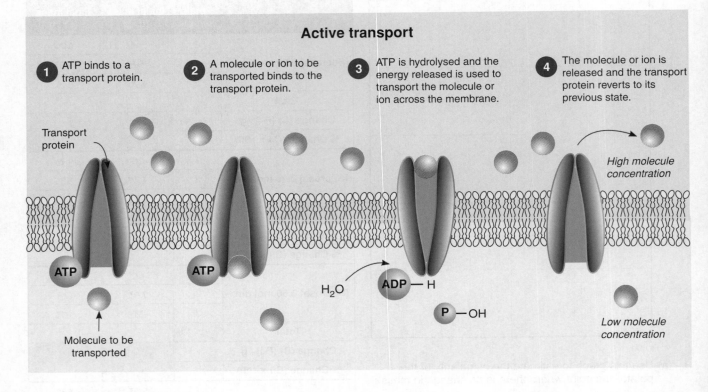

Active transport

1 ATP binds to a transport protein.

2 A molecule or ion to be transported binds to the transport protein.

3 ATP is hydrolysed and the energy released is used to transport the molecule or ion across the membrane.

4 The molecule or ion is released and the transport protein reverts to its previous state.

Transport protein

High molecule concentration

Low molecule concentration

Molecule to be transported

ATP

ATP

H_2O

ADP—H

P—OH

1. What is **active transport**? _____

_____

_____

_____

2. Where does the energy for active transport come from? _____

3. What is the difference between primary active transport and secondary active transport? _____

_____

_____

_____

© 2015 **BIOZONE** International
ISBN: 978-1-927309-19-3
Photocopying Prohibited

106 Ion Pumps

Key Idea: Ion pumps are transmembrane proteins that use energy to move ions and molecules across a membrane against their concentration gradient.

Sometimes molecules or ions are needed in concentrations that diffusion alone cannot supply to the cell, or they cannot diffuse through the plasma membrane. In this case ion pumps move ions (and some molecules) across the plasma membrane. The sodium-potassium pump (below) is found in almost all animal cells and is common in plant cells also. The concentration gradient created by ion pumps is often coupled to the transport of other molecules such as glucose across the membrane.

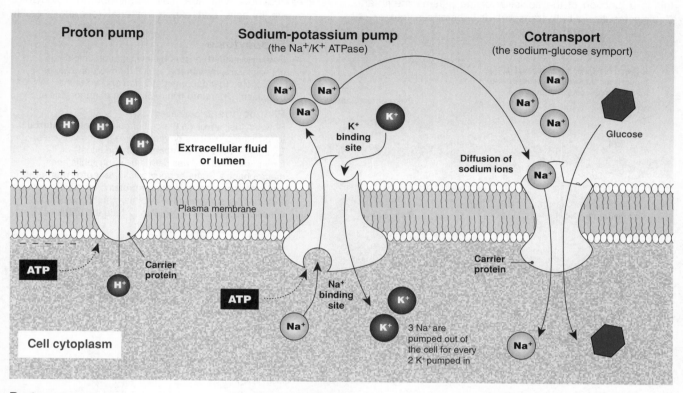

Proton pump

Sodium-potassium pump
(the Na$^+$/K$^+$ ATPase)

Cotransport
(the sodium-glucose symport)

Extracellular fluid or lumen

Plasma membrane

Cell cytoplasm

K$^+$ binding site

Diffusion of sodium ions

Glucose

ATP

Carrier protein

ATP

Na$^+$ binding site

3 Na$^+$ are pumped out of the cell for every 2 K$^+$ pumped in

Carrier protein

Proton pumps

ATP driven proton pumps use energy to remove hydrogen ions (H$^+$) from inside the cell to the outside. This creates a large difference in the proton concentration either side of the membrane, with the inside of the plasma membrane being negatively charged. This potential difference can be coupled to the transport of other molecules.

Sodium-potassium pump

The sodium-potassium pump is a specific protein in the membrane that uses energy in the form of ATP to exchange sodium ions (Na$^+$) for potassium ions (K$^+$) across the membrane. The unequal balance of Na$^+$ and K$^+$ across the membrane creates large concentration gradients that can be used to drive transport of other substances (e.g. cotransport of glucose).

Cotransport (coupled transport)

A gradient in sodium ions drives the active transport of **glucose** in intestinal epithelial cells. The specific transport protein couples the return of Na$^+$ down its concentration gradient to the transport of glucose into the intestinal epithelial cell. A low intracellular concentration of Na$^+$ (and therefore the concentration gradient) is maintained by a sodium-potassium pump.

1. Why is ATP required for membrane pump systems to operate? _____

_____

2. (a) Explain what is meant by cotransport: _____

_____

   (b) How is cotransport used to move glucose into the intestinal epithelial cells? _____

_____

_____

   (c) What happens to the glucose that is transported into the intestinal epithelial cells? _____

_____

3. Describe two consequences of the extracellular accumulation of sodium ions: _____

_____

_____

LINK 165   LINK 140   WEB 106   KNOW

107 Exocytosis and Endocytosis

Key Idea: Endocytosis and exocytosis are active transport processes. Endocytosis involves the cell engulfing material. Exocytosis involves the cell expelling material.

Most cells carry out **cytosis**, a type of active transport in which the plasma membrane folds around a substance to transport it across the plasma membrane. The ability of cells to do this is a function of the flexibility of the plasma membrane. Cytosis results in bulk transport of substances into or out

of the cell and is achieved through the localised activity of the cell's cytoskeleton. **Endocytosis** involves material being engulfed and taken into the cell. It typically occurs in protozoans and some white blood cells of the mammalian defence system (phagocytes). **Exocytosis** is the reverse of endocytosis and involves expelling material from the cell in vesicles that fuse with the plasma membrane. Exocytosis is common in cells that export material (secretory cells).

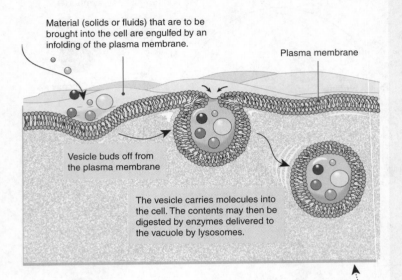

Material (solids or fluids) that are to be brought into the cell are engulfed by an infolding of the plasma membrane.

Plasma membrane

Vesicle buds off from the plasma membrane

The vesicle carries molecules into the cell. The contents may then be digested by enzymes delivered to the vacuole by lysosomes.

Endocytosis

Endocytosis (left) occurs by invagination (infolding) of the plasma membrane, which then forms vesicles or vacuoles that become detached and enter the cytoplasm. There are two main types of endocytosis:

Phagocytosis: 'cell-eating'
Phagocytosis involves the cell engulfing **solid material** to form large vesicles or vacuoles (e.g. food vacuoles). Examples: Feeding in *Amoeba*, phagocytosis of foreign material and cell debris by neutrophils and macrophages. Some endocytosis is **receptor mediated** and is triggered when receptor proteins on the extracellular surface of the plasma membrane bind to specific substances. Examples include the uptake of lipoproteins by mammalian cells.

Pinocytosis: 'cell-drinking'
Pinocytosis involves the non-specific uptake of **liquids** or fine suspensions into the cell to form small pinocytic vesicles. Pinocytosis is used primarily for absorbing extracellular fluid. Examples: Uptake in many protozoa, some cells of the liver, and some plant cells.

Both endocytosis and exocytosis require energy in the form of ATP.

Areas of enlargement

The contents of the vesicle are expelled into the intercellular space.

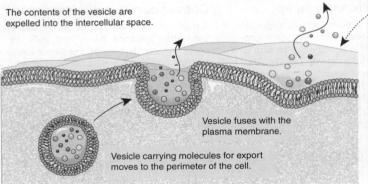

Vesicle fuses with the plasma membrane.

Vesicle carrying molecules for export moves to the perimeter of the cell.

Exocytosis

Exocytosis (left) is the reverse process to endocytosis. In multicellular organisms, various types of cells are specialised to manufacture and export products, such as proteins, from the cell to elsewhere in the body or outside it. Exocytosis occurs by fusion of the vesicle membrane and the plasma membrane, followed by release of the vesicle contents to the outside of the cell.

1. Distinguish between **phagocytosis** and **pinocytosis**: _____

_____

_____

2. Describe an example of phagocytosis and identify the cell type involved: _____

_____

3. Describe an example of exocytosis and identify the cell type involved: _____

_____

4. How does each of the following substances enter a living macrophage:

    (a) Oxygen: _____ (c) Water: _____

    (b) Cellular debris: _____ (d) Glucose: _____

© 2015 **BIOZONE** International
ISBN: 978-1-927309-19-3
Photocopying Prohibited

108 Cell Recognition

Key Idea: Cell surface MHC antigens enable the body to distinguish its own tissues from foreign material.

Each cell type has unique protein molecules on the surface, which distinguish them from other cell types. These surface proteins allow the body to recognise its own tissues (self) and distinguish itself from foreign material (non-self). The ability to recognise foreign material allows the immune system to destroy it before it can cause damage. Pathogens (disease-causing organisms), toxins, abnormal cells, and transplanted tissue are all examples of material recognised by the immune system as foreign. Even a healthy pregnancy involves suppression of specific features of the self recognition system, allowing the mother to tolerate a nine month relationship with a foreign body (a fetus).

Distinguishing self from non-self

The human immune system achieves self-recognition through the major histocompatibility complex (**MHC**). This is a cluster of tightly linked genes on chromosome 6. These genes code for protein molecules (MHC antigens) that are attached to the surface of body cells. They are used by the immune system to recognise its own or foreign material. Class I MHC antigens are found on the surfaces of almost all human cells. Class II MHC antigens occur only on macrophages and B-cells of the immune system.

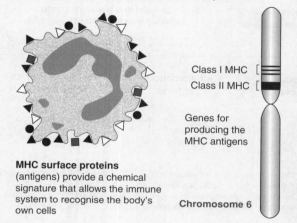

MHC surface proteins
(antigens) provide a chemical signature that allows the immune system to recognise the body's own cells

Class I MHC [
Class II MHC [

Genes for producing the MHC antigens

Chromosome 6

When self recognition fails

Failure of self/non-self recognition can lead to autoimmune disorders, in which the immune system mistakenly destroys its own tissues. Rheumatoid arthritis (right), type 1 diabetes mellitus, and multiple sclerosis, are all caused by an aberrant immune system reaction to the body's own tissues.

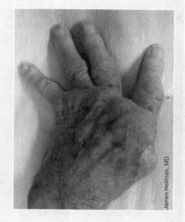

James Heilman, MD

Tissue transplants

The MHC is responsible for the rejection of tissue grafts and organ transplants. The transplanted tissue contains foreign MHC molecules which are antigenic, causing the immune system attack and reject the tissue. To minimise rejection, attempts are made to match the MHC of the organ donor to that of the recipient as closely as possible.

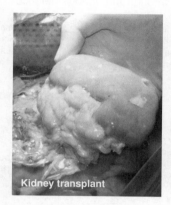

Kidney transplant

Pathogens

The immune system must detect and destroy many different types of pathogens. Pathogens can evade detection in a variety of ways including altering their surface proteins so the immune system does not immediately recognise it as foreign, or hiding within a host cell. In these ways, the pathogen can multiply undetected within its host.

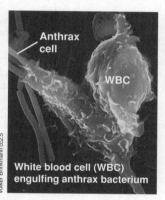

Volker Brinkmann cc2.5

Anthrax cell

WBC

White blood cell (WBC) engulfing anthrax bacterium

Abnormal tissue

Some cancerous cells are detected and destroyed by the immune system because they often produce surface proteins that the immune system recognises as foreign. However, some cancerous cells go undetected because the immune system does not recognise the surface proteins as abnormal. When this occurs, the cancerous cells continue to divide and they form tumours.

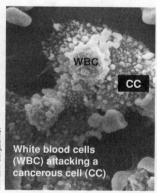

Dr. Raowf Guirguis, NCI

WBC

CC

White blood cells (WBC) attacking a cancerous cell (CC)

1. (a) What is the nature and purpose of the **major histocompatibility complex** (MHC)? _____

_____

_____

_____

   (b) Explain the importance of such a self recognition system: _____

_____

2. Name two situations when the body's MHC is undesirable: _____

_____

LINK 110   LINK 109   WEB 108   KNOW

109 The Body's Defences

Key Idea: The human body has a tiered system of defences against disease-causing organisms.

The body has several lines of defence against disease causing organisms (**pathogens**). The first line of defence consists of an external barrier to stop pathogens entering the body. If this fails, a second line of defence targets any foreign bodies (including pathogens) that enter. Lastly, the immune system provides specific or targeted defence against the pathogen. The ability to ward off disease through the various defence mechanisms is called **resistance**. **Non-specific** (or innate) **resistance** protects against a broad range of pathogens and is provided by the first and second lines of defence. **Specific resistance** (the immune response) is the third tier of defence and is specific to a particular pathogen. Part of the immune response involves the production of **antibodies** (proteins that identify and neutralise foreign material). Antibodies recognise and respond to **antigens**, foreign or harmful substances that cause an immune response.

Most microorganisms find it difficult to get inside the body. If they succeed, they face a range of other defences.

The natural populations of harmless microbes living on the skin and mucous membranes inhibit the growth of most pathogenic microbes

Microorganisms are trapped in sticky mucus and expelled by cilia (tiny hairs that move in a wavelike fashion).

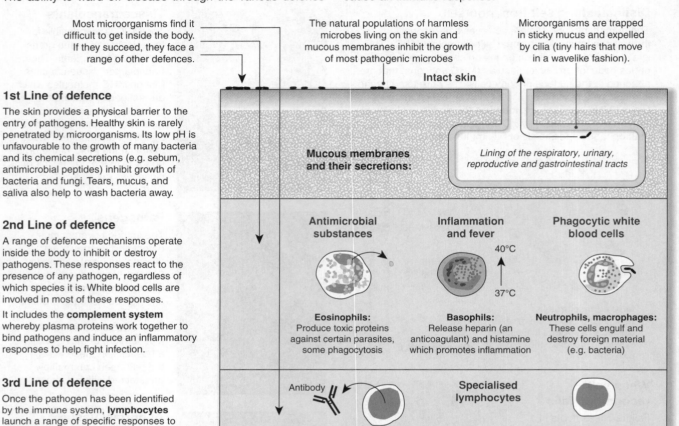

Intact skin

Mucous membranes and their secretions:

Lining of the respiratory, urinary, reproductive and gastrointestinal tracts

1st Line of defence

The skin provides a physical barrier to the entry of pathogens. Healthy skin is rarely penetrated by microorganisms. Its low pH is unfavourable to the growth of many bacteria and its chemical secretions (e.g. sebum, antimicrobial peptides) inhibit growth of bacteria and fungi. Tears, mucus, and saliva also help to wash bacteria away.

2nd Line of defence

A range of defence mechanisms operate inside the body to inhibit or destroy pathogens. These responses react to the presence of any pathogen, regardless of which species it is. White blood cells are involved in most of these responses.

It includes the **complement system** whereby plasma proteins work together to bind pathogens and induce an inflammatory responses to help fight infection.

Antimicrobial substances

Eosinophils: Produce toxic proteins against certain parasites, some phagocytosis

Inflammation and fever

40°C

37°C

Basophils: Release heparin (an anticoagulant) and histamine which promotes inflammation

Phagocytic white blood cells

Neutrophils, macrophages: These cells engulf and destroy foreign material (e.g. bacteria)

3rd Line of defence

Once the pathogen has been identified by the immune system, **lymphocytes** launch a range of specific responses to the pathogen, including the production of **antibodies**. Each type of antibody is produced by a B cell clone and is specific against a particular antigen.

Antibody

Specialised lymphocytes

B-cells: Recognise specific antigens and divide to form antibody-producing clones.

T-cells: Recognise specific antigens and activate specific defensive cells.

Tears contain antimicrobial substances as well as washing contaminants from the eyes.

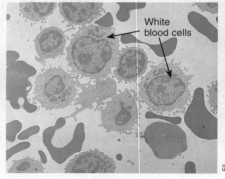

White blood cells

A range of white blood cells (arrowed above) form the second line of defence.

Coughing

Expulsive reflexes such as coughing and vomiting help remove pathogens from the body.

1. Distinguish between specific and non-specific resistance: _____

_____

_____

_____

_____

WEB
109
LINK
111
LINK
112

KNOW

© 2015 **BIOZONE** International
ISBN: 978-1-927309-19-3
Photocopying Prohibited

110 Antigenic Variability

Key Idea: Antigens are foreign substances that generate a defensive or immune response. Antigenic variability allows pathogens to avoid detection by the immune system.

Antigens are foreign substances (e.g. viral proteins) that invoke an immune response involving the production of antibodies (proteins that bind to and destroy the antigens).

Many pathogens are continually undergoing genetic changes (**mutations**) that lead to changes in their surface proteins (antigens). This is called **antigenic variability** and it enables the pathogen to escape detection by the immune system and reproduce in its host and cause disease. Antigenic variability can make the treatment and prevention of disease difficult.

Influenzavirus

Influenza (flu) is a disease of the upper respiratory tract caused by the virus *Influenzavirus*. Three strains (A, B, and C) affect humans, distinguished on the basis of their nuclear material. Influenzaviruses are able to combine and rearrange the 8 RNA segments of their genome, which alters the protein composition of their glycoprotein spikes. The changes make it difficult for the immune system to detect the virus.

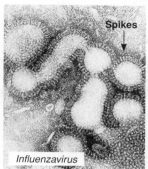

Spikes

Influenzavirus

How does the *Influenzavirus* change?

Antigenic drifts are small, sequential changes within a virus sub-type caused by point mutations in a gene. All strains of *Influenzavirus* show antigenic drift but only influenza A is a public health concern because it is associated with epidemic disease. Changes due to antigenic drift mean that the influenza vaccine must be adjusted regularly to include the most recently circulating subtypes.

Antigenic shift occurs when exchange of genetic material between influenza A viruses results in a new subtype with major antigenic differences from existing subtypes. The changes are large and sudden and most people lack immunity to the new subtype. Antigenic shifts are responsible for the influenza pandemics that have killed millions over the last century.

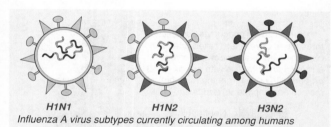

| H1N1 | H1N2 | H3N2 |

Influenza A virus subtypes currently circulating among humans

Type A influenza has a number of subtypes that are determined (and named) by the surface antigens hemagglutinin (H) and neuraminidase (N). Type A is harboured in wild fowl populations and periodically (every 10-40 years) undergoes an antigenic shift to produce a novel subtype.

HIV

The human immunodeficiency virus (HIV) infects the T lymphocytes of the immune system, eventually causing AIDS, a fatal disease, which acts by impairing the body's ability to fight disease.

Budding HIV

HIV replicates quickly, producing billions of copies of itself each day, so its ability to infect new cells (and new hosts) is high. HIV shows high genetic variability and mutates frequently. It can also combine its genetic material with other HIV viruses to form new strains. These factors have important consequences for the prevention and treatment of HIV. Any vaccine would quickly become ineffective because the virus changes so rapidly and so many different strains are present. Resistance to drugs used for treatment also arises quickly because of rapid mutation rates and short generation times. Preventing new HIV infections is critical to halting the spread of the disease.

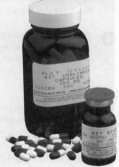

Diseases caused by genetically stable pathogens are easier to treat and prevent

it is much easier to develop vaccines to protect against pathogens that are genetically stable (have low mutation rates).

The virus that causes measles (right) is genetically stable. Prior to a measles vaccine being developed, the UK regularly had over half a million cases each year. Now fewer than 4000 are reported annually, most of which occur in unvaccinated individuals.

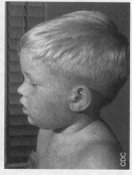

1. (a) What are the consequences of antigenic variability in type A influenzaviruses? _____

_____

_____

_____

   (b) Why is a virus capable of antigenic shift more dangerous to humans than a virus undergoing antigenic drift?

_____

_____

2. Why is it easier to treat and prevent diseases caused by genetically stable viruses? _____

_____

_____

LINK **110** LINK **109** WEB **110** KNOW

111 The Action of Phagocytes

Key Idea: Phagocytes are types of mobile white blood cells that ingest microbes and digest them by phagocytosis.

All types of **phagocytes** (e.g. neutrophils and macrophages) are white blood cells. These specialised cells have receptors on their surfaces that can detect foreign material, such as

bacteria. They then ingest the microbes and digest them by **phagocytosis.** During many kinds of infections, the total number of white blood cells increases by two to four times the normal number. The ratio of various white blood cell types changes during the course of an infection.

How a phagocyte destroys microbes

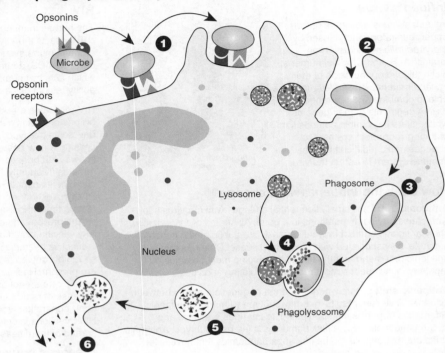

1 **Detection and interaction**
Microbe coated in opsonins is detected by the phagocyte and attaches to it. Opsonins are molecules in the blood and coat foreign material (e.g. a bacterial cell), marking it as a target for phagocytosis.

2 **Engulfment**
The opsonin markers trigger engulfment of the microbe by the phagocyte. The microbe is taken in by endocytosis.

3 **Phagosome forms**
A phagosome forms, enclosing the microbe in a membrane.

4 **Fusion with lysosome**
Phagosome fuses with a lysosome containing powerful antimicrobial proteins. The fusion forms a phagolysosome.

5 **Digestion**
The microbe is broken down into its chemical constituents.

6 **Discharge**
Indigestible material is discharged from the phagocyte.

Neutrophils

Neutrophils, named for their neutral staining cytoplasm, are the most abundant type of white blood cell, constituting up to three-quarters of all white blood cells. Neutrophils are one of four types of granulocytes, distinguished by the granular appearance of the cytoplasm and their lobed nucleus.

When activated, neutrophils become highly mobile and amoeboid-like. They are some of the first immune cells to arrive at an infection site, attracted by microbial chemicals and by **cytokines** (proteins involved in cell signalling) expressed by macrophages and damaged endothelial cells. This movement to a site based on a gradient in chemical signals is called **chemotaxis**.

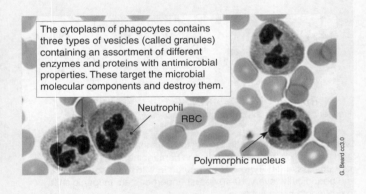

The cytoplasm of phagocytes contains three types of vesicles (called granules) containing an assortment of different enzymes and proteins with antimicrobial properties. These target the microbial molecular components and destroy them.

1. Identify the most common type of phagocytic white blood cell: _____

2. What is the role of chemotaxis in the body's response to infection? _____
_____

3. How can a blood sample be used to diagnose a microbial infection (without looking for the microbes themselves)?
_____
_____

4. Explain the role of opsonins and phagocyte receptors in enhancing phagocytosis: _____
_____
_____

© 2015 **BIOZONE** International
ISBN: 978-1-927309-19-3
Photocopying Prohibited

112 The Immune System

Key Idea: The defence provided by the immune system is based on its ability to respond specifically against foreign substances and hold a memory of this response.

There are two main components of the immune system: the humoral and the cell-mediated responses. They work separately and together to provide protection against disease. The **humoral immune response** is associated with the serum (the non-cellular part of the blood) and involves the action of antibodies secreted by B-cell lymphocytes. Antibodies are found in extracellular fluids including lymph, plasma, and mucus secretions. They protect the body against viruses, and bacteria and their toxins. The **cell-mediated immune response** is associated with the production of specialised lymphocytes called **T-cells**.

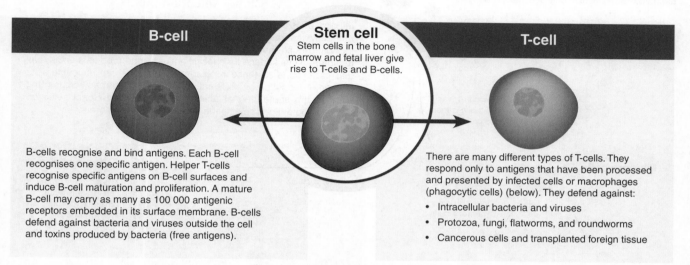

B-cell

Stem cell
Stem cells in the bone marrow and fetal liver give rise to T-cells and B-cells.

T-cell

B-cells recognise and bind antigens. Each B-cell recognises one specific antigen. Helper T-cells recognise specific antigens on B-cell surfaces and induce B-cell maturation and proliferation. A mature B-cell may carry as many as 100 000 antigenic receptors embedded in its surface membrane. B-cells defend against bacteria and viruses outside the cell and toxins produced by bacteria (free antigens).

There are many different types of T-cells. They respond only to antigens that have been processed and presented by infected cells or macrophages (phagocytic cells) (below). They defend against:

• Intracellular bacteria and viruses

• Protozoa, fungi, flatworms, and roundworms

• Cancerous cells and transplanted foreign tissue

B-cell and T-cell activation

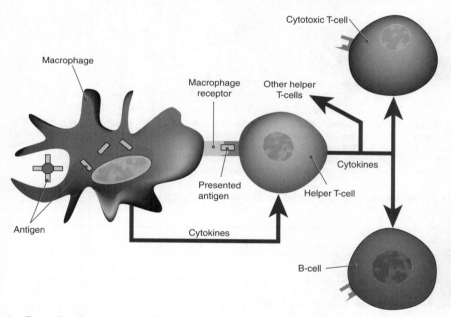

Macrophage

Macrophage receptor

Cytotoxic T-cell

Other helper T-cells

Presented antigen

Helper T-cell

Cytokines

Antigen

Cytokines

B-cell

Helper T-cells are activated by direct cell-to-cell signalling and by signalling to nearby cells using **cytokines** from macrophages.

Macrophages ingest antigens, process them, and present them on the cell surface where they are recognised by helper T-cells. The helper T-cell binds to the antigen and to the macrophage receptor, which leads to activation of the helper T-cell.

The macrophage also produces and releases cytokines, which enhance T-cell activation. The activated T-cell then releases more cytokines which causes the proliferation of other helper T-cells (positive feedback) and helps to activate cytotoxic T-cells and antibody-producing B-cells.

Lymphocyte

1. Describe the general action of the two major divisions in the immune system:

   (a) Humoral immune system: _____

   _____

   (b) Cell-mediated immune system: _____

   _____

2. Explain how an antigen causes the activation and proliferation of T-cells and B-cells: _____

   _____

   _____

   _____

113 Clonal Selection

Key Idea: Clonal selection theory explains how lymphocytes can respond to a large and unpredictable range of antigens. The **clonal selection theory** explains how the immune system can respond to the large and unpredictable range of potential antigens in the environment. The diagram below describes clonal selection after antigen exposure for B cells. In the same way, a T cell stimulated by a specific antigen will multiply and develop into different types of T cells. Clonal selection and differentiation of lymphocytes provide the basis for **immunological memory.**

Five (a-e) of the many B cells generated during development. Each one can recognise only one specific antigen.

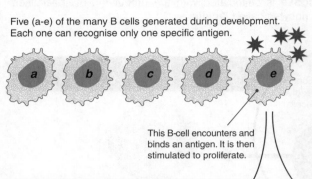

This B-cell encounters and binds an antigen. It is then stimulated to proliferate.

Clonal selection theory

Millions of B cells form during development. Antigen recognition is randomly generated, so collectively they can recognise many antigens, including those that have never been encountered. Each B cell has receptors on its surface for specific antigens and produces antibodies that correspond to these receptors. When a B cell encounters its antigen, it responds by proliferating and producing many clones that produce the same kind of antibody. This is called clonal selection because the antigen selects the B cells that will proliferate.

Memory cells

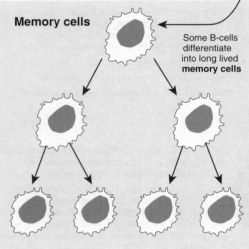

Some B-cells differentiate into long lived **memory cells**

Plasma cells

Some B-cells differentiate into **plasma cells**

The antibody produced corresponds to the antigenic receptors on the cell surface.

Antibodies are secreted into the blood by plasma cells where they inactivate antigens.

Some B cells differentiate into long lived **memory cells**. These are retained in the lymph nodes to provide future immunity (**immunological memory**). In the event of a second infection, memory B cells react more quickly and vigorously than the initial B cell reaction to the first infection.

Plasma cells secrete antibodies specific to the antigen that stimulated their development. Each plasma cell lives for only a few days, but can produce about 2000 antibody molecules per second. Note that during development, any B cells that react to the body's own antigens are selectively destroyed in a process that leads to **self tolerance** (acceptance of the body's own tissues).

1. Describe how clonal selection results in the proliferation of one particular B cell: _____

_____

_____

_____

2. (a) What is the function of the plasma cells in the immune system response? _____

_____

(b) What is the significance of B cells producing antibodies that correspond to (match) their antigenic receptors?

_____

_____

3. (a) Explain the basis of **immunological memory**: _____

_____

_____

(b) Why are memory B cells able to respond so rapidly to an encounter with an antigen long after an initial infection?

_____

© 2015 **BIOZONE** International
ISBN: 978-1-927309-19-3
Photocopying Prohibited

114 Antibodies

Key Idea: Antibodies are large, Y-shaped proteins, made by plasma cells, which destroy specific antigens.

Antibodies and antigens play key roles in the response of the immune system. **Antigens** are foreign molecules which promote a specific immune response. Antigens include pathogenic microbes and their toxins, as well as substances such as pollen grains, blood cell surface molecules, and the surface proteins on transplanted tissues. **Antibodies** (or immunoglobulins) are proteins made in response to antigens. They are secreted from B cells into the plasma where they can recognise, bind to, and help destroy antigens. There are five classes of antibodies, each plays a different role in the immune response. Each type of antibody is specific to only one particular antigen.

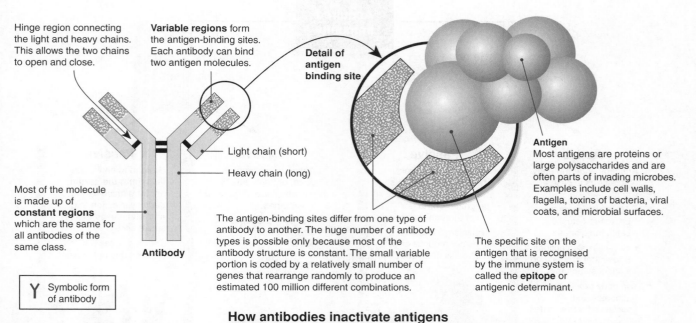

Hinge region connecting the light and heavy chains. This allows the two chains to open and close.

Variable regions form the antigen-binding sites. Each antibody can bind two antigen molecules.

Detail of antigen binding site

Light chain (short)

Heavy chain (long)

Most of the molecule is made up of **constant regions** which are the same for all antibodies of the same class.

Antibody

The antigen-binding sites differ from one type of antibody to another. The huge number of antibody types is possible only because most of the antibody structure is constant. The small variable portion is coded by a relatively small number of genes that rearrange randomly to produce an estimated 100 million different combinations.

Antigen
Most antigens are proteins or large polysaccharides and are often parts of invading microbes. Examples include cell walls, flagella, toxins of bacteria, viral coats, and microbial surfaces.

The specific site on the antigen that is recognised by the immune system is called the **epitope** or antigenic determinant.

Y Symbolic form of antibody

How antibodies inactivate antigens

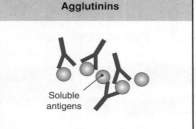

Agglutinins

Soluble antigens

Antibodies can act as agglutinins and cause antigens to bind together, forming inactivated clumps.

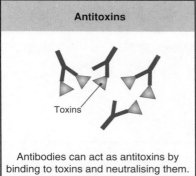

Antitoxins

Toxins

Antibodies can act as antitoxins by binding to toxins and neutralising them.

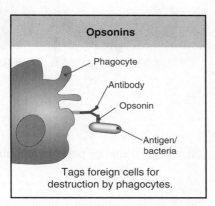

Opsonins

Phagocyte

Antibody

Opsonin

Antigen/ bacteria

Tags foreign cells for destruction by phagocytes.

1. Describe the structure of an antibody, identifying the specific features of its structure that contribute to its function:

_____

_____

_____

2. Explain how the following actions by antibodies enhance the immune systems ability to stop infections:

   (a) Acting as agglutinins: _____

   _____

   (b) Acting as antitoxins: _____

   _____

   (c) Working with opsonins: _____

   _____

LINK
111 WEB
114

KNOW

115 Acquired Immunity

Key Idea: Acquired immunity is a resistance to specific pathogens acquired over the life-time of an organism.

We are born with natural or **innate resistance** which provides non-specific immunity to certain illnesses. In contrast, **acquired immunity** is protection developed over time to specific antigens. **Active immunity** develops after the immune system responds to being exposed to microbes or foreign substances. **Passive immunity** is acquired when antibodies are transferred from one person to another. Immunity may also be naturally acquired, through natural exposure to microbes, or artificially acquired as a result of medical treatment (below).

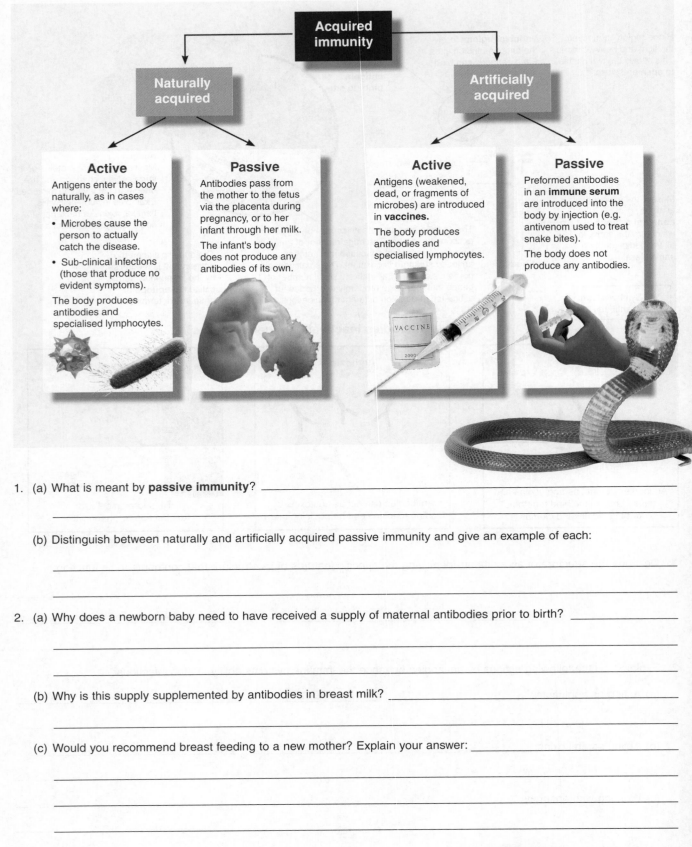

Acquired immunity

Naturally acquired

Active

Antigens enter the body naturally, as in cases where:

- Microbes cause the person to actually catch the disease.
- Sub-clinical infections (those that produce no evident symptoms).

The body produces antibodies and specialised lymphocytes.

Passive

Antibodies pass from the mother to the fetus via the placenta during pregnancy, or to her infant through her milk.

The infant's body does not produce any antibodies of its own.

Artificially acquired

Active

Antigens (weakened, dead, or fragments of microbes) are introduced in **vaccines.**

The body produces antibodies and specialised lymphocytes.

Passive

Preformed antibodies in an **immune serum** are introduced into the body by injection (e.g. antivenom used to treat snake bites).

The body does not produce any antibodies.

VACCINE

1. (a) What is meant by **passive immunity**? _____
_____

(b) Distinguish between naturally and artificially acquired passive immunity and give an example of each:
_____
_____

2. (a) Why does a newborn baby need to have received a supply of maternal antibodies prior to birth? _____
_____
_____

(b) Why is this supply supplemented by antibodies in breast milk? _____
_____

(c) Would you recommend breast feeding to a new mother? Explain your answer: _____
_____
_____
_____

LINK
116

KNOW

© 2015 **BIOZONE** International
ISBN: 978-1-927309-19-3
Photocopying Prohibited

Primary and secondary responses to antigens

When the B cells encounter antigens and produce antibodies, the body develops **active immunity** against that antigen.

The initial response to antigenic stimulation, caused by the sudden increase in B cell clones, is called the **primary response**. Antibody levels as a result of the primary response peak a few weeks after the response begins and then decline. However, because the immune system develops an immunological memory of that antigen, it responds much more quickly and strongly when presented with the same antigen subsequently (the **secondary response**).

This forms the basis of immunisation programmes where one or more booster shots are provided following the initial vaccination.

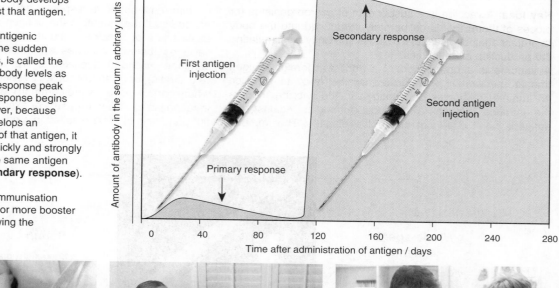

Amount of antibody in the serum / arbitrary units

First antigen injection

Secondary response

Second antigen injection

Primary response

Time after administration of antigen / days

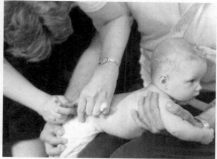

Vaccines against common diseases are given at various stages during childhood according to an immunisation schedule. Vaccination has been behind the decline of some once-common childhood diseases, such as mumps.

Many childhood diseases for which vaccination programmes exist are kept at a low level because of **herd immunity**. If most of the population is immune, those that are not immunised may be protected because the disease is uncommon.

Most vaccinations are given in childhood, but adults may be vaccinated against a disease (e.g. TB, influenza) if they are in a high risk group (e.g. the elderly) or if they are travelling to a region in the world where a disease is prevalent.

3. (a) What is **active immunity**? _____

_____

(b) Distinguish between naturally and artificially acquired active immunity and give an example of each: _____

_____

_____

4. (a) Describe two differences between the primary and secondary responses to presentation of an antigen: _____

_____

_____

(b) Why is the secondary response so different from the primary response? _____

_____

_____

5. (a) Explain the principle of **herd immunity**: _____

_____

_____

(b) Why are health authorities concerned when the vaccination rates for an infectious disease fall? _____

_____

_____

© 2015 **BIOZONE** International
ISBN: 978-1-927309-19-3
Photocopying Prohibited

116 Vaccines and Vaccination

Key Idea: A vaccine is a suspension of microorganisms (or pieces of them) that is deliberately introduced into the body to protect against disease. It induces immunity by stimulating the production of antibodies.

A **vaccine** is a preparation of a harmless foreign antigen that is deliberately introduced into the body to produce an immune response. The antigen in the vaccine triggers the immune system to produce antibodies against the antigen, but it does not cause the disease. The immune system remembers its response and will produce the same antibodies if it encounters the antigen again. There are two basic types of vaccine, subunit vaccines and whole-agent vaccines (below). Vaccines are routinely given to prevent common childhood diseases, to prevent seasonal diseases (e.g. the flu), or given to people travelling to parts of the world where certain diseases are common. Vaccines are developed in response to a new disease. For example, the H1N1 "swine flu" pandemic of 2009 resulted in a new vaccine.

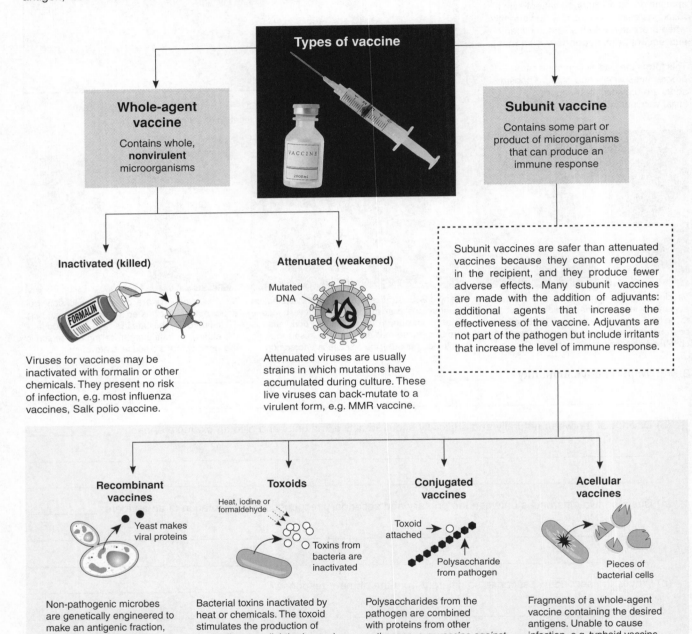

Types of vaccine

Whole-agent vaccine

Contains whole, **nonvirulent** microorganisms

Subunit vaccine

Contains some part or product of microorganisms that can produce an immune response

Inactivated (killed)

Viruses for vaccines may be inactivated with formalin or other chemicals. They present no risk of infection, e.g. most influenza vaccines, Salk polio vaccine.

Attenuated (weakened)

Mutated DNA

Attenuated viruses are usually strains in which mutations have accumulated during culture. These live viruses can back-mutate to a virulent form, e.g. MMR vaccine.

Subunit vaccines are safer than attenuated vaccines because they cannot reproduce in the recipient, and they produce fewer adverse effects. Many subunit vaccines are made with the addition of adjuvants: additional agents that increase the effectiveness of the vaccine. Adjuvants are not part of the pathogen but include irritants that increase the level of immune response.

Recombinant vaccines

Yeast makes viral proteins

Non-pathogenic microbes are genetically engineered to make an antigenic fraction, e.g. the hepatitis B vaccine.

Toxoids

Heat, iodine or formaldehyde

Toxins from bacteria are inactivated

Bacterial toxins inactivated by heat or chemicals. The toxoid stimulates the production of antibodies, e.g. diphtheria vaccine, tetanus vaccine.

Conjugated vaccines

Toxoid attached

Polysaccharide from pathogen

Polysaccharides from the pathogen are combined with proteins from other pathogens, e.g. *vaccine against Haemophilus* influenzae b.

Acellular vaccines

Pieces of bacterial cells

Fragments of a whole-agent vaccine containing the desired antigens. Unable to cause infection, e.g. typhoid vaccine.

1. **Attenuated viruses** provide long term immunity to their recipients and generally do not require booster shots. Why do you think attenuated viruses provide such effective long-term immunity when inactivated viruses do not?

_____

_____

_____

_____

© 2015 **BIOZONE** International
ISBN: 978-1-927309-19-3
Photocopying Prohibited

Whooping cough notifications and vaccine coverage (England and Wales) 1940-2008

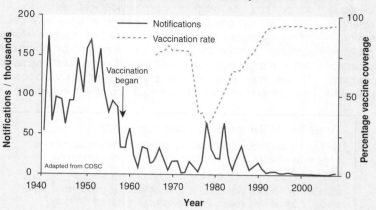

Adapted from CDSC

Changes in vaccination programmes

National vaccination programmes can have new vaccines added and others removed depending on the prevalence of certain diseases at any one time. For example, in 2013, influenza and rotavirus vaccines were added to the NHS childhood vaccination schedule to lower transmission of these diseases in the community and reduce the burden on the health system.

Changes may also be made to the frequency of a vaccination to give better protection to those most at risk from a particular disease. In the UK, children under the age of one, and youth aged from 15-19 years old are most at risk from the bacterial disease meningitis C. The UK vaccination schedule was changed recently to offer better protection to these particular groups.

Whooping cough is caused by the bacterium *Bordetella pertussis*, and may last for two to three months. It is characterised by a whooping cough and painful coughing spasms, which may be followed by periods of vomiting. Infants under six months of age are most at risk of developing complications or dying because they are too young to be fully protected by the vaccine. Inclusion of the whooping cough vaccine into the UK immunisation schedule has greatly reduced the incidence rates of the disease (above).

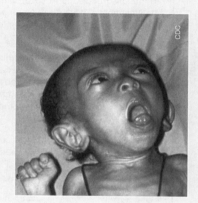

CDC

Changes to vaccines

Influenzavirus causes the 'flu' and is constantly undergo genetic changes that prevent it from being detected by the immune system. The ability of the virus to recombine its RNA enables it to change each year, so that different strains occur each 'flu' season. The 'flu' vaccination is updated annually to be effective against the current flu strains. Three strains are chosen for each year's vaccination. Selection is based on estimates of which strains will be predominant in the following year.

CDC

2. How can vaccination help lead to the eradication of an infectious disease? _____

_____

_____

_____

3. What factors would make eradication by vaccination difficult to achieve? _____

_____

_____

_____

4. (a) Suggest why influenza is difficult to eradicate by vaccination? _____

_____

_____

   (b) Predict what would happen if the wrong influenza strains were chosen for the seasonal flu vaccine: _____

_____

_____

5. In 1975, the UK vaccination rate for whooping cough decreased to 30% because of concerns about the vaccine's safety. Use the data in the graph above to describe what effect this had on rates of whooping cough reported:

_____

_____

117 Questions about Vaccines

Key Idea: People choose not to vaccinate for ethical reasons or because they perceive the vaccine to carry an unacceptable level of risk. Perceptions of risk are not supported by scientific data. Vaccines are rigorously tested to ensure their safety.

Despite the proven efficacy of vaccination in protecting against disease, some people choose to opt out of vaccination programmes. Their reasons for doing so include concerns about the testing and research protocols associated with vaccine development, the potential side effects of vaccination, or religious or philosophical objections. For childhood vaccinations, parents decide whether to vaccinate or not. Some people argue that the child cannot give informed consent (permission to vaccinate) and therefore their rights are compromised. A different ethical issue concerns access to vaccines when supply is limited. Who should get the vaccine and who should miss out and be left vulnerable?

Testing vaccine safety

Vaccines are tested using a rigorous scientific process before they are given routinely. Several regulating authorities ensure that the trials are carried out properly and that the vaccine meets safety guidelines. The steps are outlined below.

▶ Literature review and theoretical planning

▶ Laboratory testing and development

▶ Phase I clinical study. Initial safety trial on a small group of adults to determine dose.

▶ Phase II clinical study. Administration to a large target group to determine if the vaccine produces an immune response.

▶ Phase III clinical study. Administered to an even larger group to gain statistically significant safety and efficacy data.

▶ Licensing. Regulating bodies review all the data to see it is effective and safe.

▶ Phase IV clinical study. Continued surveillance to monitor the vaccine's effects in the population.

Does the MMR vaccine cause autism?

Some people choose not to vaccinate their children because they believe vaccination causes autism. Autism is a developmental disability affecting the ability to communicate and relate to others.

In 1998, Dr Andrew Wakefield and his colleagues published a paper linking the measles, mumps, and rubella vaccine (MMR) to an increase in autism rates. As a result, the uptake of the MMR vaccine in the UK dropped, and several measles outbreaks occurred. Dr Wakefield's paper has since been retracted by the journal in which it was published as it was found to be fraudulent and flawed in several aspects, e.g. sample size of only 12, with no control group.

Since the publication of Wakefield's paper, 20 large scale epidemiologic studies into MMR and autism have been carried out in several countries. All have shown that the MMR vaccine does not cause autism. However, the damage has been done, and health authorities must now convince the public the vaccine is still safe.

Autism in birth cohorts to age seven years and MMR vaccination rate in Japan

Cumulative incidence of autism to age 7 years per 10 000 — *Percent vaccinated* — *Year of birth of cohort*

— MMR vaccination rate
— Autism

Japan stopped using the MMR vaccine in 1993, opting to administer three single vaccines instead. Autism rates have continued to increase despite the fact that the MMR vaccine is no longer given. The data indicate there is no link between autism and the MMR vaccine. Many experts say the increase in autism is largely due to better diagnosis methods and a broadening of the definition and symptoms of autism.

1. (a) Describe the trend in UK MMR vaccination rates shown right:

_____

_____

_____

(b) What happened to the measles cases during this time?

_____

_____

_____

_____

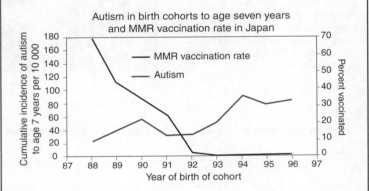

Confirmed measles cases in the UK and vaccination rate (1996-2013)

— Measles cases
— MMR vaccination rate

Confirmed cases — *Vaccination rate / %*

2. (a) Review the reasons people use to justify opting out of a vaccination programme. On a separate piece of paper, give your opinion about the validity of each reason. Attach it to this workbook.

(b) Herd immunity refers to the protection afforded to non-vaccinated individuals because most of the population is immune (and transmission of the disease is therefore limited). Parents who do not vaccinate their children rely on herd immunity to reduce the risk of their own children contracting a disease such as mumps. On a separate piece of paper, give your opinion on this issue. Should these people benefit from the action of others? Give your reasons.

© 2015 **BIOZONE** International
ISBN: 978-1-927309-19-3
Photocopying Prohibited

KNOW

118 HIV/AIDS

Key Idea: The human immunodeficiency virus infects lymphocyte cells, eventually causing AIDS, a fatal disease, which acts by impairing the immune system.

HIV (human immunodeficiency virus) is a retrovirus, a single-stranded RNA virus which infects lymphocytes called helper T-cells. Over time, a disease called **AIDS** (acquired immunodeficiency syndrome) develops and the immune system loses its ability to fight off infections as more helper T-cells are destroyed. There is no cure or vaccine for HIV, but some drugs can slow the progress of the disease. Antibiotics are ineffective against viruses because they only target specific aspects of bacterial metabolism.

HIV infects lymphocytes

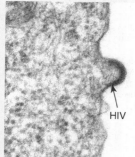

HIV budding from a lymphocyte

HIV infects helper T-cell lymphocytes. It uses the cells to replicate itself in great numbers, then the newly formed viral particles exit the cell to infect more helper T-cells. Many helper T-cells are destroyed in the process of HIV replication.

Helper T-cells are part of the body's immune system, so when their levels become too low, the immune system can no longer fight off infections.

The graph below shows the relationship between the level of HIV infection and the number of helper T-cells in an individual.

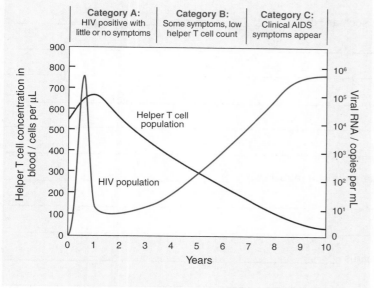

AIDS: The end stage of an HIV infection

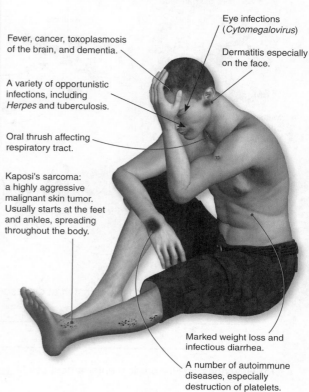

- Fever, cancer, toxoplasmosis of the brain, and dementia.
- A variety of opportunistic infections, including *Herpes* and tuberculosis.
- Oral thrush affecting respiratory tract.
- Kaposi's sarcoma: a highly aggressive malignant skin tumor. Usually starts at the feet and ankles, spreading throughout the body.
- Eye infections (*Cytomegalovirus*)
- Dermatitis especially on the face.
- Marked weight loss and infectious diarrhea.
- A number of autoimmune diseases, especially destruction of platelets.

The range of symptoms resulting from HIV infection is huge, but are not the result of the HIV infection directly. The symptoms arise from secondary infections that gain a foothold in the body due to the weakened immune system (due to the reduced number of helper T-cells). People with healthy immune systems can be exposed to pathogens and not suffer serious effects because their immune system fights them off. However, people with HIV are susceptible to all pathogens because their immune system is too weak to fight them off. As the immune system become progressively weaker, the infected person becomes sicker.

1. (a) What type of cells does HIV infect? _____

　　 (b) What effect does HIV have on the body's immune system? _____

　　 _____

　　 _____

　　 _____

2. Study the graph above showing how HIV affects the number of helper T-cells. Describe how the viral population changes with the progression of the disease:

　　 _____

　　 _____

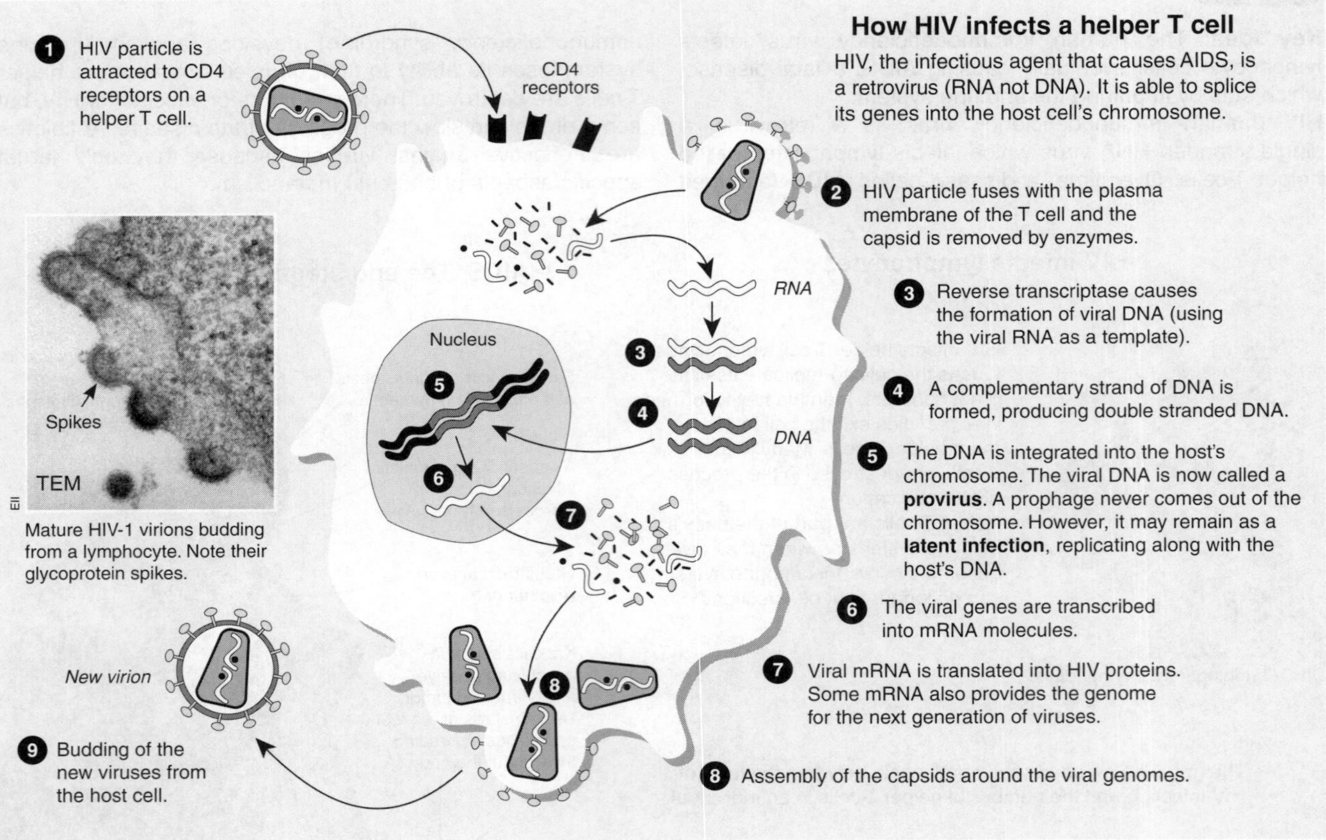

1 HIV particle is attracted to CD4 receptors on a helper T cell.

CD4 receptors

Spikes

TEM

Mature HIV-1 virions budding from a lymphocyte. Note their glycoprotein spikes.

Nucleus

5

6

RNA

3

4 DNA

7

New virion

9 Budding of the new viruses from the host cell.

8

How HIV infects a helper T cell

HIV, the infectious agent that causes AIDS, is a retrovirus (RNA not DNA). It is able to splice its genes into the host cell's chromosome.

2 HIV particle fuses with the plasma membrane of the T cell and the capsid is removed by enzymes.

3 Reverse transcriptase causes the formation of viral DNA (using the viral RNA as a template).

4 A complementary strand of DNA is formed, producing double stranded DNA.

5 The DNA is integrated into the host's chromosome. The viral DNA is now called a **provirus**. A prophage never comes out of the chromosome. However, it may remain as a **latent infection**, replicating along with the host's DNA.

6 The viral genes are transcribed into mRNA molecules.

7 Viral mRNA is translated into HIV proteins. Some mRNA also provides the genome for the next generation of viruses.

8 Assembly of the capsids around the viral genomes.

3. Why are antibiotics ineffective against viral diseases such as HIV? _____

_____

_____

4. (a) How does an HIV particle enter a host cell? _____

_____

_____

   (b) What is the role of reverse transcriptase in the life cycle of a retrovirus? _____

_____

_____

   (c) Explain the significance of the formation of a provirus: _____

_____

_____

_____

_____

5. (a) Explain why retroviral infections are difficult to treat: _____

_____

_____

   (b) Some of the drugs for treating HIV inhibit reverse transcriptase. Why is this an effective strategy?

_____

_____

_____

© 2015 **BIOZONE** International
ISBN: 978-1-927309-19-3
Photocopying Prohibited

119 Monoclonal Antibodies

Key Idea: Monoclonal antibodies are artificially produced antibodies that neutralise specific antigens. They have many diagnostic and therapeutic applications.

A **monoclonal antibody** is an artificially produced antibody that binds to and neutralises one specific type of antigen. A monoclonal antibody binds an antigen in the same way that a normally produced antibody does. Monoclonal antibodies are useful because they are identical (i.e. clones), they can be produced in large quantities, and they are highly specific for a particular antigen. Most monoclonal antibodies are produced in mice, although in some people the foreign mouse proteins can cause an unwanted immune response. Monoclonal antibodies have wide applications in diagnosing and treating disease, in detecting pregnancy, and in food safety tests.

Applications of monoclonal antibodies

Diagnostic uses

- Detecting the presence of pathogens such as *Chlamydia* and streptococcal bacteria, distinguishing between *Herpesvirus* I and II, and diagnosing AIDS.

- Measuring protein, toxin, or drug levels in serum.

- Blood and tissue typing.

- Detection of antibiotic residues in milk.

Therapeutic uses

- Neutralising endotoxins produced by bacteria in blood infections.

- Used to prevent organ rejection, e.g. in kidney transplants, by interfering with the T-cells involved with the rejection of transplanted tissue.

- Used in the treatment of some auto-immune disorders such as rheumatoid arthritis and allergic asthma. The monoclonal antibodies bind to and inactivate factors involved in the cascade leading to the inflammatory response.

- Immunodetection and immunotherapy of cancer. Herceptin is a monoclonal antibody for the targeted treatment of breast cancer. Herceptin recognises receptor proteins on the outside of cancer cells and binds to them. The immune system can then identify the antibodies as foreign and destroy the cell.

- Inhibition of platelet clumping, which is used to prevent reclogging of coronary arteries in patients who have undergone angioplasty. The monoclonal antibodies bind to the receptors on the platelet surface that are normally linked by fibrinogen during the clotting process.

Using monoclonal antibodies in organ transplants

Organ transplants often fail because the recipient's immune system identifies the donor organ as a foreign body and launches an immune response against it. A monoclonal antibody called OKT3 (or anti-CD3) is used to reduce transplant rejection rates. It works by inactivating the killer T-cells (below) that would otherwise attack and destroy transplanted organs.

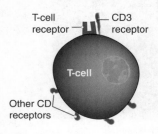

- The CD3 receptor is a signalling molecule found on the surface of T-cells. It is involved in signal transduction, and is critical to T-cell proliferation and development.

- The CD3 receptor forms a complex with the T-cell receptor (TCR), the molecule responsible for identifying antigens. The CD3/TCR complex is only found on T-cells and one other cell type.

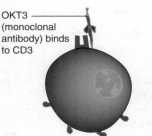

- The OKT3 monoclonal antibody is highly specific, it only binds to the CD3 receptor.

- OKT3 binds to the CD3 receptor. Because of CD3's close proximity to the TCR, the complex is no longer functional. The transplanted organ is remains safe from attack by the immune system.

- T-cells are still produced, but they lack the CD3 receptor. The other CD receptors are still present, and carry out their normal functions.

- Once OKT3 treatment is stopped, the body begins to produce normal T-cells (containing CD3) again.

1. (a) What is a monoclonal antibody? _____

_____

_____

(b) In what way are monoclonal antibodies the same as a regular antibody?_____

_____

2. (a) How does the OKT3 monoclonal antibody prevent the rejection of transplanted organs? _____

_____

_____

(b) What feature of OKT3 makes it an effective monoclonal antibody? _____

_____

_____

What is ELISA?

ELISA stands for enzyme-linked immunosorbent assay. ELISA is a technique used to detect and quantify a specific antigen (e.g. peptides, proteins, and hormones). Antigens from the sample being tested are attached to a surface, such as a microtiter plate (below). An antibody specific to the antigen is applied and binds to the antigen. The antibody has an enzyme attached. Lastly, a solution containing the enzyme's substrate is added. The reaction between the enzyme and its substrate produces a colour change in the substrate. The colour change indicates how much antigen is present in the sample. Several variations in ELISA methods exist. Pregnancy testing (right), is an example of use of ELISA.

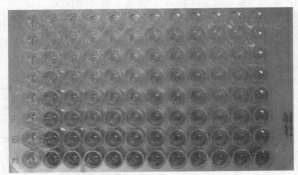

A well that undergoes a dark colour indicates more antigen is present than in a sample that has a lighter colour change.

Ethical issues associated with the use of monoclonal antibodies

Some people object to the use of monoclonal antibodies based on ethical reasons. The main ethical arguments against the use of monoclonal antibodies include:

▸ **Animal testing**: Most antibodies are produced and harvested from mice. However new *in vitro* techniques are in development where no animals will be required to produce monoclonal antibodies.

▸ **Genetic engineering**: To make monoclonal antibodies stable for use in humans, human genes are transplanted into mice.

▸ **Human safety**: When used, some monoclonal antibodies have caused deaths in recipients.

Pregnancy testing using ELISA

When a woman becomes pregnant, she produces a hormone called human chorionic gonadotropin (HCG), which accumulates in the blood and is excreted in the urine. Antibodies (**Ab**) can be produced against HCG and used in test kits to determine if a woman is pregnant.

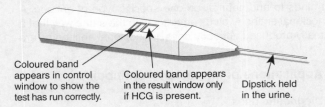

Coloured band appears in control window to show the test has run correctly.

Coloured band appears in the result window only if HCG is present.

Dipstick held in the urine.

How ELISA-based pregnancy detection kits work

Pregnancy tests use a sandwich ELISA method using three different antibody (Ab) preparations (below). The centre test zone contains polyclonal antibodies (Ab from different lines), which detect different antigenic regions of the HCG molecule.

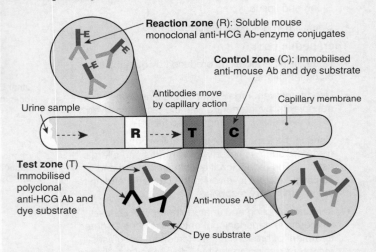

Reaction zone (R): Soluble mouse monoclonal anti-HCG Ab-enzyme conjugates

Control zone (C): Immobilised anti-mouse Ab and dye substrate

Antibodies move by capillary action

Capillary membrane

Urine sample

Test zone (T) Immobilised polyclonal anti-HCG Ab and dye substrate

Anti-mouse Ab

Dye substrate

1 In the reaction zone, HCG moves by capillary action and binds with anti-HCG Ab-enzyme conjugates. The HCG-Ab-enzyme complexes continue to move up the dipstick along with any unbound conjugates.

2 At the test zone, other parts of the HCG molecules in the HCG-Ab-E complexes bind to the polyclonal HCG Ab. The enzyme catalyses a reaction with the dye to create a colour change in the test zone.

3 In the control zone, unbound Ab-enzyme conjugates bind to the anti-mouse antibodies. The enzyme catalyses a colour change in the test zone confirming the test activity.

---

3. In the ELISA-based pregnancy test kit described above, what is the nature and purpose of each of the three zones:

(a) The reaction zone: _____

_____

(b) The test zone: _____

_____

(c) The control zone: _____

_____

4. What reaction would you expect in the windows if a woman was not pregnant? _____

_____

5. On a separate sheet, write a short essay (150 words) giving your view of the ethical issues associated with the use of monoclonal antibodies. Discuss any solutions to these issues:

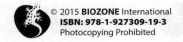

120 Herceptin: A Modern Monoclonal

Key Idea: Herceptin is a monoclonal antibody that attaches to the HER2 receptor protein on cells to help T-cells target them for destruction.

Herceptin is the patented name of a monoclonal antibody for the treatment of breast cancer. It targets the HER2 receptor proteins on cancerous cells that signal to the cell when it should divide. The proteins are produced by the proto-oncogene HER2. Cancerous cells contain 20-30% more of the HER2 gene than normal cells and this causes over-expression of HER2, and large amounts of HER2 protein. The over-expression causes the cell to divide more often than normal, producing a tumour. HER2 protein is not a foreign protein, so cancerous (**HER2⁺**) cells are not recognised by the immune system as abnormal. Herceptin binds to the HER2 protein on the surface of the cancerous cell so that the immune system can recognise it as foreign and destroy it.

Herceptin targeted destruction of cancer cells

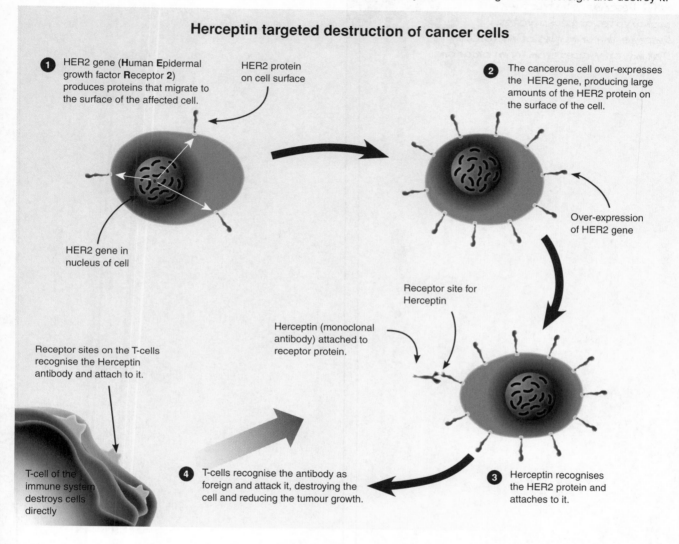

1 HER2 gene (**H**uman **E**pidermal growth factor **R**eceptor **2**) produces proteins that migrate to the surface of the affected cell.

HER2 protein on cell surface

HER2 gene in nucleus of cell

2 The cancerous cell over-expresses the HER2 gene, producing large amounts of the HER2 protein on the surface of the cell.

Over-expression of HER2 gene

Receptor site for Herceptin

Herceptin (monoclonal antibody) attached to receptor protein.

Receptor sites on the T-cells recognise the Herceptin antibody and attach to it.

T-cell of the immune system destroys cells directly

4 T-cells recognise the antibody as foreign and attack it, destroying the cell and reducing the tumour growth.

3 Herceptin recognises the HER2 protein and attaches to it.

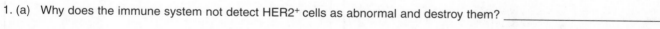

1. (a) Why does the immune system not detect HER2⁺ cells as abnormal and destroy them? _____

_____

(b) How does Herceptin detect and destroy HER2⁺ cells?

_____

_____

(c) Study the graph (right). What effect does Herceptin have on survival rates of women treated for HER2⁺?

_____

_____

_____

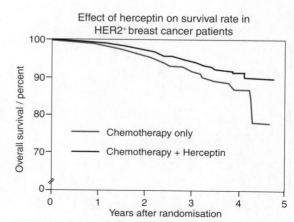

Effect of herceptin on survival rate in HER2⁺ breast cancer patients

Overall survival / percent

— Chemotherapy only
— Chemotherapy + Herceptin

Years after randomisation

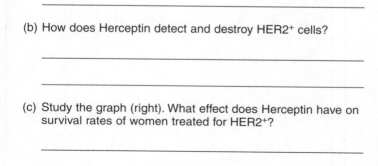

© 2015 **BIOZONE** International
ISBN: 978-1-927309-19-3
Photocopying Prohibited

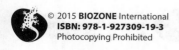

LINK **119** LINK **114** **KNOW**

121 Chapter Review

Summarise what you know about this topic under the headings and sub-headings provided. You can draw diagrams or mind maps, or write short notes to organise your thoughts. Use the images and hints to help you and refer back to the introduction to check the points covered:

Cells

HINT: Describe cell structure in prokaryotes and eukaryotes.
Describe the principles of microscopy.
Distinguish viruses from living organisms.

All cells arise from other cells

HINT: Contrast cell division in eukaryotic and prokaryotic cells.

REVISE

Transport across cell membranes

HINT: Describe membrane structure. Explain diffusion, osmosis, and active transport.

Cell recognition and the immune system

HINT: How does the body recognise and protect itself against pathogens.

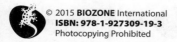

122 KEY TERMS: Did You Get It?

1. Test your vocabulary by matching each term to its definition, as identified by its preceding letter code.

antibody

antigen

cell wall

chloroplast

clonal selection

eukaryotic

magnification

mitochondrion

nucleus

optical microscope

organelle

pathogen

plasma membrane

prokaryotic

resolution

vaccination

virus

A A highly specialised intracellular parasite which replicates only inside the living cells of a host organism.

B How many times larger an image is than the original object.

C The ability to distinguish between close together but separate objects.

D An organelle found in photosynthetic organisms such as plants, which contains chlorophyll and in which the reactions of photosynthesis take place.

E A disease-causing organism.

F A structural and functional part of the cell usually bound within its own membrane. Examples include the mitochondria and chloroplasts.

G A structure, present in plants and bacteria, which is found outside the plasma membrane and gives rigidity to the cell.

H The deliberate introduction of antigenic material to produce immunity to a disease.

I Membrane-bound region within a eukaryotic cell where the chromosomes are found.

J A molecule that is recognised by the immune system as foreign.

K Organelle responsible for producing the cell's ATP. It appears oval in shape with an outer double membrane and a convoluted interior membrane. Contains its own circular DNA.

L With reference to cells, lacking a distinct nucleus and with no membrane-bound organelles DNA is present as a single, circular, naked chromosome.

M A model for how B and T cells are selected to target specific antigens invading the body.

N Lipid bilayer membrane surrounding the cell. Proteins are embedded in it and are responsible for the passage of material into and out of the cell.

O Cell types with a distinct membrane-bound nucleus and membrane-bound organelles.

P Microscope that uses lenses to focus visible light waves passing through an object into an image.

Q Protein in the blood that identifies and neutralises foreign material (e.g. bacteria).

2. (a) Identify organelle 1: _____

    (b) The organelle in (a) is found in a plant cell / animal cell / both plant and animal cells (circle the correct answer).

    (c) Identify organelle 2: _____

    (d) The organelle in (c) is found in a plant / animal cell / plant and animal cell (circle the correct answer).

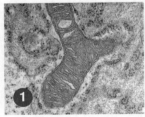

3. Match the statements in the table below to form a complete paragraph. The left hand column is in the correct order, the right hand column is not.

Transport of molecules though the plasma membrane...	....to the movement of molecules or ions against their concentration gradient.
Active transport requires the input of energy...	...high concentration to low concentration (down a concentration gradient).
Passive transport involves the movement of molecules from...	...can be active or passive.
Simple diffusion can occur...	...directly across the membrane.
Facilitated diffusion involves proteins in the plasma membrane...	...which help molecules or ions to move through.
Active transport involves membrane proteins, which couple the energy provided by ATP...	...whereas passive transport does not.

© 2015 **BIOZONE** International
ISBN: 978-1-927309-19-3
Photocopying Prohibited

TEST

Topic 3

Organisms exchange substances with their environment

3.1 Surface area to volume ratio
Learning outcomes

Activity number

☐ 1 Using model cells if you wish, describe the relationship between the size of an organism or structure and its surface area to volume ratio.
10 123

☐ 2 Explain how the evolution of body shape and specialised systems in multicellular organisms are adaptations to facilitate exchanges with the environment as organisms become larger and their surface area to volume ratio reduces.
124 129

☐ 3 **PS** Use agar blocks containing indicator to determine the effect of SA:V ratio and concentration gradient on the diffusion of an acid or an alkali.
123

3.2 Gas exchange
Learning outcomes

Activity number

☐ 4 Describe the adaptations of gas exchange surfaces in single-celled and multicellular organisms as shown by gas exchange:
124

☐ i Across the body surface in a single celled organism, such as *Paramecium*.
123 124

☐ ii In the tracheal system (tracheae, tracheoles, and spiracles) of an insect.
124-126

☐ iii Countercurrent exchange across the gills of fish (gill lamellae and filaments).
125 127

☐ iv By the leaves of dicotyledonous plants (mesophyll and stomata).
128

☐ 5 **AT** Dissect the gas exchange system of a mammal, bony fish, or insect.
168

☐ 6 **AT** Use a light microscope to examine prepared mounts of gas exchange surfaces of a mammal, fish, or insect.
124 130

☐ 7 Describe the gross structure of the human gas exchange system to include the alveoli, bronchioles, bronchi, trachea, and lungs. Describe the essential features of the gas exchange (alveolar-capillary) membrane in mammalian lungs.
130

☐ 8 Describe ventilation (breathing) and the exchange of gases in the lungs. Include reference to the role of the diaphragm and antagonistic muscle action in bringing about pressure changes in the thoracic cavity.
131

☐ 9 **AT** Use a respirometer to measure volumes of air involved in gas exchange. Use the equation PVR = tidal volume x breathing rate to calculate aspects of lung function (cross reference MS 2.2).
132 133

☐ 10 Explain what is meant by lung disease and give examples. Interpret information and data relating to the effects of lung disease on gas exchange or ventilation, and the effects of pollution and smoking on the incidence of lung disease.
134 135

☐ 11 Analyse and interpret data associated with specific risk factors and the incidence of lung cancer. Explain how experimental data led to statutory restrictions on the sources of risk factors (e.g. tobacco smoking). Distinguish between correlation and causation.
19 135 136

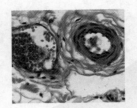

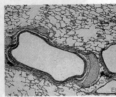

3.3 Digestion and absorption

Learning outcomes

☐ 12 Describe what happens during digestion and explain its purpose. Describe the digestion in mammals of:
- carbohydrates by amylases and membrane-bound disaccharidases.
- lipids by lipase, including the role of bile salts.
- proteins by endo- and exopeptidases and membrane-bound dipeptidases.

137 138

☐ 13 **PS** Investigate the effect of pH on the rate of a reaction catalysed by a named digestive enzyme (e.g. α-amylase or pepsin).

139

☐ 14 Identify the products of fat, carbohydrate, and protein digestion and describe how these are absorbed by the cells lining the ileum. Include:
- cotransport for the absorption of amino acids and monosaccharides.
- the role of micelles in lipid absorption.

140

☐ 15 **PS** Use Visking (dialysis) tubing models to investigate the absorption of the products of digestion.

140

3.4 Mass transport

Learning outcomes

☐ 15 Explain what is meant by mass transport and describe its role in the efficient movement of substances to and from exchange surfaces in plants and animals.

141 165

☐ 16 Describe the nature and role of haemoglobin (Hb) proteins in animals. Describe how the different oxygen transporting properties of haemoglobins reflect adaptation to environment.

142 143

☐ 17 Describe the role of Hb and red blood cells in the transport of oxygen in mammals. Interpret the oxyhaemoglobin dissociation curve in terms of cooperative binding and the Bohr effect.

144

☐ 18 Describe the pattern of blood circulation in a mammal, identifying the coronary arteries and the blood vessels leaving and entering the heart, lungs, and kidneys.

145

☐ 19 Describe the gross structure of the mammalian heart including the heart chambers, heart valves, and the main blood vessels.

151

☐ 20 **PR-5** Dissect, examine, and draw a mammalian heart to show its external and internal structure.

153

☐ 21 Describe the cardiac cycle, including the pressure and volume changes and the associated valve movements. Analyse and interpret data relating to pressure and volume changes during the cardiac cycle.

152

☐ 22 **AT** Investigate the effect of a named variable on human heart rate.

154

☐ 23 Describe and explain differences in the structure and function of blood vessels in mammals, including arteries, arterioles, capillaries, and veins.

146-148

☐ 24 Explain the importance of capillary networks (beds) as exchange surfaces. Describe the formation of tissue fluid and its return to the circulation.

149 150

☐ 25 Analyse and interpret data associated with specific risk factors and the incidence of heart disease. Evaluate conflicting evidence and recognise correlations and causal relationships.

19

155-158

☐ 26 Describe the structure and function of the vascular system in the roots and stems of herbaceous dicotyledonous plants. Describe the composition, arrangement, and role of phloem and xylem tissue.

159-161

☐ 27 Describe the movement of water through the plant. Include reference to the pathways for water movement and their relative importance.

162

☐ 28 Describe transpiration in plants as a consequence of gas exchange. Identify the environmental factors affecting the rate of transpiration and explain their effect. Explain the cohesion-tension hypothesis of water transport in the xylem.

163

☐ 29 **AT** Use a potometer to investigate the effect of an environmental variable on transpiration rate. Interpret data from investigations of transpiration.

164

☐ 30 Describe translocation in plants as an energy requiring process. Explain how sucrose is transported in the phloem, including reference to the mass-flow hypothesis and the active loading of sucrose at sources and unloading at sinks.

165

☐ 31 Interpret evidence from radiotracer and ringing experiments and evaluate evidence for and against the mass flow hypothesis.

166

123 Limitations to Cell Size

Key Idea: Diffusion is less efficient in cells with a small surface area relative to their volume than in cells with a large surface area relative to their volume.

When an object (e.g. a cell) is small it has a large surface area in comparison to its volume. Diffusion is an effective way to transport materials (e.g. gases) into the cell. As an object becomes larger, its surface area compared to its volume is smaller. Diffusion is no longer an effective way to transport materials to the inside. This places a physical limit on the size a cell can grow, with the effectiveness of diffusion being the controlling factor. Larger organisms overcome this constraint by becoming multicellular.

Single-celled organisms

Single-celled organisms (e.g. *Amoeba*), are small and have a large surface area relative to the cell's volume. The cell's requirements can be met by the diffusion or active transport of materials into and out of the cell (below).

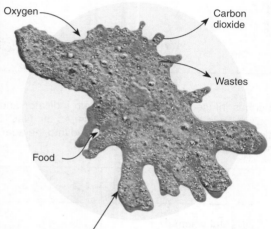

Oxygen

Carbon dioxide

Wastes

Food

The **plasma membrane**, which surrounds every cell, regulates movements of substances into and out of the cell. For each square micrometre of membrane, only so much of a particular substance can cross per second.

Multicellular organisms

Multicellular organisms (e.g. plants and animals) are often quite large and large organisms have a small surface area compared to their volume. They require specialised systems to transport the materials they need to and from the cells and tissues in their body.

In a multicellular organism, such as an elephant, the body's need for respiratory gases cannot be met by diffusion through the skin.

A specialised gas exchange surface (lungs) and circulatory (blood) system are required to transport substances to the body's cells.

The diagram below shows four hypothetical cells of different sizes. They range from a small 2 cm cube to a 5 cm cube. This exercise investigates the effect of cell size on the efficiency of diffusion.

2 cm cube

3 cm cube

4 cm cube

5 cm cube

1. Calculate the volume, surface area and the ratio of surface area to volume for each of the four cubes above (the first has been done for you). When completing the table below, show your calculations.

Cube size	Surface area	Volume	Surface area to volume ratio
2 cm cube	$2 \times 2 \times 6 = 24 \, cm^2$ (2 cm x 2 cm x 6 sides)	$2 \times 2 \times 2 = 8 \, cm^3$ (height x width x depth)	24 to 8 = 3:1
3 cm cube			
4 cm cube			
5 cm cube			

LINK WEB
124 123 **DATA**

2. Create a graph, plotting the surface area against the volume of each cube, on the grid on the right. Draw a line connecting the points and label axes and units.

3. Which increases the fastest with increasing size: the **volume** or the **surface area**?

   _____

4. Explain what happens to the ratio of surface area to volume with increasing size.

   _____

   _____

   _____

   _____

   _____

5. The diffusion of molecules into a cell can be modelled by using agar cubes infused with phenolphthalein indicator and soaked in sodium hydroxide (NaOH). Phenolphthalein turns a pink colour when in the presence of a base. As the NaOH diffuses into the agar, the phenolphthalein changes to pink and thus indicates how far the NaOH has diffused into the agar. By cutting an agar block into cubes of various sizes, it is possible to show the effect of cell size on diffusion.

   (a) Use the information below to fill in the table on the right:

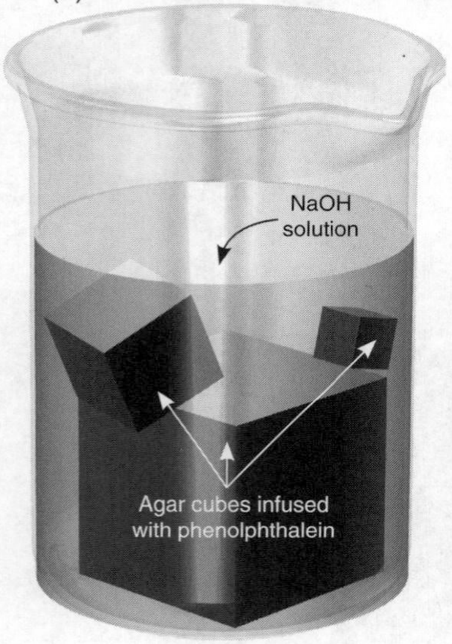

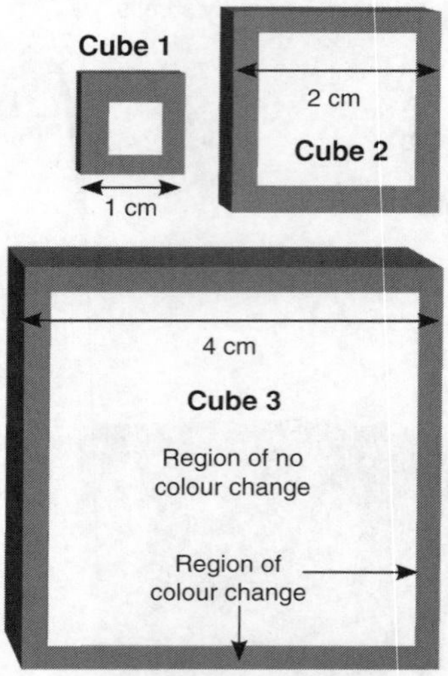

   NaOH solution

   Agar cubes infused with phenolphthalein

   Cube 1
   2 cm
   Cube 2
   1 cm

   4 cm
   Cube 3
   Region of no colour change
   Region of colour change

   Cubes shown to same scale

Cube	1	2	3
1. Total volume / cm^3			
2. Volume not pink / cm^3			
3. Diffused volume / cm^3 (subtract value 2 from value 1)			
4. Percentage diffusion			

   (b) Diffusion of substances into and out of a cell occurs across the plasma membrane. For a cuboid cell, explain how increasing cell size affects the effective ability of diffusion to provide the materials required by the cell:

   _____

   _____

   _____

   _____

6. Explain why a single large cell of 2 cm x 2 cm x 2 cm is less efficient in terms of passively acquiring nutrients than eight cells of 1 cm x 1 cm x 1 cm:

   _____

   _____

   _____

   _____

© 2015 **BIOZONE** International
ISBN: 978-1-927309-19-3
Photocopying Prohibited

124 Exchange Surfaces

Key Idea: Gas exchange is the process by which respiratory gases are exchanged between the cells of an organism and the environment. Large, complex organisms require special adaptations to ensure adequate gas exchange.

Energy is released in cells by the breakdown of sugars and other substances in cellular respiration. As a consequence of this process, respiratory gases (carbon dioxide and oxygen)

need to be exchanged by diffusion. Gas are exchanged in opposite directions across a gas exchange surface between the lungs (or gills) and the external environment. Diffusion gradients are maintained by transport of gases away from the gas exchange surface. Gas exchange surfaces must be in close proximity to the blood for this to occur effectively.

The need for gas exchange

Gas exchange is the process by which respiratory gases (oxygen and carbon dioxide) enter and leave the body by diffusion across **gas exchange surfaces**. To achieve effective gas exchange rates, gas exchange surfaces must be thin, they must have a high surface area, and there must be a concentration gradient for diffusion. The concentration gradients for diffusion are maintained by transport of gases away from the gas exchange surface. Because gases must be in solution to cross the membrane, gas exchange surfaces are also moist.

Carbon dioxide gas

Oxygen gas

Gas exchange surfaces provide a means for gases to enter and leave the body. Some organisms use the body surface as the sole gas exchange surface, but many have specialised gas exchange structures (e.g. lungs, gills, or stomata). Amphibians use the body surface and simple lungs to provide for their gas exchange requirements.

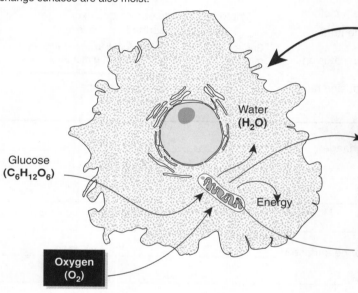

Water (H$_2$O)

Carbon dioxide (CO$_2$)

Glucose (C$_6$H$_{12}$O$_6$)

Energy

Oxygen (O$_2$)

Cellular respiration takes place in every cell of an organism's body. Cellular respiration creates a constant demand for oxygen (O$_2$) and a need to eliminate carbon dioxide gas (CO$_2$).

Living cells require energy for the activities of life. **Mitochondria** are the main sites where glucose is broken down to release energy. In the process, oxygen is used to make water, and carbon dioxide is released as a waste product.

Features of gas exchange surfaces

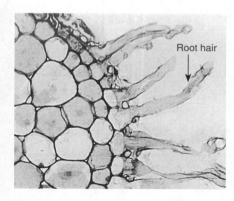

Root hair

Nephron

Alveolar walls

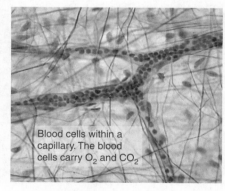

Blood cells within a capillary. The blood cells carry O$_2$ and CO$_2$

Root hair cells are thin-walled extensions of the root epidermis that greatly increase the surface area over which the plant can absorb minerals and dissolved gases. A study of the roots of a four-month old rye plant (*Secale cereale*) found the root system covered 639 m^2 (of which the root hair cells made up 401 m^2), 130 times the area of the shoot system. It was estimated there were 14 billion root hair cells. The volume of space occupied by the root system was just 6 dm^3.

In mammalian lungs, the surface area for gas exchange is greatly increased by alveoli, the microscopic air sacs at the terminal ends of the airways. The walls of the alveoli are only one cell thick and are enveloped by capillaries. Oxygen diffuses across the alveolar walls into the blood in the capillaries and is transported away to the body's cells. Carbon dioxide is brought from the body's cells to the alveoli, where it diffuses into the alveolar space and is breathed out.

Effective gas exchange relies on maintaining a concentration gradient for the diffusion of gases. Oxygen is transported from the alveoli or gills by the blood, reducing its concentration relative to the environmental side of the gas exchange surface (respiratory membrane). Carbon dioxide is transported to the alveoli or gills, increasing its concentration relative to the environmental side of the membrane. It then diffuses out of the blood, across the membrane, and into the external environment.

LINK 125 WEB 124 **KNOW**

Gas exchange in unicellular and multicellular organisms

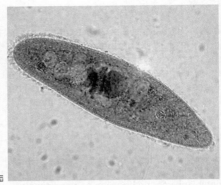

Single celled organisms are small enough that gases can diffuse into their interior without the need for gas exchange or transport systems. Oxygen and carbon dioxide diffuse into and out of the cell over the cell's entire surface.

Gills

Larger animals require specialised systems to obtain and transport oxygen to the cells of the body and remove carbon dioxide. Aquatic animals have gills, thin feathery structures, which remain moist and functional in water.

Spiracle

Terrestrial animals protect their respiratory membranes internally. Insects exchange gases by way of tubes called tracheae, which open to the outside through spiracles. Terrestrial vertebrates have lungs, which are ventilated to maintain gas exchange rates.

Fick's law of diffusion expresses the rate of diffusion of a given molecule across a membrane at a given temperature. At a given temperature the rate is affected by three main factors:

▶ **Concentration gradient**: The greater the concentration gradient, the greater the diffusion rate.

▶ **Surface area**: The larger the area across which diffusion occurs, the greater the rate of diffusion.

▶ **Barriers to diffusion**: Thicker barriers slow diffusion rate. Pores in a barrier enhance diffusion.

Fick's law

The diffusion rate across gas exchange surfaces is described by Fick's law:

$$\frac{\text{Surface area of membrane} \times \text{Difference in concentration across the membrane}}{\text{Thickness of the membrane}}$$

1. Distinguish between cellular respiration and gas exchange: _____

_____

_____

2. (a) What gases are involved in cellular respiration? _____

(b) How do these gases move across the gas exchange surface? _____

3. What is the main function of a gas exchange surface? _____

_____

4. Describe the three properties that all gas exchange surfaces have in common and state the significance of each:

(a) _____

(b) _____

(c) _____

5. Explain the function of root hairs: _____

_____

6. State the effect on diffusion rate in the following situations:

(a) The surface area for diffusion is increased: _____

(b) The thickness of the membrane is decreased: _____

(c) The difference in concentration on either side of the membrane is decreased: _____

7. Explain how mammals maintain a gradient for oxygen uptake across the gas exchange surface: _____

_____

_____

© 2015 **BIOZONE** International
ISBN: 978-1-927309-19-3
Photocopying Prohibited

125 Gas Exchange in Animals

Key Idea: Animal gas exchange systems are suited to the animal's environment, body form, and metabolic needs. The way an animal exchanges gases with its environment is influenced by the animal's body form and by the environment in which the animal lives. Small or flat organisms in moist or aquatic environments, such as sponges and flatworms, require no specialised structures for gas exchange. Larger or more complex animals have specialised systems to supply the oxygen to support their metabolic activities. The type and complexity of the exchange system reflects the demands of metabolism for gas exchange (oxygen delivery and carbon dioxide removal) and the environment (aquatic or terrestrial).

1. Describe two reasons for the development of gas exchange structures and systems in animals:

   (a) _____

   _____

   (b) _____

   _____

2. Describe two ways in which air breathers manage to keep their gas exchange surfaces moist:

   (a) _____

   _____

   (b) _____

   _____

3. Explain why gills would not work in a terrestrial environment:

   _____

   _____

   _____

   _____

   _____

   _____

   _____

4. Explain why mammals must ventilate their lungs (breathe in and out):

   _____

   _____

   _____

   _____

   _____

   _____

Representative gas exchange systems

Oxygen

Carbon dioxide

Simple organisms
The high surface area to volume ratio of very flat or very small organisms, such as this nematode, enables them to use the body surface as the gas exchange surface.

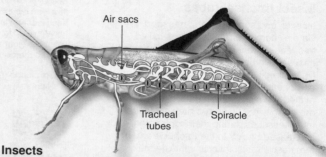

Air sacs

Tracheal tubes

Spiracle

Insects
Insects transport gases via a system of branching tubes called **tracheae** (or tracheal tubes). The tracheae deliver oxygen directly to the tissues. Larger insects can increase the air moving in and out of these tubes by contracting and expanding the abdomen.

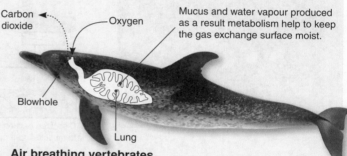

Carbon dioxide

Oxygen

Mucus and water vapour produced as a result metabolism help to keep the gas exchange surface moist.

Blowhole

Lung

Air breathing vertebrates
The gas exchange surface in mammals and other air breathing vertebrates is located in internal **lungs**. Their internal location within the body keeps the exchange surfaces moist and prevents them from drying out. The many alveoli of the lungs provide a large surface area for maximising gas exchange. For example, human lungs have 600 million alveoli with a total surface area of 100 m².

Oxygen

Carbon dioxide

Gills under gill cover (operculum).

Bony fish, sharks, and rays
Fish extract oxygen dissolved in water using **gills**. Gills achieve high extraction rates of oxygen from the water which is important because there is less oxygen in water than air. Bony fish ventilate the gill surfaces by movements of the gill cover. The water supports the gills, and the gill lamellae (the gas exchange surface) can be exposed directly to the environment without drying out.

LINK 130   LINK 127   LINK 126   WEB 125   **KNOW**

126 Gas Exchange in Insects

Key Idea: Insects transport air throughout their bodies via a system of tracheal tubes. Spiracles allow air to enter and leave the body.

Terrestrial air breathers lose water from their gas exchange surfaces to the environment. Most terrestrial insects have a large surface area to volume ratio and so are at risk of drying out. They minimise water losses with a waxy outer layer to their exoskeleton and a system of **tracheal tubes** for gas exchange that loses very little water to the environment.

Tracheal systems, which open to the air via paired openings (**spiracles**) in the body wall, are the most common gas exchange organs of insects. Filtering devices stop the system clogging and valves control the degree to which the spiracles are open. In small insects, diffusion is the only mechanism needed to exchange gases, because it occurs so rapidly through the air-filled tubules. Larger, active insects, such as locusts, have air sacs, which can be compressed and expanded to assist in moving air through the tubules.

Insect tracheal tubes

Insects, and some spiders, transport gases via a system of branching tubes called tracheae or tracheal tubes. Respiratory gases move by diffusion across the moist lining directly to and from the tissues. The end of each tube contains a small amount of fluid in which the respiratory gases are dissolved. The fluid is drawn into the muscle tissues during their contraction, and is released back into the tracheole when the muscle rests. Insects ventilate their tracheal system by making rhythmic body movements to help move the air in and out of the tracheae.

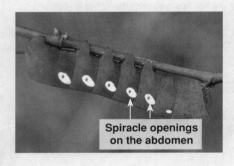

Spiracle openings on the abdomen

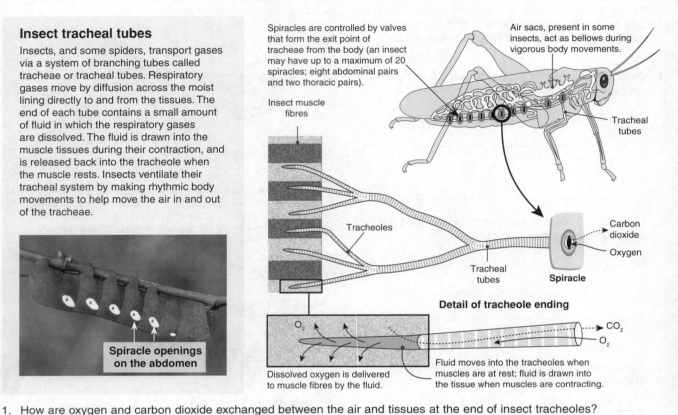

Spiracles are controlled by valves that form the exit point of tracheae from the body (an insect may have up to a maximum of 20 spiracles; eight abdominal pairs and two thoracic pairs).

Insect muscle fibres

Air sacs, present in some insects, act as bellows during vigorous body movements.

Tracheal tubes

Tracheoles

Carbon dioxide

Oxygen

Tracheal tubes

Spiracle

Detail of tracheole ending

O_2

CO_2

O_2

Dissolved oxygen is delivered to muscle fibres by the fluid.

Fluid moves into the tracheoles when muscles are at rest; fluid is drawn into the tissue when muscles are contracting.

1. How are oxygen and carbon dioxide exchanged between the air and tissues at the end of insect tracheoles?

_____

_____

_____

_____

2. Valves in the spiracles can regulate the amount of air entering the tracheal system. Suggest a reason for this adaptation:

_____

_____

3. How is ventilation achieved in a terrestrial insect? _____

_____

_____

4. Even though most insects are small, they have evolved an efficient and highly developed gas exchange system that is independent of diffusion across the body surface. Why do you think this is the case?

_____

_____

_____

© 2015 **BIOZONE** International
ISBN: 978-1-927309-19-3
Photocopying Prohibited

127 Gas Exchange in Fish

Key Idea: The gills of fish exchange gases between the blood and the environment. Gills are thin filamentous, vascular structures located just behind the head.

Fish obtain the oxygen they need from the water using gills, which are membranous structures supported by cartilaginous or bony struts. Gill surfaces are very large and as water flows over the gill surface, respiratory gases are exchanged between the blood and the water. The percentage of dissolved oxygen in a volume of water is much less than in the same volume of air. Air is 21% oxygen, whereas in water, dissolved oxygen is about 1% by volume. Active organisms with gills must therefore be able to extract oxygen efficiently from the water. In fish, high oxygen extraction rates are achieved using countercurrent mechanisms and by pumping water across the gill surface (bony fish) or swimming continuously with the mouth open (sharks and rays).

Fish gills

The gills of fish have a great many folds, which are supported and kept apart from each other by the water. This gives them a high surface area for gas exchange. The outer surface of the gill is in contact with the water, and blood flows in vessels inside the gill. Gas exchange occurs by diffusion between the water and blood across the gill membrane and capillaries. The operculum (gill cover) permits exit of water and acts as a pump, drawing water past the gill filaments. The gills of fish are very efficient and achieve an 80% extraction rate of oxygen from water; over three times the rate of human lungs from air.

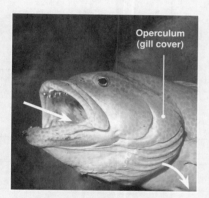

Operculum (gill cover)

Ventilation of the gills

Bony fish ventilate the gills by opening and closing the mouth in concert with opening and closing the operculum. The mouth opens, increasing the volume of the buccal (mouth) cavity and causing water to enter. The operculum bulges slightly, moving water into the opercular cavity. The mouth closes and the operculum opens and water flows out over the gills. These continual pumping movements keep oxygenated water flowing over the gills, maintaining the concentration gradient for diffusion.

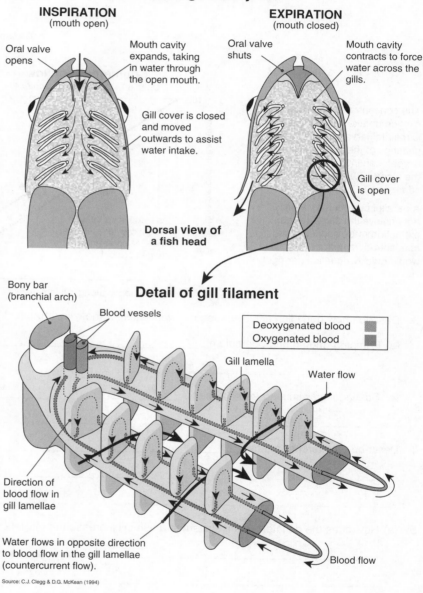

Breathing in bony fish

INSPIRATION
(mouth open)

Oral valve opens

Mouth cavity expands, taking in water through the open mouth.

Gill cover is closed and moved outwards to assist water intake.

EXPIRATION
(mouth closed)

Oral valve shuts

Mouth cavity contracts to force water across the gills.

Gill cover is open

Dorsal view of a fish head

Detail of gill filament

Bony bar (branchial arch)

Blood vessels

Deoxygenated blood
Oxygenated blood

Gill lamella

Water flow

Direction of blood flow in gill lamellae

Water flows in opposite direction to blood flow in the gill lamellae (countercurrent flow).

Blood flow

Source: C.J. Clegg & D.G. McKean (1994)

1. Describe three features of a fish gas exchange system (gills and related structures) that facilitate gas exchange:

   (a) _____

   (b) _____

   (c) _____

2. Why do fish need to ventilate their gills? _____

   _____

   _____

LINK
125
WEB
127
KNOW

Countercurrent flow

▶ The structure of fish gills and their physical arrangement in relation to the blood flow maximises gas exchange rates. A constant stream of oxygen-rich water flows over the gill filaments in the opposite direction to the blood flowing through the gill filaments.

▶ This is called countercurrent flow (below left) and it is an adaptation for maximising the amount of O_2 removed from the water. Blood flowing through the gill capillaries encounters water of increasing oxygen content.

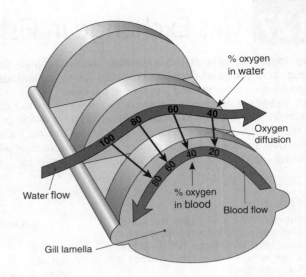

The concentration gradient (for oxygen uptake) across the gill is maintained across the entire distance of the gill lamella and oxygen continues to diffuse into the blood (CO_2 diffuses out at the same time).

A parallel current flow would not achieve the same oxygen extraction rates because the concentrations across the gill would quickly equalise (far right).

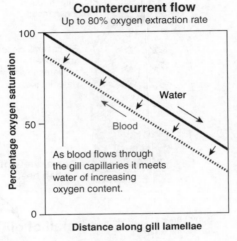

Countercurrent flow
Up to 80% oxygen extraction rate

As blood flows through the gill capillaries it meets water of increasing oxygen content.

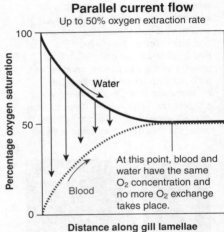

Parallel current flow
Up to 50% oxygen extraction rate

At this point, blood and water have the same O_2 concentration and no more O_2 exchange takes place.

3. Describe how bony fish achieve adequate ventilation of the gills through:

(a) Pumping (mouth and operculum): _____

_____

(b) Continuous swimming (mouth open): _____

_____

4. Describe countercurrent flow: _____

_____

_____

5. (a) How does the countercurrent system in a fish gill increase the efficiency of oxygen extraction from the water?

_____

_____

_____

(b) Explain why parallel flow would not achieve the same rates of oxygen extraction: _____

_____

_____

6. In terms of the amount of oxygen available in the water, explain why fish are very sensitive to increases in water temperature or suspended organic material in the water:

_____

_____

128 Gas Exchange in Plants

Key Idea: Gas exchange through stomata is associated with water losses. Plants have adaptations to limit this loss.

The leaf epidermis of angiosperms is covered with tiny pores, called **stomata**. Angiosperms have many air spaces between the cells of the stems, leaves, and roots. These air spaces are continuous and gases are able to move freely through them and into the plant's cells via the stomata. Each stoma is bounded by two **guard cells**, which together regulate the entry and exit of gases and water vapour. Although stomata permit gas exchange between the air and the photosynthetic cells inside the leaf, they are also the major routes for water loss through transpiration.

Gas exchanges and the function of stomata

Gases enter and leave the leaf by way of stomata. Inside the leaf (as illustrated by a dicot, right), the large air spaces and loose arrangement of the spongy mesophyll facilitate the diffusion of gases and provide a large surface area for gas exchanges.

Respiring plant cells use oxygen (O_2) and produce carbon dioxide (CO_2). These gases move in and out of the plant and through the air spaces by diffusion.

When the plant is photosynthesising, the situation is more complex. Overall there is a net consumption of CO_2 and a net production of oxygen. The fixation of CO_2 maintains a gradient in CO_2 concentration between the inside of the leaf and the atmosphere. Oxygen is produced in excess of respiratory needs and diffuses out of the leaf. These **net** exchanges are indicated by the arrows on the diagram.

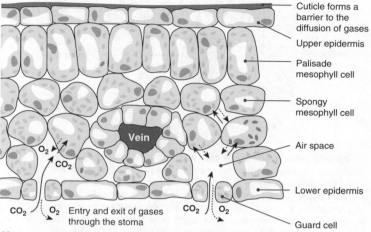

Net gas exchanges in a photosynthesising dicot leaf

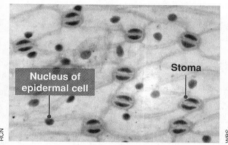

A surface view of the leaf epidermis of a dicot (above) illustrating the density and scattered arrangement of stomata. In dicots, stomata are usually present only on the lower leaf surface.

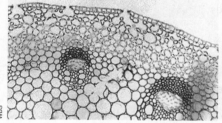

The stems of some plants (e.g. the buttercup above) are photosynthetic. Gas exchange between the stem tissues and the environment occurs through stomata in the outer epidermis.

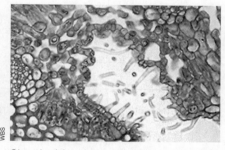

Oleander (above) has many water conserving features. The stomata are in pits on the leaf underside. The pits restrict water loss to a greater extent than they reduce CO_2 uptake.

The cycle of opening and closing of stomata
The opening and closing of stomata shows a daily cycle that is largely determined by the hours of light and dark.

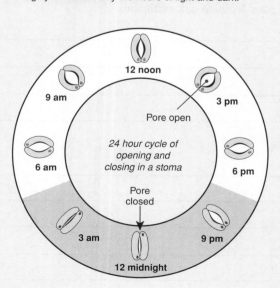

The image left shows a scanning electron micrograph (SEM) of a single stoma from the leaf epidermis of a dicot.

Note the guard cells (G), which are swollen tight and open the pore (S) to allow gas exchange between the leaf tissue and the environment.

Factors influencing stomatal opening

Stomata	Guard cells	Daylight	CO_2	Soil water
Open	Turgid	Light	Low	High
Closed	Flaccid	Dark	High	Low

The opening and closing of stomata depends on environmental factors, the most important being light, carbon dioxide concentration in the leaf tissue, and water supply. Stomata tend to open during daylight in response to light, and close at night (left and above). Low CO_2 levels also promote stomatal opening. Conditions that induce water stress cause the stomata to close, regardless of light or CO_2 level.

The guard cells on each side of a stoma control the diameter of the pore by changing shape. When the guard cells take up water by osmosis they swell and become turgid, making the pore wider. When the guard cells lose water, they become flaccid, and the pore closes up. By this mechanism a plant can control the amount of gas entering, or water leaving, the plant. The changes in turgor pressure that open and close the pore result mainly from the reversible uptake and loss of potassium ions (and thus water) by the guard cells.

Stomatal pore open

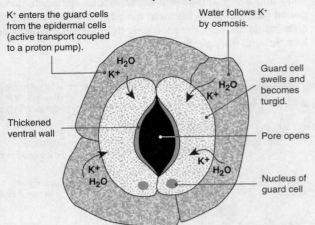

K⁺ enters the guard cells from the epidermal cells (active transport coupled to a proton pump).

Water follows K⁺ by osmosis.

Guard cell swells and becomes turgid.

Thickened ventral wall

Pore opens

Nucleus of guard cell

Stomatal pore closed

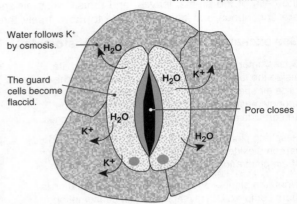

K⁺ leaves the guard cell and enters the epidermal cells.

Water follows K⁺ by osmosis.

The guard cells become flaccid.

Pore closes

Ψguard cell < Ψepidermal cell: water enters the guard cells
Stomata open when the guard cells actively take up K⁺ from the neighboring epidermal cells. The ion uptake causes the water potential (Ψ) to become more negative in the guard cells. As a consequence, water is taken up by the cells and they swell and become turgid. The walls of the guard cells are thickened more on the inside surface (the ventral wall) than the outside wall, so that when the cells swell they buckle outward, opening the pore.

ψepidermal cell < ψguard cell: water leaves the guard cells
Stomata close when K⁺ leaves the guard cells. The loss causes the water potential (Ψ) to become less negative in the guard cells, and more negative in the epidermal cells. As a consequence, water is lost by osmosis and the cells sag together and close the pore. The K⁺ movements in and out of the guard cells are thought to be triggered by blue-light receptors in the plasma membrane, which activate the active transport mechanisms involved.

1. Describe two adaptive features of leaves:

   (a) _____

   (b) _____

2. With respect to a mesophytic, terrestrial flowering plant:

   (a) Describe the **net** gas exchanges between the air and the cells of the mesophyll in the dark (no photosynthesis):

   _____

   (b) Explain how this situation changes when a plant is photosynthesising: _____

   _____

   _____

3. Describe two ways in which the continuous air spaces through the plant facilitate gas exchange:

   (a) _____

   (b) _____

4. Outline the role of stomata in gas exchange in an angiosperm: _____

   _____

5. Summarise the mechanism by which the guard cells bring about:

   (a) Stomatal opening: _____

   _____

   _____

   (b) Stomatal closure: _____

   _____

   _____

© 2015 **BIOZONE** International
ISBN: 978-1-927309-19-3
Photocopying Prohibited

129 Adaptations of Xerophytes

Key Idea: Xerophytes are plants with adaptations that allow them to survive in dry conditions and conserve water. Plants adapted to dry conditions are called **xerophytes**. Xerophytes are found in a number of environments, but all show adaptations to conserve water. These adaptations include small, hard leaves, an epidermis with a thick cuticle, sunken stomata, succulence, and permanent or temporary absence of leaves.

▶ Most xerophytes are found in deserts, but they may be found in humid environments, provided that their roots are in dry micro-environments (e.g. the roots of epiphytic plants that grow on tree trunks or branches).

▶ Many xerophytes are have a succulent morphology. Their stem are often thickened and retain a large amount of water in the tissues, e.g. *Aloe*.

▶ Many xerophytes have a low surface area to volume ratio, reducing the amount of water lost through transpiration.

▶ Salt tolerant plants and alpine species may show xeromorphic features in response to the lack of free water and high transpirational losses in these environments.

Desert xerophytes in Arizona have a succulent photosynthetic stem

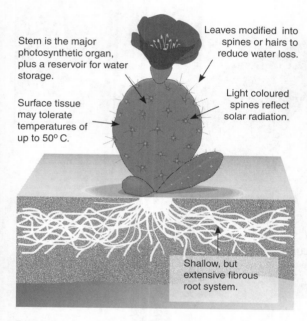

Leaves modified into spines or hairs to reduce water loss.

Stem is the major photosynthetic organ, plus a reservoir for water storage.

Light coloured spines reflect solar radiation.

Surface tissue may tolerate temperatures of up to 50° C.

Shallow, but extensive fibrous root system.

Desert plants, such as cacti (above), must cope with low or sporadic rainfall and high (potential) transpiration rates. Numerous structural adaptations reduce water losses, and enable them to access and store available water. Adaptations such as waxy leaves also reduce water loss and, in many desert plants, germination is triggered only by a certain quantity of rainfall.

Acacia trees have deep root systems, allowing them to draw water from sources deep underground.

Hairs

An outer surface coated in fine hairs traps air close to the surface and reduces the transpiration rate.

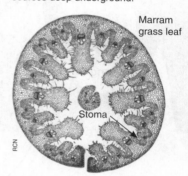
Marram grass leaf

Stoma

Grasses on coastal sand dunes curl their leaves. Stomata are sunken in pits, creating a moist microclimate around the pore, which reduces transpiration rate, e.g. marram grass.

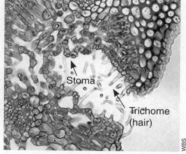
Stoma

Trichome (hair)

Oleander has a thick multi-layered epidermis and the stomata are sunken in trichome-filled pits on the leaf underside which restrict water loss.

1. Define the term xerophyte: _____

_____

2. Describe three xeromorphic adaptations of plants that reduce water loss:

   (a) _____

   (b) _____

   (c) _____

3. How does creating a moist microclimate around the areas of water loss reduce the transpiration rate? _____

_____

4. How does a low surface area to volume ratio in a plant such as a cactus reduce water loss? _____

_____

130 The Human Gas Exchange System

Key Idea: Lungs are internal sac-like organs connected to the outside by a system of airways. The smallest airways end in thin-walled alveoli, where gas exchange occurs.

The gas exchange (or respiratory system) includes all the structures associated with exchanging respiratory gases with the environment. In humans, this system consists of paired lungs connected to the outside air by way of a system of tubular passageways: the trachea, bronchi, and bronchioles. The details of exchanges across the gas exchange membrane are described on the next page.

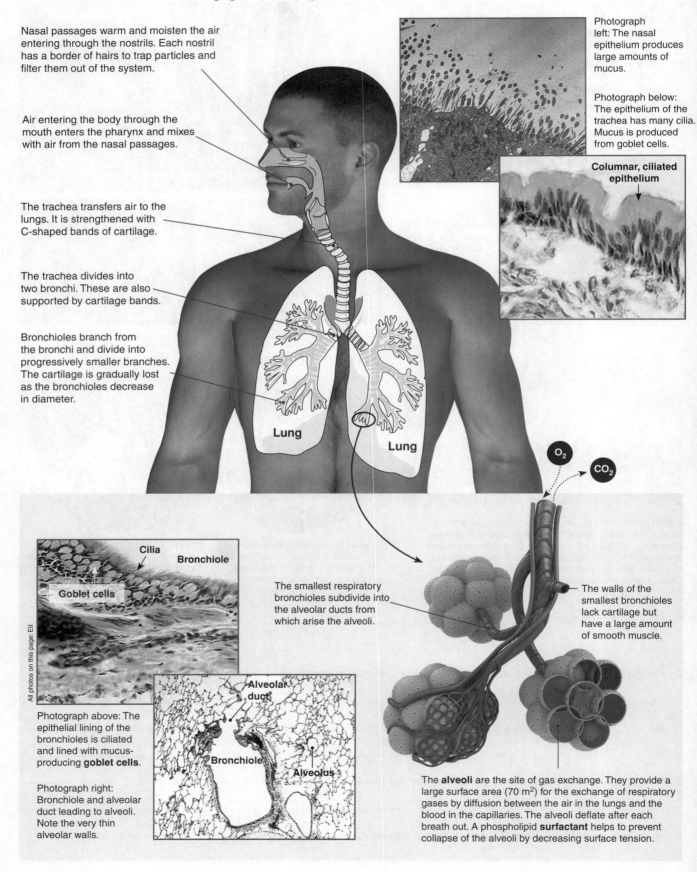

Nasal passages warm and moisten the air entering through the nostrils. Each nostril has a border of hairs to trap particles and filter them out of the system.

Air entering the body through the mouth enters the pharynx and mixes with air from the nasal passages.

The trachea transfers air to the lungs. It is strengthened with C-shaped bands of cartilage.

The trachea divides into two bronchi. These are also supported by cartilage bands.

Bronchioles branch from the bronchi and divide into progressively smaller branches. The cartilage is gradually lost as the bronchioles decrease in diameter.

Lung

Lung

Photograph left: The nasal epithelium produces large amounts of mucus.

Photograph below: The epithelium of the trachea has many cilia. Mucus is produced from goblet cells.

Columnar, ciliated epithelium

O_2

CO_2

Cilia

Bronchiole

Goblet cells

All photos on this page: EII

Photograph above: The epithelial lining of the bronchioles is ciliated and lined with mucus-producing **goblet cells**.

Photograph right: Bronchiole and alveolar duct leading to alveoli. Note the very thin alveolar walls.

Alveolar duct

Bronchiole

Alveolus

The smallest respiratory bronchioles subdivide into the alveolar ducts from which arise the alveoli.

The walls of the smallest bronchioles lack cartilage but have a large amount of smooth muscle.

The **alveoli** are the site of gas exchange. They provide a large surface area (70 m^2) for the exchange of respiratory gases by diffusion between the air in the lungs and the blood in the capillaries. The alveoli deflate after each breath out. A phospholipid **surfactant** helps to prevent collapse of the alveoli by decreasing surface tension.

© 2015 **BIOZONE** International
ISBN: 978-1-927309-19-3
Photocopying Prohibited

Cross section through an alveolus

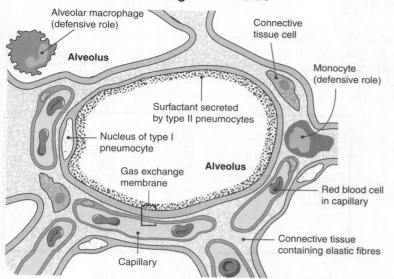

Alveolar macrophage (defensive role)

Connective tissue cell

Alveolus

Monocyte (defensive role)

Surfactant secreted by type II pneumocytes

Nucleus of type I pneumocyte

Alveolus

Gas exchange membrane

Red blood cell in capillary

Connective tissue containing elastic fibres

Capillary

The gas exchange membrane

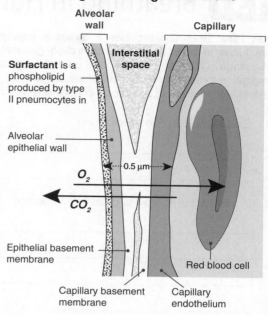

Alveolar wall

Capillary

Surfactant is a phospholipid produced by type II pneumocytes in

Interstitial space

Alveolar epithelial wall

0.5 μm

O_2

CO_2

Epithelial basement membrane

Red blood cell

Capillary basement membrane

Capillary endothelium

The alveoli are very close to the blood-filled capillaries. The alveolus is lined with alveolar epithelial cells or **pneumocytes**. Type I pneumocytes (90-95% of aveolar cells) contribute to the gas exchange membrane (right). Type II pneumocytes secrete a **surfactant**, which decreases surface tension within the alveoli and prevents them from collapsing and sticking to each other. Macrophages and monocytes defend the lung tissue against pathogens. Elastic connective tissue gives the alveoli their ability to expand and recoil.

The **gas exchange membrane** is the term for the layered junction between the alveolar epithelial cells (pneumocytes), the endothelial cells of the capillary, and their associated basement membranes (thin, collagenous layers that underlie the epithelial tissues). Gases move freely across this membrane.

1. (a) Explain how the basic structure of the human gas exchange system provides such a large area for gas exchange:

_____

_____

(b) Identify the general region of the lung where exchange of gases takes place: _____

2. Describe the structure and purpose of the alveolar-capillary membrane: _____

_____

_____

3. Describe the role of the surfactant in the alveoli: _____

_____

4. Using the information above and opposite, complete the table below summarising the **histology of the gas exchange pathway**. Name each numbered region and use a tick or cross to indicate the presence or absence of particular tissues.

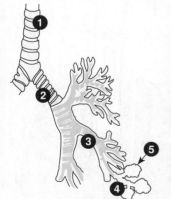

	Region	Cartilage	Ciliated epithelium	Goblet cells (mucus)	Smooth muscle	Connective tissue
1						✓
2						
3		gradually lost				
4	Alveolar duct		✗	✗		
5					very little	

5. Babies born prematurely are often deficient in surfactant. This causes respiratory distress syndrome; a condition where breathing is very difficult. From what you know about the role of surfactant, explain the symptoms of this syndrome:

_____

_____

131 Breathing in Humans

Key Idea: Breathing provides a continual supply of air to the lungs to maintain the concentration gradients for gas exchange. Different muscles are used in inspiration and expiration to force air in and out of the lungs.

Breathing (ventilation) provides a continual supply of oxygen-rich air to the lungs and expels air high in carbon dioxide. Together with the cardiovascular system, which transports respiratory gases between the alveolar and the cells of the body, breathing maintains concentration gradients for gas exchange. Breathing is achieved by the action of muscles.

1. Explain the purpose of breathing: _____

_____

_____

2. In general terms, how is breathing achieved?

_____

_____

_____

_____

3. (a) Describe the sequence of events involved in quiet breathing:

_____

_____

_____

_____

_____

   (b) What is the essential difference between this and the situation during forced breathing:

_____

_____

_____

4. During inspiration, which muscles are:

   (a) Contracting: _____

_____

   (b) Relaxed: _____

_____

5. During forced expiration, which muscles are:

   (a) Contracting: _____

_____

   (b) Relaxed: _____

_____

6. Explain the role of antagonistic muscles in breathing:

_____

_____

_____

Breathing and muscle action

Muscles can only do work by contracting, so they can only perform movement in one direction. To achieve motion in two directions, muscles work as antagonistic pairs. Antagonistic pairs of muscles have opposing actions and create movement when one contracts and the other relaxes. Breathing in humans involves two sets of antagonistic muscles. The external and internal intercostal muscles of the ribcage, and the diaphragm and abdominal muscles.

Inspiration (inhalation or breathing in)

During quiet breathing, inspiration is achieved by increasing the thoracic volume (therefore decreasing the pressure inside the lungs). Air then flows into the lungs in response to the decreased pressure inside the lung. Inspiration is always an active process involving muscle contraction.

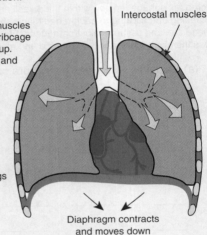

1 External intercostal muscles contract causing the ribcage to expand and move up. Diaphragm contracts and moves down.

2 Thoracic volume increases, lungs expand, and the pressure inside the lungs decreases.

3 Air flows into the lungs in response to the pressure gradient.

Intercostal muscles

Diaphragm contracts and moves down

Expiration (exhalation or breathing out)

In quiet breathing, expiration is a passive process, achieved when the external intercostals and diaphragm relax and thoracic volume decreases. Air flows passively out of the lungs to equalise with the air pressure. In active breathing, muscle contraction is involved in bringing about both inspiration and expiration.

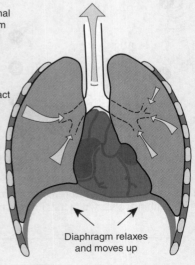

1 In **quiet breathing**, external intercostals and diaphragm relax. The elasticity of the lung tissue causes recoil.

In **forced breathing**, the internal intercostals and abdominal muscles contract to compress the thoracic cavity and increase the force of the expiration.

2 Thoracic volume decreases and the pressure inside the lungs increases.

3 Air flows passively out of the lungs in response to the pressure gradient.

Diaphragm relaxes and moves up

© 2015 **BIOZONE** International
ISBN: 978-1-927309-19-3
Photocopying Prohibited

132 Measuring Lung Function

Key Idea: A lung function test, called spirometry, measures changes in lung volume and can be used diagnostically.

The volume of gases exchanged during breathing varies according to the physiological demands placed on the body (e.g. by exercise) and an individual's lung function. **Spirometry** measures changes in lung volume by measuring how much air a person can breathe in and out and how fast the air can be expelled. Spirometry can measure changes in ventilation rates during exercise and can be used to assess impairments in lung function, as might occur as a result of disease. In humans, the total adult lung capacity varies between 4 and 6 dm^3 and is greater in males.

Determining changes in lung volume using spirometry

The apparatus used to measure the amount of air exchanged during breathing and the rate of breathing is a **spirometer** (also called a respirometer). A simple spirometer consists of a weighted drum, containing oxygen or air, inverted over a chamber of water. A tube connects the air-filled chamber with the subject's mouth, and soda lime in the system absorbs the carbon dioxide breathed out. Breathing results in a trace called a spirogram, from which lung volumes can be measured directly.

During inspiration
Air is removed from the chamber, the drum sinks, and an upward deflection is recorded on the paper on the rotating drum.

During expiration
Air is added to the chamber, the drum rises, and a downward deflection is recorded.

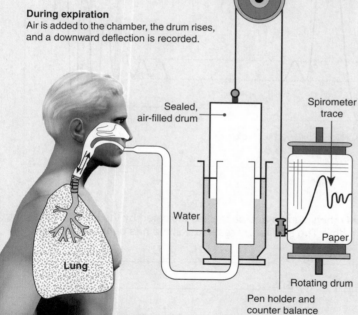

Pulley
Sealed, air-filled drum
Spirometer trace
Water
Paper
Lung
Rotating drum
Pen holder and counter balance

Lung volumes and capacities

The air in the lungs can be divided into volumes. Lung capacities are combinations of volumes.

DESCRIPTION OF VOLUME	Vol (dm^3)
Tidal volume (TV) Volume of air breathed in and out in a single breath	**0.5**
Inspiratory reserve volume (IRV) Volume breathed in by a maximum inspiration at the end of a normal inspiration	**3.3**
Expiratory reserve volume (ERV) Volume breathed out by a maximum effort at the end of a normal expiration	**1.0**
Residual volume (RV) Volume of air remaining in the lungs at the end of a maximum expiration	**1.2**

DESCRIPTION OF CAPACITY	
Inspiratory capacity (IC) = TV + IRV Volume breathed in by a maximum inspiration at the end of a normal expiration	**3.8**
Vital capacity (VC) = IRV + TV + ERV Volume that can be exhaled after a maximum inspiration.	**4.8**
Total lung capacity (TLC) = VC + RV The total volume of the lungs. Only a fraction of TLC is used in normal breathing	**6.0**

PRIMARY INDICATORS OF LUNG FUNCTION

Forced expiratory volume in 1 second (FEV_1)
The volume of air that is maximally exhaled in the first second of exhalation.

Forced vital capacity (FVC)
The total volume of air that can be forcibly exhaled after a maximum inspiration.

---

1. Describe how each of the following might be expected to influence values for lung volumes and capacities obtained using spirometry:

   (a) Height: _____

   (b) Gender: _____

   (c) Age: _____

2. A percentage decline in FEV_1 and FVC (to <80% of normal) are indicators of impaired lung function, e.g in asthma:

   (a) Explain why a forced volume is a more useful indicator of lung function than tidal volume:

   _____

   (b) Asthma is treated with drugs to relax the airways. Suggest how spirometry could be used during asthma treatment:

   _____

LINK 134   LINK 133   WEB 132   DATA

Respiratory gas	Approximate percentages of O_2 and CO_2		
	Inhaled air	Air in lungs	Exhaled air
O_2	21.0	13.8	16.4
CO_2	0.04	5.5	3.6

Above: The percentages of respiratory gases in air (by volume) during normal breathing. The percentage volume of oxygen in the alveolar air (in the lung) is lower than that in the exhaled air because of the influence of the **dead air volume** (the air in the spaces of the nose, throat, larynx, trachea and bronchi). This air (about 30% of the air inhaled) is unavailable for gas exchange.

Left: During exercise, the breathing rate, tidal volume, and **pulmonary ventilation** rate or **PV** (the amount of air exchanged with the environment per minute) increase up to a maximum (as indicated below).

Spirogram for a male during quiet and forced breathing, and during exercise

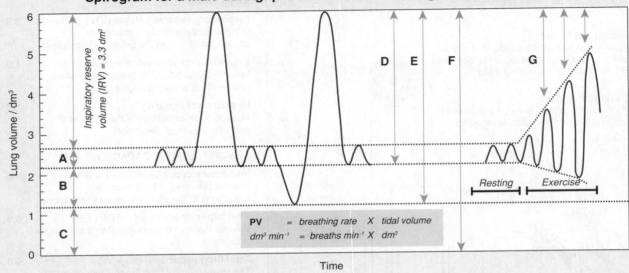

$$PV = breathing\ rate\ X\ tidal\ volume$$
$$dm^3\ min^{-1} = breaths\ min^{-1}\ X\ dm^3$$

3. Using the definitions given on the previous page, identify the volumes and capacities indicated by the letters **A-F** on the spirogram above. For each, indicate the volume (vol) in dm^3. The inspiratory reserve volume has been identified:

(a) **A:** _____ Vol: _____ (d) **D:** _____ Vol: _____

(b) **B:** _____ Vol: _____ (e) **E:** _____ Vol: _____

(c) **C:** _____ Vol: _____ (f) **F:** _____ Vol: _____

4. Explain what is happening in the sequence indicated by the letter **G:** _____

_____

5. Calculate PV when breathing rate is 15 breaths per minute and tidal volume is 0.4 dm^3: _____

6. (a) Describe what would happen to PV during strenuous exercise: _____

   (b) Explain how this is achieved: _____

7. The table above gives approximate percentages for respiratory gases during breathing. Study the data and then:

   (a) Calculate the difference in CO_2 between inhaled and exhaled air: _____

   (b) Explain where this 'extra' CO_2 comes from: _____

   (c) Explain why the dead air volume raises the oxygen content of exhaled air above that in the lungs: _____

_____

_____

© 2015 **BIOZONE** International
ISBN: 978-1-927309-19-3
Photocopying Prohibited

133 Investigating Ventilation in Humans

Key Idea: Vital capacity can be affected by several factors including age, gender, height, ethnicity, and disease.

Vital capacity is the greatest volume of air that can be expelled from the lungs after taking the deepest possible breath. It is easily measured using a spirometer or a bell jar system (as described below). In healthy adults, vital capacity ranges between 4-6 dm³, but is influenced by several factors including gender, age, height, ethnicity, and fitness.

Measuring vital capacity

Vital capacity can be measured using a 6 dm³ calibrated glass bell jar, supported in a sink of water (right). The jar is calibrated by inverting it, pouring in known volumes of water, and marking the level on the bell jar with a marker pen.

To measure vital capacity, a person breathes in as far as possible (maximal inhalation), and then exhales as far as possible (maximal exhalation) into a mouth piece connected to tubing. The drop in volume within the bell jar is measured (this is the vital capacity in dm³).

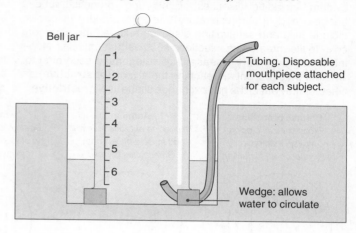

Bell jar

Tubing. Disposable mouthpiece attached for each subject.

Wedge: allows water to circulate

Investigating vital capacity

A class of high school biology students investigated the vital capacity of the whole class using the bell jar method described above.

The students recorded their heights as well as their vital capacity. The results are presented on the table (right).

1. Calculate the mean vital capacity for:

   (a) Females: _____

   (b) Males: _____

   (c) Explain if these results are what you would expect?

   _____

   _____

   _____

   _____

Females		Males	
Height / cm	Vital capacity / dm³	Height / cm	Vital capacity / dm³
156	2.75	181	4.00
145	2.50	163	2.50
155	3.25	167	4.00
170	4.00	174	4.00
162	2.75	177	4.00
164	2.75	177	3.75
163	3.40	176	3.75
158	2.75	177	3.25
167	4.00	178	4.00
165	3.00	178	3.75

2. (a) Plot height versus vital capacity as a scatter graph on the grid provided (right). Use different symbols or colours for each set of data (female and male).

   (b) Draw a line of best fit through each set of points. For a line of best fit, the points should fall equally either side of the line.

   (c) Describe the relationship between height and vital capacity:

   _____

   _____

   _____

   _____

   _____

   _____

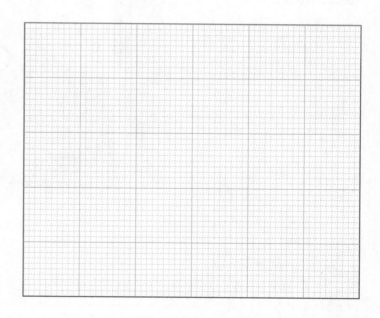

134 Respiratory Diseases

Key Idea: Respiratory diseases may be restrictive or obstructive and severely limit the functioning of the gas exchange surface.

Respiratory diseases are diseases of the gas exchange system, including diseases of the lung, bronchial tubes, trachea, and upper respiratory tract. Respiratory diseases include mild and self-limiting diseases such as the common cold, to life-threatening infections such as tuberculosis. Non-infectious respiratory diseases are categorised according to whether they prevent air reaching the alveoli (**obstructive**) or whether they affect the gas exchange tissue itself (**restrictive**).

Such diseases ultimately have similar effects and the end result is that gas exchange rates are too low to meet metabolic requirements. Non-infectious respiratory diseases are strongly correlated with certain behaviours and are made worse by exposure to air pollutants. Obstructive diseases, such as emphysema, are associated with an inflammatory response of the lung to noxious particles or gases, most commonly tobacco smoke. In contrast, scarring (**fibrosis**) of the lung tissue underlies restrictive lung diseases such as **asbestosis** and **silicosis**. Such diseases are often called occupational lung diseases.

Chronic bronchitis
Excess mucus blocks airway, leading to inflammation and infection

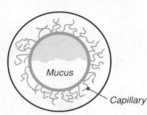

Mucus

Capillary

Asthma
Thickening of bronchiole wall and muscle hypertrophy. Bronchioles narrow.

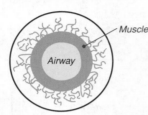

Muscle

Airway

Emphysema
Destruction of capillaries and structures supporting the small airways and lung tissue

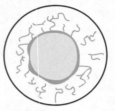

A peak flow meter is a small, hand-held device used to monitor a person's ability to breathe out air. It measures the airflow through the bronchi and thus the degree of obstruction in the airways.

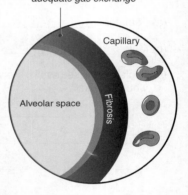

Cross sections through a bronchiole with various types of obstructive lung disease

Obstructive lung disease
– passage blockage –

In obstructive lung diseases, a blockage prevents the air getting to the gas exchange surface.

The flow of air may be obstructed because of constriction of the airways (as in **asthma**), excess mucus secretion (as in chronic **bronchitis**), or because of reduced lung elasticity, which causes alveoli and small airways to collapse (as in **emphysema**). Shortness of breath is a symptom in all cases and chronic bronchitis is also associated with a persistent cough.

Chronic bronchitis and emphysema often occur together and are commonly associated with cigarette smoking, but can also occur with chronic exposure to air pollution.

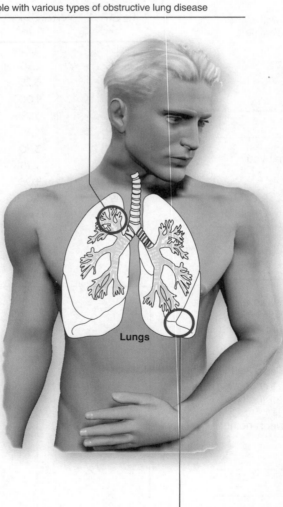

Lungs

Scarring (fibrosis) makes the lung tissue stiffer and prevents adequate gas exchange

Capillary

Alveolar space

Fibrosis

Restrictive lung disease
– scarring –

Restrictive lung diseases are characterised by scarring or **fibrosis** within the gas exchange tissue of the lung (above). As a result of the scarring, the lung tissue becomes stiffer and more difficult to expand, leading to shortness of breath.

Restrictive lung diseases are usually the result of exposure to inhaled substances (especially dusts) in the environment, including **inorganic dusts** such as silica, asbestos, or coal dust, and **organic dusts**, such as those from bird droppings or moldy hay. Like most respiratory diseases, the symptoms are exacerbated by poor air quality (such as occurs in smoggy cities).

Nephron

Micrograph showing alveoli affected by emphysema. The top of the image shows the large open airways resulting from emphysema. The bottom of the image shows healthy alveoli.

LINK
132
LINK
135
LINK
136
KNOW

© 2015 **BIOZONE** International
ISBN: 978-1-927309-19-3
Photocopying Prohibited

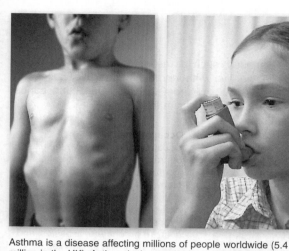

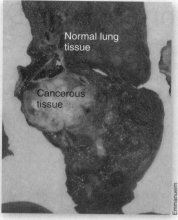

Normal lung tissue

Cancerous tissue

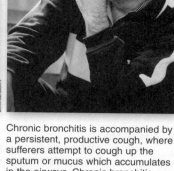

Asthma is a disease affecting millions of people worldwide (5.4 million in the UK). Asthma is the result of a hypersensitive reaction to allergens such as house dust or pollen, but attacks can be triggered by environmental factors such as cold air, exercise, or air pollutants. During an attack, sufferers show laboured breathing with overexpansion of the chest cavity (above left). Asthma is treated with drugs that help to expand the airways (bronchodilators). These are usually delivered via a nebuliser or inhaler (above).

Lung cancer is the second most common form of cancer in the UK, with around 43 000 people diagnosed and 35 000 dying from the disease each year. Most (90%) of lung cancer cases are linked to lifestyle choices, with the majority of these being associated with cigarette smoking.

Chronic bronchitis is accompanied by a persistent, productive cough, where sufferers attempt to cough up the sputum or mucus which accumulates in the airways. Chronic bronchitis is indicated using spirometry by a reduced FEV1/FVC ratio that is not reversed with bronchodilator therapy.

1. Distinguish between obstructive and restrictive lung diseases, and provide some examples:

2. Physicians may use spirometry to diagnosis certain types of respiratory disease. Explain the following typical results:

(a) In patients with chronic obstructive pulmonary disease, the FEV_1 / FVC ratio declines (to <70% of normal):

(b) Patients with asthma also have a FEV_1 / FVC ratio of <70%, but this improves following use of bronchodilators:

(c) In patients with restrictive lung disease, both FEV_1 and FVC are low but the FEV_1 / FVC ratio is normal to high:

3. Describe the mechanisms by which restrictive lung diseases reduce lung function and describe an example:

4. Suggest why many restrictive lung diseases are also classified as occupational lung diseases:

5. Describe the role of histamine in the occurrence of an asthma attack:

135 Risk Factors for Lung Disease

Key Idea: Risk factors associated with lung disease include age, sex, occupational hazards, and behavioural factors. Lung disease includes a wide range of aliments including lung cancer, obstructive diseases such as emphysema, and restrictive diseases, such as asbestosis. In the UK, about 3 million people live with chronic obstructive pulmonary disease, and 23 000 die from it every year. Lung cancer accounts for 6% of all deaths in the UK.

▶ **Behavioural**:
Smoking is the number one behavioural risk factor for lung disease, with lung cancer rates being 15 times higher in smokers than in non-smokers. Second-hand smoke also contributes to lung disease. Indoor living increases the risk of lung disease due to increased levels of radon gas released from the soil which becomes trapped indoors, especially in basement areas.

▶ **Age and sex**:
The risk of developing lung disease increases with age. Frequent occurrences of lung disease when young increases the risk of chronic lung disease later in life. Males tend to have slightly higher risk of developing lung disease than females.

▶ **Genetic and socioeconomic factors**:
Occurrence of lung disease increases in those with a family history of lung disease. Some socioeconomic factors (e.g. living in poorly heated and ventilated housing) also increase the risk of lung disease.

▶ **Occupational**:
Occupations that involve the use of, or proximity to, hazardous substances increase the risk of lung diseases. Many of these substances cause change to the DNA (mutation) and include paints, machine exhaust and airborne particles such as industrial dusts (e.g. concrete, asbestos, and coal dust), which are inhaled.

Asbestosis is a restrictive lung disease caused by breathing in asbestos fibres. The asbestos fibres make their way into the alveoli where they cause damage and scarring. Symptoms may not appear for 20 years or more. Asbestos has not been widely used as building or insulating material for many decades. In the photo, left, workers removing old asbestos sheets must wear full protective equipment.

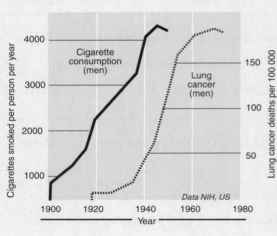

Rates of smoking vs rates of lung cancer

Data NIH, US

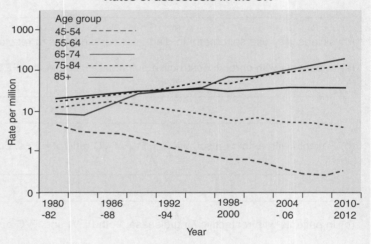

Rates of asbestosis in the UK

Age group
45-54 – – – –
55-64 – – – –
65-74 ——
75-84 - - - -
85+ ——

1. A long term study showed the correlation between smoking and lung cancer, providing supporting evidence for the adverse effects of smoking (above left):

    (a) Explain why a long term study was important: _____

    _____

    _____

    (b) The study made a link between cigarette consumption and mortality from lung cancer. What else did it show?

    _____

    _____

2. In the UK, cases of asbestosis between age groups were not significantly different in the 1970s and early 1980s. Since then, there has been a steady fall in young to middle age people with asbestosis, but a rising incidence rate in older age groups. Explain why this has occurred:

    _____

    _____

© 2015 **BIOZONE** International
ISBN: 978-1-927309-19-3
Photocopying Prohibited

136 Reducing the Risk of Lung Disease

Key Idea: Data gathered over several decades has identified causes of lung disease. Increasing the public's awareness about risk factors can reduce incidence of lung disease. The link between common causes of lung disease, such as smoking, industrial contaminants, and air pollution are undisputable. Public education and legislation designed to increase the awareness of risk factors have helped to reduce the incidence of lung disease.

Time line of smoking in the United States

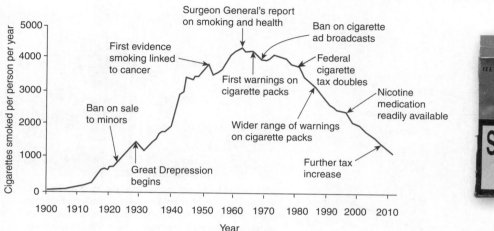

Reducing the risks of lung disease has important health and economic consequences. In the UK, about £2 billion a year is spent on treating smoking related diseases. In order to reduce the health cost of smoking, emphasis is put on preventative measures, such as public education. In the United States, legislation requiring cigarette packets to display warning labels began around 1960, soon after the Surgeon General's report on smoking and health was released. As the evidence for the detrimental health effects of smoking have increased, efforts to reduce the number of people smoking have increased. Strategies include increased cigarette taxes, health warnings on packets, and making it easier and less expensive to obtain products to help people stop smoking.

Effect of stopping smoking on lung cancer

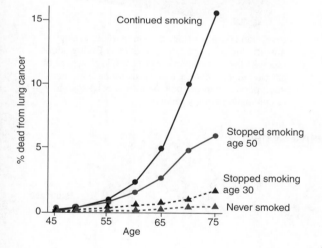

Survival to age 70+ in British doctors

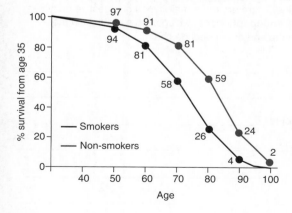

1. (a) What has been the apparent effect of increased federal warnings and taxes on smoking in the United States?

_____

_____

_____

_____

(b) What event might be called the "turning point" in United States public's opinion of smoking?

_____

_____

_____

2. Based on the data presented, what is the simplest way to reduce the risk of dying from lung cancer?

_____

3. What percentage of doctors were alive at age 70 who were:

(a) Smokers: _____

(b) Non-smokers: _____

4. What is the effect of stopping smoking early in life on the risk of dying from lung cancer?

_____

_____

_____

LINK 135 LINK 134 LINK 19

KNOW

137 The Role of the Digestive System

Key Idea: The digestive tract is specialised to maximise the physical and chemical breakdown of food (**digestion**), absorption of nutrients, and elimination of undigested material. Nutrients are substances required by the body for energy, metabolism, and tissue growth and repair. Nutrients occur in food, which must be broken down by mechanical and chemical processes before the nutrients can be absorbed into the bloodstream and assimilated by the body. Digestion in humans is extracellular (occurs outside the cells). The breakdown products are then absorbed by the cells.

Processes in the digestive system

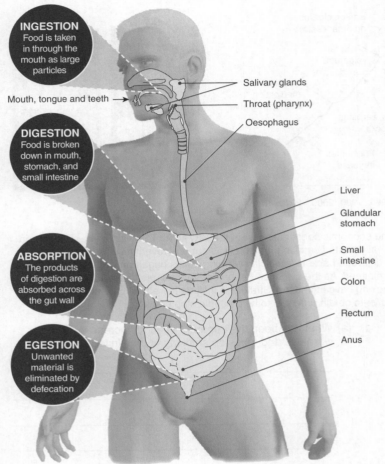

INGESTION Food is taken in through the mouth as large particles

Mouth, tongue and teeth →

Salivary glands

Throat (pharynx)

Oesophagus

DIGESTION Food is broken down in mouth, stomach, and small intestine

Liver

Glandular stomach

Small intestine

ABSORPTION The products of digestion are absorbed across the gut wall

Colon

Rectum

Anus

EGESTION Unwanted material is eliminated by defecation

Before the body can incorporate the food we eat into its own tissues (a process called assimilation), it must be broken down into smaller components that can be absorbed across the intestinal wall. The breakdown of proteins, fats, and carbohydrates is achieved by enzymes and mechanical processes (such as chewing).

Some foods are specially designed to be quickly absorbed (e.g. sports gels and drinks). Energy foods (such as the one shown above) contain a mixture of simple monomers (e.g. monosaccharides) for quick absorption and larger polymers (e.g. polysaccharides) for longer lasting energy release.

Enzymes in the digestive system

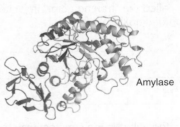

Amylase

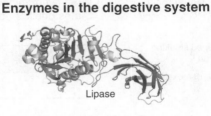

Lipase

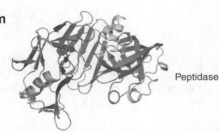

Peptidase

Amylases hydrolyse carbohydrates | **Lipases** hydrolyse lipids | **Peptidases** hydrolyse protein or peptides

Enzymes are essential to the digestion of food, catalysing the breakdown of food polymers (e.g. protein) into smaller monomers (e.g. amino acids) that can be absorbed by the intestinal villi of the small intestine. There are three main types of digestive enzymes: amylases, **lipases**, and **peptidases** (also called proteases). Peptidases can be **endopeptidases**, which cleave proteins in the middle of the peptide chain, or **exopeptidases**, which cleave amino acids from the end of the peptide chain.

1. (a) How is food broken down during the digestive process? _____

_____

(b) Why must large food molecules be broken down into smaller molecules? _____

_____

2. Explain the role of enzymes in the digestive system: _____

_____

© 2015 **BIOZONE** International
ISBN: 978-1-927309-19-3
Photocopying Prohibited

138 Digestion

Key Idea: Different parts of the digestive system have specific enzymes, which act on specific types of food molecules. Specific digestive enzymes work in specific parts of the digestive tract and on specific types of molecules. Digestion begins in the mouth where food is chewed and mixed with salivary enzymes. In the stomach, food is mixed in an acidic environment to produce a slurry called chyme. Peptidases are activated in the acid stomach and begin protein digestion. The chyme enters the small intestine where enzymes secreted by the pancreas and bound to the surfaces of the intestinal epithelial cells themselves complete the chemical digestion of proteins, carbohydrates, and lipids.

The stomach

The **stomach** is a hollow, muscular organ between the oesophagus and small intestine. The low pH of the stomach destroys microbes, denatures proteins, and activates a protein-digesting enzyme precursor. There is very little absorption in the stomach, although small molecules (glucose, alcohol) are absorbed across the stomach wall into the surrounding blood vessels.

The liver cells produce bile, which is stored and released from the gall bladder. **Bile** helps the digestion of fats in the small intestine by emulsifying the fat, i.e. promoting dispersion of the fat molecules. This makes the fat molecules more available to the intestinal lipase. Fat and acid in the duodenum stimulate release of bile from the gall bladder.

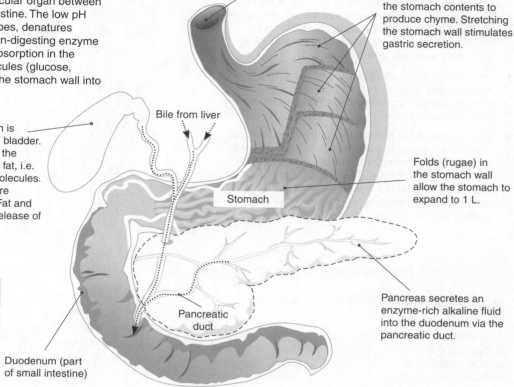

Oesophagus

Three layers of muscle mix the stomach contents to produce chyme. Stretching the stomach wall stimulates gastric secretion.

Bile from liver

Stomach

Folds (rugae) in the stomach wall allow the stomach to expand to 1 L.

Pancreatic duct

Duodenum (part of small intestine)

Pancreas secretes an enzyme-rich alkaline fluid into the duodenum via the pancreatic duct.

Stomach secretions

Gastric juice
Acid (HCl) secretion
Pepsin (optimal pH 1.5-2.0)
Protein → peptides

Detail of a gastric gland (stomach wall)

The stomach's secretions are produced by gastric glands in the lining of the stomach (gastric means stomach):

► Some cells secrete pepsinogen, a precursor of the enzyme pepsin.

► Some cells produce hydrochloric acid, which activates the pepsinogen.

► Goblet cells at the neck of the gastric gland secrete mucus to protect the stomach lining from the acid.

► Some cells secrete a hormone (gastrin) which acts on the stomach to increase acid secretion and gastric motility.

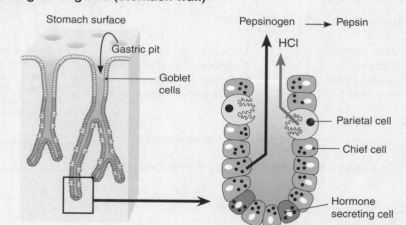

Stomach surface

Gastric pit

Goblet cells

Pepsinogen → Pepsin

HCl

Parietal cell

Chief cell

Hormone secreting cell

---

1. What is the purpose of the hydrochloric acid produced by the parietal cells of the stomach? _____

_____

2. What is the purpose of bile and why is its release from the gall bladder triggered by acid and fat in the duodenum?

_____

_____

LINK LINK WEB
140 **139** **138** KNOW

The small intestine

The small intestine is divided into the **duodenum**, where most chemical digestion occurs, and the **jejunum** and **ileum**, where most absorption occurs. The main roles of the small intestine are to complete digestion and absorb the breakdown products into the blood.

▶ The small intestine is a tubular structure between the stomach and the large intestine. It receives the chyme (food and enzyme mixture) directly from the stomach.

▶ The intestinal lining is folded into many **intestinal villi**, which project into the gut lumen (the space enclosed by the gut). They increase the surface area for nutrient absorption. The **epithelial cells** of each villus in turn have a brush-border of many **microvilli**, which increase the surface area further.

▶ Pancreatic juice is an alkaline liquid secreted by the pancreas, which contains a variety of enzymes, including pancreatic amylase, trypsin, chymotrypsin, and pancreatic lipase.

▶ Enzymes bound to the surfaces of the epithelial cells, and in the pancreatic and intestinal juices, break down peptides and carbohydrate molecules (tables below). Cellulose is not digested. The breakdown products are then absorbed into the underlying blood and lymph vessels. Tubular exocrine glands and goblet cells secrete alkaline fluid and mucus into the lumen.

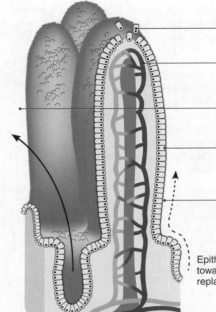

Epithelial cells

Capillaries surround a central lymph vessel

Intestinal glands secrete alkaline fluid and mucus into the lumen.

Disaccharidases bound to the surfaces of the epithelial cells break down the disaccharides lactose, sucrose, and maltose.

Dipeptidases bound to the surfaces of the epithelial cells break down dipeptides.

Epithelial cells migrate toward the tip of the villus to replace lost and worn cells.

Nutrients are transported away

Enzymes in pancreatic juice

Enzymes in duodenum (optimal pH)	Action
1. Pancreatic amylase (6.7-7.0)	1. Starch → maltose
2. Trypsin (7.8-8.7)	2. Protein → peptides
3. Chymotrypsin (7.8)	3. Protein → peptides
4. Pancreatic lipase (8.0)	4. Fats → fatty acids & glycerol

Membrane-bound enzymes (intestinal epithelium)

Enzymes (optimal pH)	Action
1. Maltase (6.0-6.5)	1. Maltose → glucose
2. Lactase (6.0)	2. Lactose → glucose + galactose
3. Sucrase (~6.0)	3. Sucrose → glucose + fructose
2. Peptidases (~ 8.0)	4. Polypeptides → amino acids

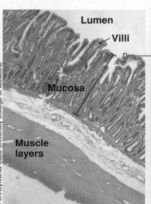

Lumen

Villi

Mucosa

Muscle layers

Pennsylvania State University College of Medicine

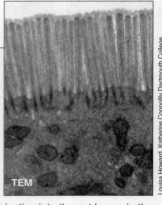

TEM

Louisa Howard, Katherine Connolly Dartmouth College

The intestinal villi are shown projecting into the gut lumen in the light microscope image (left). The microvilli forming the brush border of a single intestinal cell are shown in the transmission electron micrograph (right). The brush border contains membrane-bound enzymes that complete the digestion of proteins and carbohydrates.

3. (a) Name the three regions of the small intestine: _____

(b) Identify a functional difference between these regions: _____

_____

4. What is the brush border and why is it important?_____

_____

5. (a) Where do the enzymes in the small intestine come from? _____

_____

_____

(b) Why are the secretions of the pancreas and intestinal glands alkaline?_____

_____

© 2015 **BIOZONE** International
ISBN: 978-1-927309-19-3
Photocopying Prohibited

139 Optimal pH of Digestive Enzymes

Key Idea: The pH optimum for a digestive enzyme is correlated to the pH of the region of the digestive tract it is found in.

The optimal pH (the pH at which the activity of an enzyme is at its peak) of each digestive enzyme matches the pH of the region it works in. Enzyme activity can be monitored using a spectrophotometer to measure change in light absorbance as the enzyme reaction takes place. Two simple investigations (below) were carried out to determine the optimal pH of α-amylase and pepsin.

α-amylase (salivary enzyme)

Seven solutions containing the same concentration of α-amylase and 5% starch were made and kept at 30°C. A pH 4 buffer solution was added to one of the solutions. 0.1 cm^3 of the pH 4 mix was added to 3 cm^3 of 2% iodine solution and the absorbance measured using a spectrophotometer. The absorbance was measured every 20 seconds for a total of 120 seconds. The rate of the enzyme reaction was calculated (below). This was repeated for each of the pH buffers in the table below.

Results

pH	Rate of reaction (Δ absorbance s^{-1})
4.0	0.00
5.0	3.5×10^{-3}
6.0	1.1×10^{-2}
6.5	1.7×10^{-2}
7.0	1.5×10^{-2}
7.5	1.0×10^{-2}
8.0	7×10^{-3}

Pepsin (stomach enzyme)

Seven solutions containing 9 parts water to 1 part egg white were prepared. The solutions were cloudy when ready. Each solution was then acidified using HCl to produce a pH range from 1.1 to 2.3. Pepsin was then added to 3 cm^3 of the pH 1.1 solution and the absorbance measured using a spectrophotometer. The absorbance was measured every 20 seconds for a total of 120 seconds. The rate of the enzyme reaction was calculated (below). This was repeated for each of the pH ranges described below.

Results

pH	Rate of reaction (Δ absorbance s^{-1})
1.1	2.8×10^{-4}
1.3	2.0×10^{-3}
1.5	3.4×10^{-3}
1.7	4.0×10^{-3}
1.9	3.9×10^{-3}
2.1	2.8×10^{-3}
2.3	1.8×10^{-3}

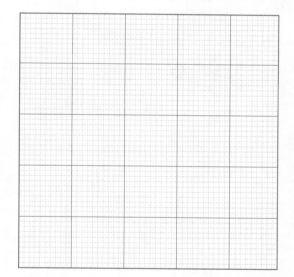

1. Graph the results of the investigations on the two grids above:

2. (a) What was the optimal pH of α-amylase? _____

   (b) Explain why this would be the expected result: _____

   _____

   (c) Why was there no activity for α-amylase at pH 4.0?_____

3. (a) What was the optimal pH of pepsin? _____

   (b) Explain why this would be the expected result: _____

   _____

   _____

LINK
49

DATA

140 Absorption

Key Idea: Food must be digested into smaller components that can be absorbed by the body's cells and assimilated. Nutrient absorption involves both active and passive transport. Digestion breaks down food molecules into forms (simple sugars, amino acids, and fatty acids) that can pass through the intestinal lining into the underlying blood and lymph vessels. For example, starch is broken down first into maltose and short chain carbohydrates such as dextrose, before being hydrolysed to glucose (below). Breakdown products of other foodstuffs include amino acids (from proteins), and fatty acids, glycerol, and acylglycerols (from fats). The passage of these molecules from the gut into the blood or lymph is called absorption. Nutrients are then transported directly or indirectly to the liver for storage or processing. After they have been **absorbed** nutrients can be **assimilated**, i.e incorporated into the substance of the body itself.

Digestion of starch

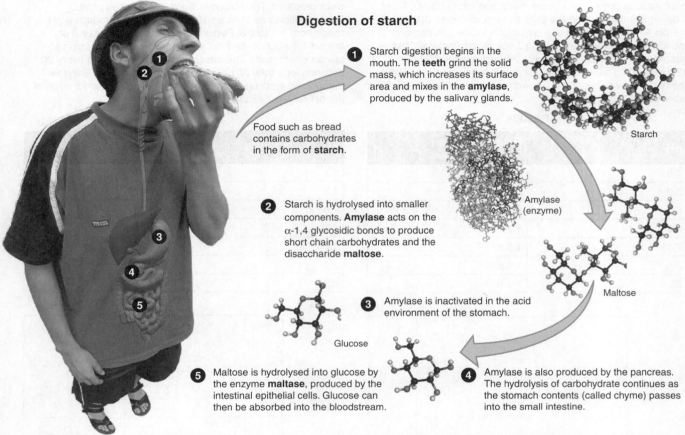

1 Starch digestion begins in the mouth. The **teeth** grind the solid mass, which increases its surface area and mixes in the **amylase**, produced by the salivary glands.

Food such as bread contains carbohydrates in the form of **starch**.

Starch

Amylase (enzyme)

2 Starch is hydrolysed into smaller components. **Amylase** acts on the α-1,4 glycosidic bonds to produce short chain carbohydrates and the disaccharide **maltose**.

Maltose

3 Amylase is inactivated in the acid environment of the stomach.

Glucose

5 Maltose is hydrolysed into glucose by the enzyme **maltase**, produced by the intestinal epithelial cells. Glucose can then be absorbed into the bloodstream.

4 Amylase is also produced by the pancreas. The hydrolysis of carbohydrate continues as the stomach contents (called chyme) passes into the small intestine.

1. The experiment on the right demonstrates why food must be digested before it can be absorbed.

   (a) Why was there no starch in the distilled water?

   _____

   _____

   _____

   _____

   (b) Use this model to explain why food must be digested before it can be absorbed.

   _____

   _____

   _____

   _____

   _____

   _____

   _____

Modelling nutrient absorption

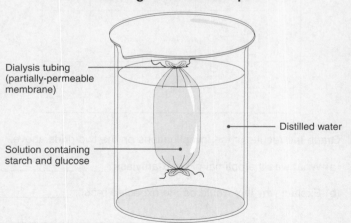

Dialysis tubing (partially-permeable membrane)

Distilled water

Solution containing starch and glucose

To model absorption of nutrients in the small intestine, a dialysis tubing was filled with a solution of starch and glucose. The outside of the tubing was washed with distilled water to remove any starch or glucose that spilled on to the outer surface during filling. The tubing was placed into a beaker of distilled water. After one hour, the distilled water was tested for the presence of starch or glucose. Only glucose was present in the distilled water.
NOTE: Dialysis tubing comes in many different pore sizes. It only allows molecules smaller than the size of the pore to pass through.

© 2015 **BIOZONE** International
ISBN: 978-1-927309-19-3
Photocopying Prohibited

Nutrient absorption by intestinal villi

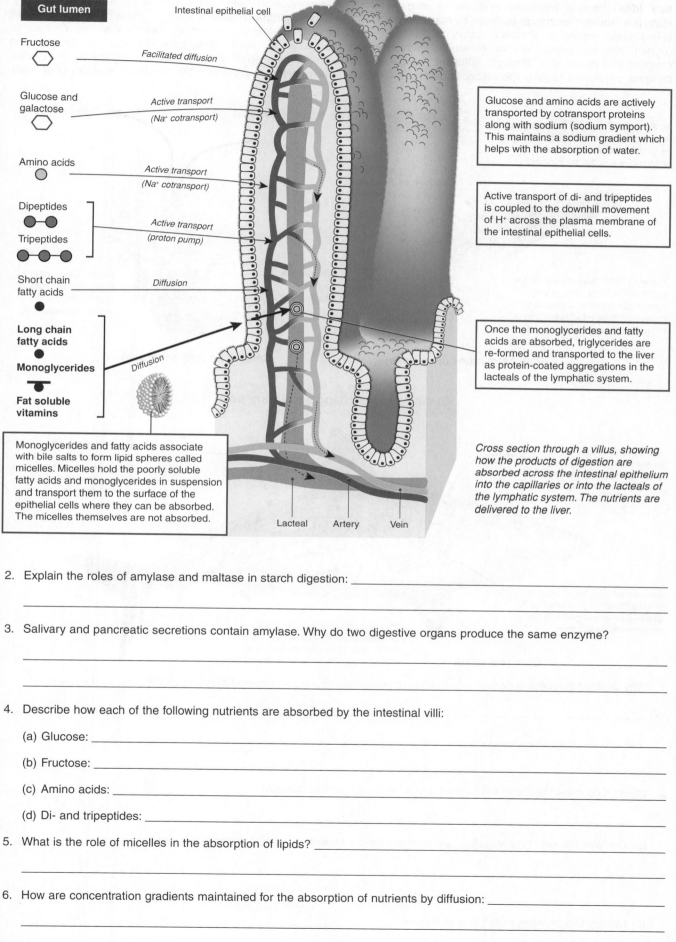

Gut lumen

Intestinal epithelial cell

Fructose — Facilitated diffusion

Glucose and galactose — Active transport (Na⁺ cotransport)

Amino acids — Active transport (Na⁺ cotransport)

Dipeptides
Tripeptides — Active transport (proton pump)

Short chain fatty acids — Diffusion

Long chain fatty acids
Monoglycerides — Diffusion
Fat soluble vitamins

Glucose and amino acids are actively transported by cotransport proteins along with sodium (sodium symport). This maintains a sodium gradient which helps with the absorption of water.

Active transport of di- and tripeptides is coupled to the downhill movement of H⁺ across the plasma membrane of the intestinal epithelial cells.

Once the monoglycerides and fatty acids are absorbed, triglycerides are re-formed and transported to the liver as protein-coated aggregations in the lacteals of the lymphatic system.

Monoglycerides and fatty acids associate with bile salts to form lipid spheres called micelles. Micelles hold the poorly soluble fatty acids and monoglycerides in suspension and transport them to the surface of the epithelial cells where they can be absorbed. The micelles themselves are not absorbed.

Lacteal   Artery   Vein

Cross section through a villus, showing how the products of digestion are absorbed across the intestinal epithelium into the capillaries or into the lacteals of the lymphatic system. The nutrients are delivered to the liver.

2. Explain the roles of amylase and maltase in starch digestion: _____

_____

3. Salivary and pancreatic secretions contain amylase. Why do two digestive organs produce the same enzyme?

_____

_____

4. Describe how each of the following nutrients are absorbed by the intestinal villi:

   (a) Glucose: _____

   (b) Fructose: _____

   (c) Amino acids: _____

   (d) Di- and tripeptides: _____

5. What is the role of micelles in the absorption of lipids? _____

_____

6. How are concentration gradients maintained for the absorption of nutrients by diffusion: _____

_____

141 Transport and Exchange in Animals

Key Idea: Internal transport systems in animals move materials between exchange surfaces by mass transport.
Living cells require a constant supply of nutrients and oxygen, and continuous removal of wastes. Simple, small organisms achieve this through diffusion. Larger, more complex organisms require specialised systems to facilitate

exchanges as their surface area to volume ratio decreases. **Mass transport** (also known as mass flow or bulk flow) describes the movement of materials at equal rates or as a single mass. Mass transport accounts for the long distance transport of fluids in living organisms. It includes the movement of blood in the circulatory systems of animals.

Exchanges across a body surface

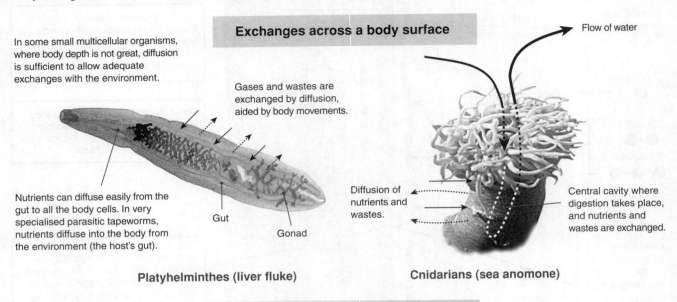

In some small multicellular organisms, where body depth is not great, diffusion is sufficient to allow adequate exchanges with the environment.

Gases and wastes are exchanged by diffusion, aided by body movements.

Flow of water

Nutrients can diffuse easily from the gut to all the body cells. In very specialised parasitic tapeworms, nutrients diffuse into the body from the environment (the host's gut).

Gut

Gonad

Diffusion of nutrients and wastes.

Central cavity where digestion takes place, and nutrients and wastes are exchanged.

Platyhelminthes (liver fluke)

Cnidarians (sea anomone)

Systems for exchange and transport

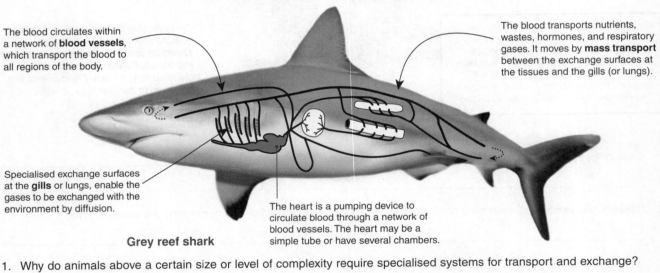

The blood circulates within a network of **blood vessels**, which transport the blood to all regions of the body.

The blood transports nutrients, wastes, hormones, and respiratory gases. It moves by **mass transport** between the exchange surfaces at the tissues and the gills (or lungs).

Specialised exchange surfaces at the **gills** or lungs, enable the gases to be exchanged with the environment by diffusion.

The heart is a pumping device to circulate blood through a network of blood vessels. The heart may be a simple tube or have several chambers.

Grey reef shark

1. Why do animals above a certain size or level of complexity require specialised systems for transport and exchange?

_____

_____

_____

2. (a) How do materials move within the circulatory system of a vertebrate? _____

_____

(b) Contrast this with how materials are transported in a flatworm or single celled eukaryote: _____

_____

_____

(c) Identify two exchange sites in a vertebrate: _____

142 Circulatory Fluids

Key Idea: Circulatory fluid transports nutrients, wastes, hormones, and often respiratory gases around the body.
The internal transport system of most animals includes a circulating fluid. In animals with closed systems, the fluid in the blood vessels is distinct from the tissue fluid outside the vessels and is called **blood**. Blood can have many different appearances, depending on the animal group, but it usually consists of cells and cell fragments suspended in a watery fluid. It serves many functions, including transporting dissolved gases, nutrients, wastes, and hormones. In animals with open systems, there is no difference between the fluid in the vessels and that in the sinuses (haemocoel) so the circulating fluid is called **haemolymph**. In insects, the haemolymph carries nutrients but not respiratory gases.

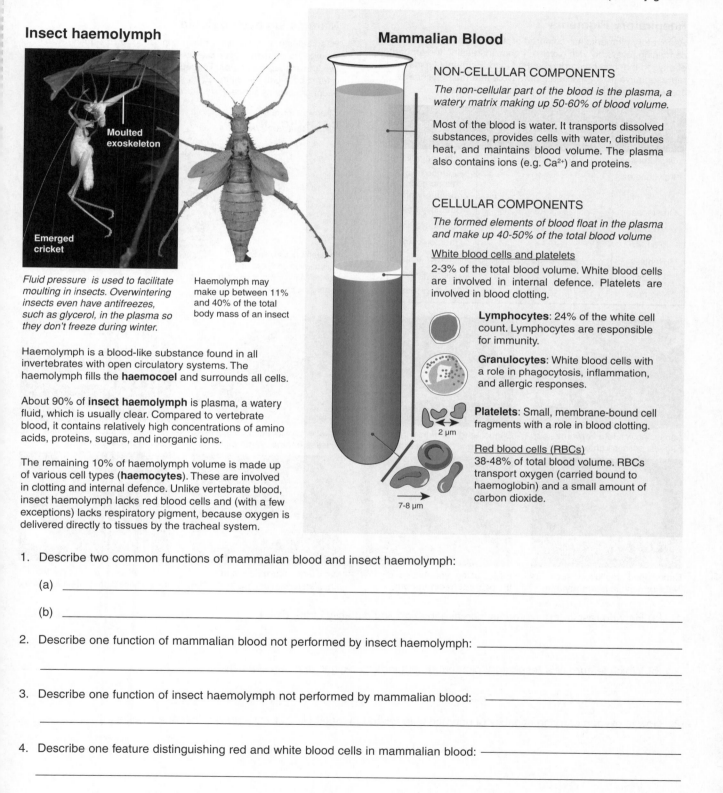

Insect haemolymph

Moulted exoskeleton

Emerged cricket

Fluid pressure is used to facilitate moulting in insects. Overwintering insects even have antifreezes, such as glycerol, in the plasma so they don't freeze during winter.

Haemolymph may make up between 11% and 40% of the total body mass of an insect

Haemolymph is a blood-like substance found in all invertebrates with open circulatory systems. The haemolymph fills the **haemocoel** and surrounds all cells.

About 90% of **insect haemolymph** is plasma, a watery fluid, which is usually clear. Compared to vertebrate blood, it contains relatively high concentrations of amino acids, proteins, sugars, and inorganic ions.

The remaining 10% of haemolymph volume is made up of various cell types (**haemocytes**). These are involved in clotting and internal defence. Unlike vertebrate blood, insect haemolymph lacks red blood cells and (with a few exceptions) lacks respiratory pigment, because oxygen is delivered directly to tissues by the tracheal system.

Mammalian Blood

NON-CELLULAR COMPONENTS

The non-cellular part of the blood is the plasma, a watery matrix making up 50-60% of blood volume.

Most of the blood is water. It transports dissolved substances, provides cells with water, distributes heat, and maintains blood volume. The plasma also contains ions (e.g. Ca^{2+}) and proteins.

CELLULAR COMPONENTS

The formed elements of blood float in the plasma and make up 40-50% of the total blood volume

<u>White blood cells and platelets</u>
2-3% of the total blood volume. White blood cells are involved in internal defence. Platelets are involved in blood clotting.

Lymphocytes: 24% of the white cell count. Lymphocytes are responsible for immunity.

Granulocytes: White blood cells with a role in phagocytosis, inflammation, and allergic responses.

Platelets: Small, membrane-bound cell fragments with a role in blood clotting.
2 µm

<u>Red blood cells (RBCs)</u>
38-48% of total blood volume. RBCs transport oxygen (carried bound to haemoglobin) and a small amount of carbon dioxide.
7-8 µm

---

1. Describe two common functions of mammalian blood and insect haemolymph:

    (a) _____

    (b) _____

2. Describe one function of mammalian blood not performed by insect haemolymph: _____

    _____

3. Describe one function of insect haemolymph not performed by mammalian blood: _____

    _____

4. Describe one feature distinguishing red and white blood cells in mammalian blood: _____

    _____

5. Contrast the proportions of cellular and non-cellular components in blood and haemolymph: _____

    _____

LINK **144** LINK **143** WEB **142** KNOW

143 Haemoglobins

Key Idea: Respiratory pigments bind oxygen and increase the efficiency of its transport through the body.

The amount of oxygen that can be carried in solution in the blood is small. The efficiency of gas transport in animals is enhanced by the presence of respiratory pigments. All respiratory pigments consist of proteins complexed with iron or copper. They combine reversibly with oxygen and greatly increase the capacity of blood to transport oxygen and deliver it to the tissues. For example, the amount of oxygen dissolved in the plasma in mammals is only about 2 mL O_2 per litre. However the amount carried bound to haemoglobin is 100 times this. Haemoglobin is the most widely distributed respiratory pigment but there is some variability in structure and oxygen carrying capacity between different taxa.

Respiratory Pigments

Respiratory pigments are coloured proteins capable of combining reversibly with oxygen, hence increasing the amount of oxygen that can be carried by the blood. Pigments typical of representative taxa are listed below. Note that the polychaetes are very variable in terms of the pigment possessed.

Taxon	Oxygen capacity mL O_2 per 100 mL blood	Pigment
Oligochaetes	1 - 10	Haemoglobin
Polychaetes	1 - 10	Haemoglobin, chlorocruorin, or haemerythrin
Crustaceans	1 - 6	Haemocyanin
Molluscs	1 - 6	Haemocyanin
Fishes	2 - 4	Haemoglobin
Reptiles	7 - 12	Haemoglobin
Birds	20 - 25	Haemoglobin
Mammals	15 - 30	Haemoglobin

Mammalian haemoglobin

Haemoglobin is a globular protein consisting of 574 amino acids arranged in four polypeptide sub-units: two identical **beta chains** and two identical **alpha chains**. The four sub-units are held together as a functional unit by bonds. Each sub-unit has an iron-containing haem group at its centre and binds one molecule of oxygen.

Chemical formula:
$C_{3032}H_{4816}O_{872}N_{780}S_8Fe_4$

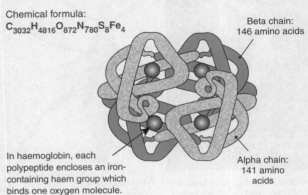

Beta chain: 146 amino acids

In haemoglobin, each polypeptide encloses an iron-containing haem group which binds one oxygen molecule.

Alpha chain: 141 amino acids

Aquatic polychaete fanworms, e.g. *Sabella,* possess **chlorocruorin**.

Oligochaete annelids, such as earthworms, have **haemoglobin**.

Aquatic crustaceans, e.g. crabs, possess **haemocyanin** pigment.

Vertebrates such as this fish have **haemoglobin** pigment.

Cephalopod molluscs such as *Nautilus* contain **haemocyanin**.

Birds, being vertebrates contain the pigment **haemoglobin**.

Many large active polychaetes, e.g. *Nereis*, contain **haemoglobin**.

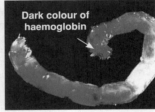

Dark colour of haemoglobin

Chironomus is one of only two insect genera to contain a pigment.

1. (a) How do respiratory pigments increase the carrying capacity of the blood? _____

_____

(b) Which feature of a respiratory pigment determines its oxygen carrying capacity? _____

_____

2. How is oxygen carrying capacity of haemoglobin related to metabolic activity across different animal taxa? _____

_____

_____

3. Why are larger molecular weight respiratory pigments carried dissolved in the plasma rather than within cells?

_____

© 2015 **BIOZONE** International
ISBN: 978-1-927309-19-3
Photocopying Prohibited

144 Gas Transport in Humans

Key Idea: Haemoglobin is a respiratory pigment in red blood cells, which binds oxygen and increases the efficiency of its transport and delivery to tissues throughout the body.

The transport of respiratory gases around the body is the role of the blood and its respiratory pigment. In vertebrates, e.g humans, oxygen is transported throughout the body chemically bound to the respiratory pigment **haemoglobin** inside the red blood cells. In the muscles, oxygen from haemoglobin is transferred to and retained by **myoglobin**, a molecule that is chemically similar to haemoglobin except that it consists of only one haem-globin unit. Myoglobin has a greater affinity for oxygen than haemoglobin and acts as an oxygen store within muscles, releasing the oxygen during periods of prolonged or extreme muscular activity.

Gas exchange and transport

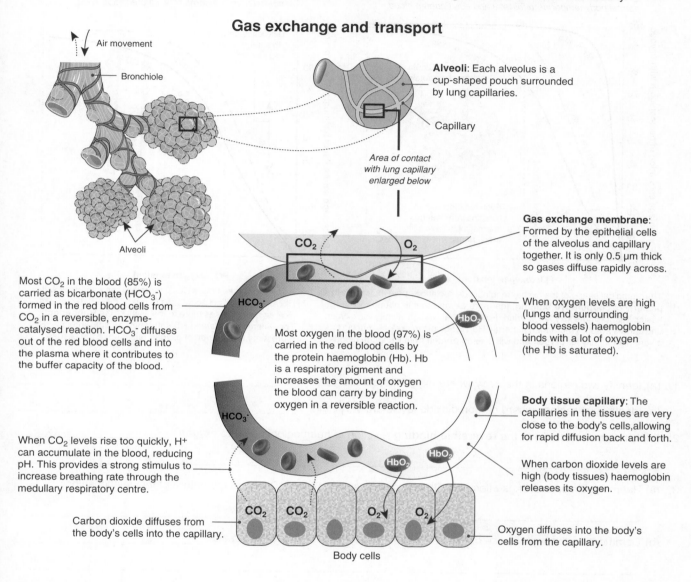

Alveoli: Each alveolus is a cup-shaped pouch surrounded by lung capillaries.

Capillary

Area of contact with lung capillary enlarged below

Gas exchange membrane: Formed by the epithelial cells of the alveolus and capillary together. It is only 0.5 μm thick so gases diffuse rapidly across.

Most CO_2 in the blood (85%) is carried as bicarbonate (HCO_3^-) formed in the red blood cells from CO_2 in a reversible, enzyme-catalysed reaction. HCO_3^- diffuses out of the red blood cells and into the plasma where it contributes to the buffer capacity of the blood.

Most oxygen in the blood (97%) is carried in the red blood cells by the protein haemoglobin (Hb). Hb is a respiratory pigment and increases the amount of oxygen the blood can carry by binding oxygen in a reversible reaction.

When oxygen levels are high (lungs and surrounding blood vessels) haemoglobin binds with a lot of oxygen (the Hb is saturated).

Body tissue capillary: The capillaries in the tissues are very close to the body's cells, allowing for rapid diffusion back and forth.

When carbon dioxide levels are high (body tissues) haemoglobin releases its oxygen.

When CO_2 levels rise too quickly, H^+ can accumulate in the blood, reducing pH. This provides a strong stimulus to increase breathing rate through the medullary respiratory centre.

Carbon dioxide diffuses from the body's cells into the capillary.

Oxygen diffuses into the body's cells from the capillary.

Body cells

Transport of carbon dioxide in the blood

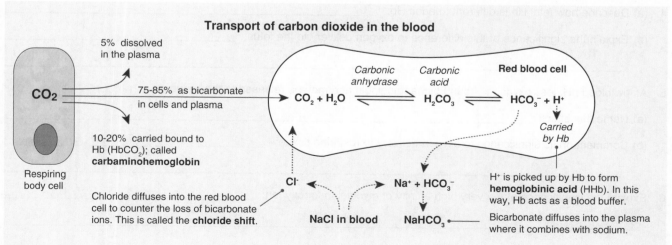

5% dissolved in the plasma

75-85% as bicarbonate in cells and plasma

10-20% carried bound to Hb ($HbCO_2$); called **carbaminohemoglobin**

Respiring body cell

Carbonic anhydrase *Carbonic acid* **Red blood cell**

$$CO_2 + H_2O \rightleftharpoons H_2CO_3 \rightleftharpoons HCO_3^- + H^+$$

Carried by Hb

Chloride diffuses into the red blood cell to counter the loss of bicarbonate ions. This is called the **chloride shift**.

Cl^-

NaCl in blood

$Na^+ + HCO_3^-$

$NaHCO_3$

H^+ is picked up by Hb to form **hemoglobinic acid** (HHb). In this way, Hb acts as a blood buffer.

Bicarbonate diffuses into the plasma where it combines with sodium.

LINK 141   LINK 124   WEB 144   **KNOW**

Oxygen does not easily dissolve in blood, but is carried in chemical combination with haemoglobin (Hb) in red blood cells. The most important factor determining how much oxygen is carried by Hb is the level of oxygen in the blood. The greater the oxygen tension, the more oxygen will combine with Hb. This relationship can be illustrated with an oxyhaemoglobin dissociation curve as shown below (Fig. 1). In the lung capillaries, (high O_2), a lot of oxygen is picked up and bound by Hb. In the tissues, (low O_2), oxygen is released. In skeletal muscle, myoglobin picks up oxygen from haemoglobin and therefore serves as an oxygen store when oxygen tensions begin to fall. The release of oxygen is enhanced by the **Bohr effect** (Fig. 2).

Respiratory pigments and the transport of oxygen

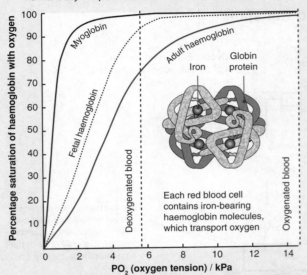

Fig.1: Dissociation curves for haemoglobin and myoglobin at normal body temperature for fetal and adult human blood.

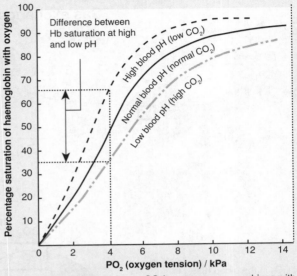

Fig.2: Oxyhaemoglobin dissociation curves for human blood at normal body temperature at different blood pH.

The sigmoidal shape of the oxyhaemoglobin dissociation curve indicates Hb's property of **cooperative binding**; the more oxygen that is bound to Hb, the easier it is for more oxygen to bind. Fetal Hb has a high affinity for oxygen and carries 20-30% more than maternal Hb. Myoglobin in skeletal muscle has a very high affinity for oxygen and will take up oxygen from Hb in the blood.

As pH increases (lower CO_2), more oxygen combines with Hb. As the blood pH decreases (higher CO_2), Hb binds less oxygen and releases more to the tissues (the **Bohr effect**). The difference between Hb saturation at high and low pH represents the amount of oxygen released to the tissues.

1. (a) Identify two regions in the body where oxygen levels are very high: _____

   (b) Identify two regions where carbon dioxide levels are very high: _____

2. Explain the significance of the **reversible binding** reaction of haemoglobin (Hb) to oxygen: _____

   _____

3. (a) Haemoglobin saturation is affected by the oxygen level in the blood. Describe the nature of this relationship:

   _____

   (b) Comment on the significance of this relationship to oxygen delivery to the tissues: _____

   _____

4. (a) Describe how fetal Hb is different to adult Hb: _____

   (b) Explain the significance of this difference to oxygen delivery to the fetus: _____

   _____

5. At low blood pH, less oxygen is bound by haemoglobin and more is released to the tissues:

   (a) Name this effect: _____

   (b) Comment on its significance to oxygen delivery to respiring tissue: _____

   _____

6. Explain the significance of the very high affinity of myoglobin for oxygen: _____

   _____

7. Identify the two main contributors to the buffer capacity of the blood: _____

145 The Mammalian Transport System

Key Idea: The mammalian circulatory system is a double circuit made up of a pulmonary circuit and a systemic circuit. The blood vessels of the circulatory system form a network of tubes that carry blood away from the heart, transport it to the tissues of the body, and then return it to the heart. The figure below shows a number of the basic circulatory routes. Mammals have a double circulatory system: a **pulmonary** **system**, which carries blood between the heart and lungs, and a **systemic system**, which carries blood between the heart and the rest of the body. The systemic circulation has many subdivisions. Two important subdivisions are the coronary (cardiac) circulation, which supplies the heart muscle, and the hepatic portal circulation, which runs from the gut to the liver.

Schematic overview of the human circulatory system

Deoxygenated blood (coloured blue below) travels to the right side of the heart via the vena cavae. The heart pumps the deoxygenated blood to the lungs where it releases carbon dioxide and receives oxygen. The oxygenated blood (coloured white below) travels via the pulmonary vein back to the heart from where it is pumped to all parts of the body. The **venous system** (figure, left) returns blood from the capillaries to the heart. The **arterial system** (figure right) carries blood from the heart to the capillaries. **Portal systems** carry blood between two capillary beds.

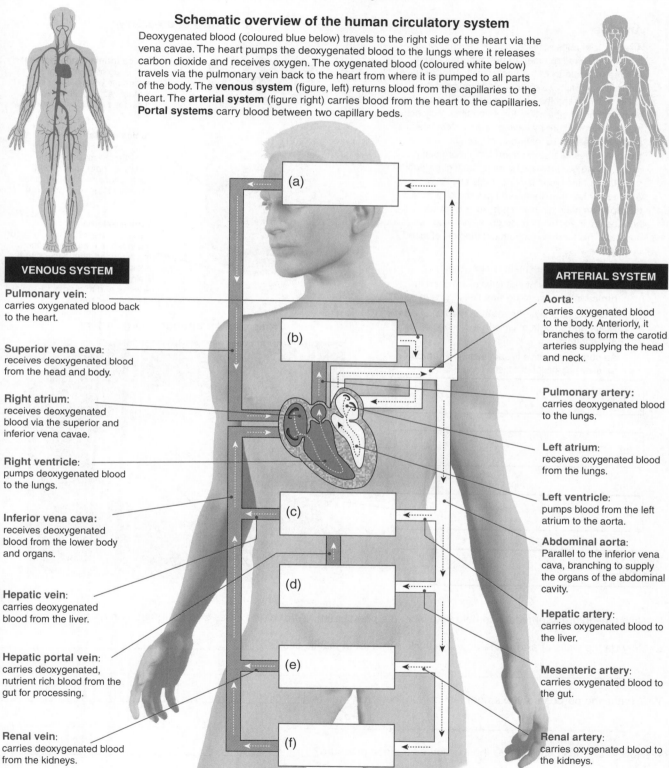

VENOUS SYSTEM

Pulmonary vein:
carries oxygenated blood back to the heart.

Superior vena cava:
receives deoxygenated blood from the head and body.

Right atrium:
receives deoxygenated blood via the superior and inferior vena cavae.

Right ventricle:
pumps deoxygenated blood to the lungs.

Inferior vena cava:
receives deoxygenated blood from the lower body and organs.

Hepatic vein:
carries deoxygenated blood from the liver.

Hepatic portal vein:
carries deoxygenated, nutrient rich blood from the gut for processing.

Renal vein:
carries deoxygenated blood from the kidneys.

ARTERIAL SYSTEM

Aorta:
carries oxygenated blood to the body. Anteriorly, it branches to form the carotid arteries supplying the head and neck.

Pulmonary artery:
carries deoxygenated blood to the lungs.

Left atrium:
receives oxygenated blood from the lungs.

Left ventricle:
pumps blood from the left atrium to the aorta.

Abdominal aorta:
Parallel to the inferior vena cava, branching to supply the organs of the abdominal cavity.

Hepatic artery:
carries oxygenated blood to the liver.

Mesenteric artery:
carries oxygenated blood to the gut.

Renal artery:
carries oxygenated blood to the kidneys.

1. Complete the diagram above by labelling the boxes with the correct organs:
   lungs, liver, head, intestines, genitals/lower body, kidneys.

2. Circle the two blood vessels involved in the pulmonary circuit.

LINK
151

WEB
145

KNOW

146 Arteries

Key Idea: Arteries are thick-walled blood vessels that carry blood away from the heart to the capillaries within the tissues. In vertebrates, **arteries** are the blood vessels that carry blood away from the heart to the capillaries within the tissues. The large arteries that leave the heart divide into medium-sized (distributing) arteries. Within the tissues and organs, these distributing arteries branch to form **arterioles**, which deliver blood to capillaries. Arterioles lack the thick layers of arteries and consist only of an endothelial layer wrapped by a few smooth muscle fibres at intervals along their length. Blood flow to the tissues is altered by contraction (**vasoconstriction**) or relaxation (**vasodilation**) of the blood vessel walls. Vasoconstriction increases blood pressure whereas vasodilation has the opposite effect.

Arteries

Arteries, regardless of size, can be recognised by their well-defined rounded **lumen** (internal space) and the muscularity of the vessel wall. Arteries have an elastic, stretchy structure that gives them the ability to withstand the high pressure of blood being pumped from the heart. At the same time, they help to maintain pressure by having some contractile ability themselves (a feature of the central muscle layer). Arteries nearer the heart have more elastic tissue, giving greater resistance to the higher blood pressures of the blood leaving the left ventricle. Arteries further from the heart have more muscle to help them maintain blood pressure. Between heartbeats, the arteries undergo elastic recoil and contract. This tends to smooth out the flow of blood through the vessel.

Arteries comprise three main regions (right):

1. A thin inner layer of epithelial cells called the **tunica intima** (endothelium) lines the artery.

2. A thick central layer (the **tunica media**) of elastic tissue and smooth muscle that can both stretch and contract.

3. An outer connective tissue layer (the **tunica externa**) has a lot of elastic tissue.

Structure of an artery

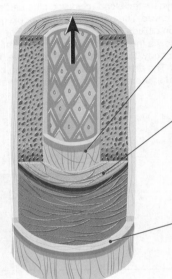

Tunica intima (endothelium)
Thin endothelial layer of squamous epithelium is in contact with the blood. Arrow indicates direction of blood flow.

Tunica media
Thick layer of elastic tissue and smooth muscle tissue allows for both stretch and contraction, maintaining blood flow without loss of pressure.

Tunica externa
Layer of elastic connective tissue (collagen and elastin) anchors the artery to other tissues and allows it to resist overexpansion. Relatively thinner in larger elastic arteries and thicker in muscular, distributing arteries.

Cross section through a large artery

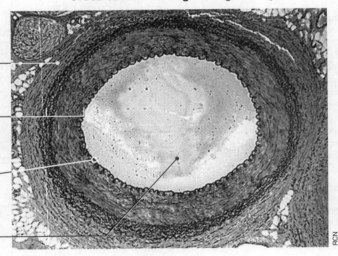

RCN

(a)

(b)

(c)

(d)

1. Using the information above to help you, label the photograph (a)-(d) of the cross section through an artery (above).

2. Why do the walls of arteries need to be thick with a lot of elastic tissue? _____

_____

3. What is the purpose of the smooth muscle in the artery walls? _____

_____

4. How to arteries contribute to the regulation of blood pressure? _____

_____

_____

_____

WEB   LINK
KNOW   146   151

© 2015 **BIOZONE** International
ISBN: 978-1-927309-19-3
Photocopying Prohibited

147 Veins

Key Idea: Veins are blood vessels that return the blood from the tissues to the heart. Veins have a large lumen.

Veins are the blood vessels that return blood to the heart from the tissues. The smallest veins (**venules**) return blood from the capillaries to the veins. Veins and their branches contain about 59% of the blood in the body. The structural differences between veins and arteries are mainly associated with differences in the relative thickness of the vessel layers and the diameter of the lumen (space within the vessel). These, in turn, are related to the vessel's functional role.

Veins

When several capillaries unite, they form small veins called **venules**. The venules collect the blood from capillaries and drain it into **veins**. Veins are made up of the same three layers as arteries but they have less elastic and muscle tissue, a relatively thicker tunica externa, and a larger, less defined **lumen**. The venules closest to the capillaries consist of an **endothelium** and a tunica externa of connective tissue. As the venules approach the veins, they also contain the tunica media characteristic of veins (right). Although veins are less elastic than arteries, they can still expand enough to adapt to changes in the pressure and volume of the blood passing through them. Blood flowing in the veins has lost a lot of pressure because it has passed through the narrow capillary vessels. The low pressure in veins means that many veins, especially those in the limbs, need to have valves to prevent backflow of the blood as it returns to the heart.

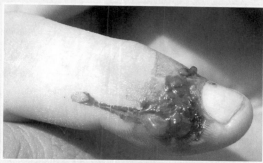

If a vein is cut, as is shown in this severed finger wound, the blood oozes out slowly in an even flow, and usually clots quickly as it leaves. In contrast, arterial blood spurts rapidly and requires pressure to staunch the flow.

Structure of a vein

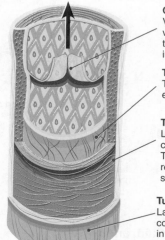

One-way valves
Valves located along the length of veins keep the blood moving towards the heart (prevent back-flow). Arrow indicates direction of blood flow.

Tunica intima (endothelium)
Thin endothelial layer of squamous epithelium lines the vein.

Tunica media
Layer of smooth muscle tissue with collagen fibres (connective tissue). The tunica media is much thinner relative to that of an artery and the smaller venules may lack this layer.

Tunica externa
Layer of connective tissue (mostly collagen) is relatively thicker than in arteries and thicker than the tunica media.

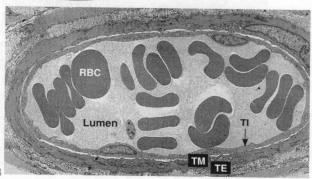

Above: TEM of a vein showing red blood cells (RBC) in the lumen, and the tunica intima (TI), tunica media (TM), and tunica externa (TE).

1. Contrast the structure of veins and arteries for each of the following properties:

   (a) Thickness of muscle and elastic tissue: _____

   _____

   (b) Size of the lumen (inside of the vessel): _____

   _____

2. With respect to their functional roles, explain the differences you have described above: _____

   _____

   _____

3. What is the role of the valves in assisting the veins to return blood back to the heart? _____

   _____

4. Why does blood ooze from a venous wound, rather than spurting as it does from an arterial wound?

   _____

   _____

   _____

© 2015 **BIOZONE** International
ISBN: 978-1-927309-19-3
Photocopying Prohibited

LINK 151   WEB 147   KNOW

148 Capillaries

Key Idea: Capillaries are small, thin-walled vessels that allow the exchange of material between the blood and the tissues. In vertebrates, **capillaries** are very small vessels that connect arterial and venous circulation and allow efficient exchange of nutrients and wastes between the blood and tissues. Capillaries form networks or beds and are abundant where metabolic rates are high. Fluid that leaks out of the capillaries has an essential role in bathing the tissues.

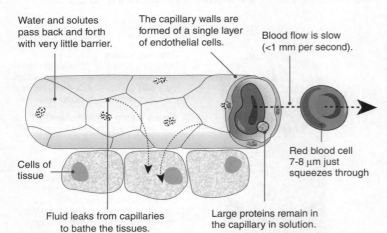

Water and solutes pass back and forth with very little barrier.

The capillary walls are formed of a single layer of endothelial cells.

Blood flow is slow (<1 mm per second).

Red blood cell 7-8 μm just squeezes through

Cells of tissue

Fluid leaks from capillaries to bathe the tissues.

Large proteins remain in the capillary in solution.

Exchanges in capillaries

Blood passes from the arterioles into the capillaries where the exchange of materials between the body cells and the blood takes place. Capillaries are small blood vessels with a diameter of just 4-10 μm. The only tissue present is an **endothelium** of squamous epithelial cells. Capillaries are so numerous that no cell is more than 25 μm from any capillary.

Blood pressure causes fluid to leak from capillaries through small gaps where the endothelial cells join. This fluid bathes the tissues, supplying nutrients and oxygen, and removing wastes (left). The density of capillaries in a tissue is an indication of that tissue's metabolic activity. For example, cardiac muscle relies heavily on oxidative metabolism. It has a high demand for blood flow and is well supplied with capillaries. Smooth muscle is far less active than cardiac muscle, relies more on anaerobic metabolism, and does not require such an extensive blood supply.

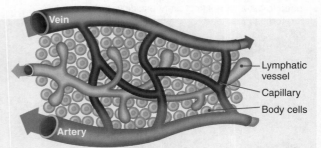

Vein

Lymphatic vessel

Capillary

Body cells

Artery

The pressure at the arterial end of the capillaries forces fluid through gaps between the capillary endothelial cells. The fluid contains nutrients and oxygen and is called tissue fluid. Some of this fluid returns to the blood at the venous end of the capillary bed, but some is drained by lymph vessels to form lymph. Blood transports nutrients, wastes, and respiratory gases to and from the tissues. Tissue fluid facilitates the transport of these between the blood and the tissues. Lymph drains excess tissue fluid and returns it to the general circulation, and it has a role in the immune system.

Blood, tissue fluid, and lymph

	Blood	Tissue fluid	Lymph
Cells	Erythrocytes, leucocytes, platelets	Some leucocytes	Lymphocytes
Proteins	Hormones and plasma proteins	Some hormones and proteins	None
Glucose	High	None	Low
Amino acids	High	Used by body cells	Low
Oxygen	High	Used by body cells	Low
Carbon dioxide	Low	Produced by body cells	High

1. What is the role of capillaries? _____

_____

2. Describe the structure of a capillary, contrasting it with the structure of a vein and an artery:

_____

_____

_____

_____

_____

3. Distinguish between blood, tissue fluid, and lymph: _____

_____

_____

_____

_____

_____

© 2015 **BIOZONE** International
ISBN: 978-1-927309-19-3
Photocopying Prohibited

149 Capillary Networks

Key Idea: Capillaries form branching networks where exchanges between the blood and tissues take place.

The flow of blood through a capillary bed is called microcirculation. In most parts of the body, there are two types of vessels in a capillary bed: the true capillaries, where exchanges take place, and a vessel called a vascular shunt, which connects the arteriole and venule at either end of the bed. The shunt diverts blood past the true capillaries when the metabolic demands of the tissue are low. When tissue activity increases, the entire network fills with blood.

1. Describe the structure of a capillary network:

_____

_____

_____

_____

_____

_____

2. Explain the role of the smooth muscle sphincters and the vascular shunt in a capillary network:

_____

_____

_____

_____

_____

_____

_____

3. (a) Describe a situation where the capillary bed would be in the condition labelled **A**:

_____

_____

_____

_____

(b) Describe a situation where the capillary bed would be in the condition labelled **B**:

_____

_____

_____

_____

4. How does a portal venous system differ from other capillary systems?

_____

_____

_____

_____

_____

_____

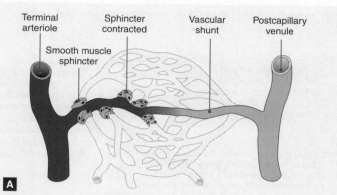

A

When the sphincters contract (close), blood is diverted via the vascular shunt to the postcapillary venule, bypassing the exchange capillaries.

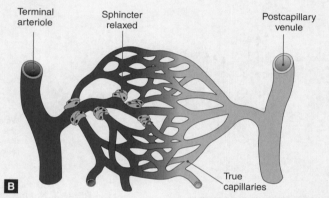

B

When the sphincters are relaxed (open), blood flows through the entire capillary bed allowing exchanges with the cells of the surrounding tissue.

Connecting capillary beds
The role of portal venous systems

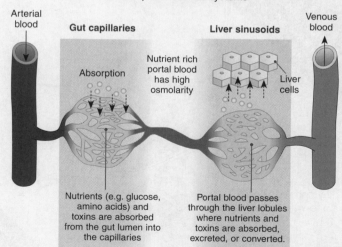

A portal venous system occurs when a capillary bed drains into another capillary bed through veins, without first going through the heart. Portal systems are relatively uncommon. Most capillary beds drain into veins which then drain into the heart, not into another capillary bed. The diagram above depicts the hepatic portal system, which includes both capillary beds and the blood vessels connecting them.

150 The Formation of Tissue Fluid

Key Idea: Tissue fluid is formed by leakage from capillaries. It provides oxygen and nutrients to tissues and removes wastes. The network of capillaries supplying the body's tissues ensures that no cell is far from a supply of nutrients and oxygen. Substances reach the cells through the tissue fluid, moving into and out of the capillaries by diffusion, by cytosis, and through gaps where the membranes are not tightly joined. Specialised capillaries, such as those in the intestine and kidney, where absorption or filtration is important, are relatively more leaky. Fluid moves across the leaky capillary membranes in a direction that depends on the balance between the blood pressure and the oncotic pressure at each end of a capillary bed. Oncotic pressure (also called colloid osmotic pressure) tends to pull water into the capillaries.

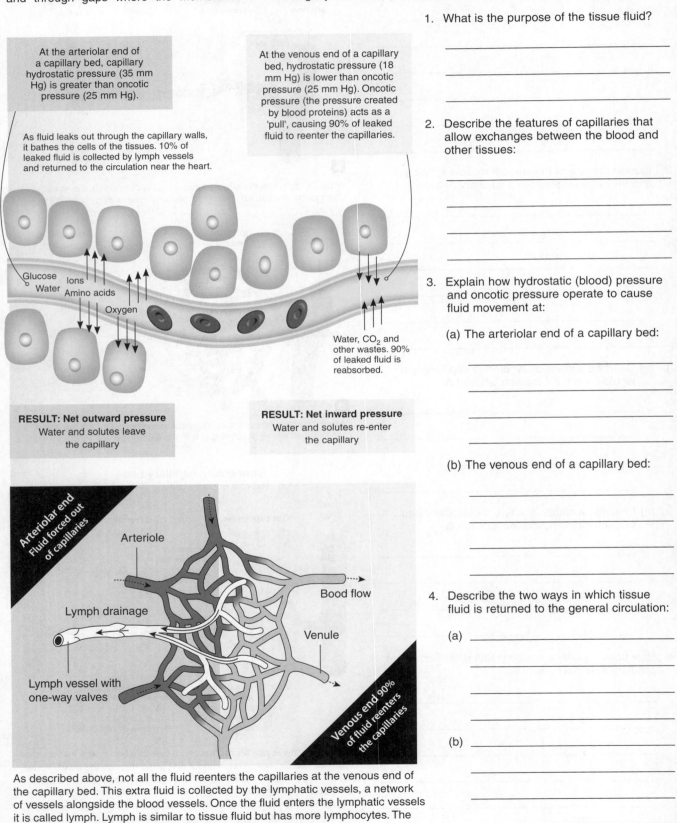

At the arteriolar end of a capillary bed, capillary hydrostatic pressure (35 mm Hg) is greater than oncotic pressure (25 mm Hg).

As fluid leaks out through the capillary walls, it bathes the cells of the tissues. 10% of leaked fluid is collected by lymph vessels and returned to the circulation near the heart.

At the venous end of a capillary bed, hydrostatic pressure (18 mm Hg) is lower than oncotic pressure (25 mm Hg). Oncotic pressure (the pressure created by blood proteins) acts as a 'pull', causing 90% of leaked fluid to reenter the capillaries.

Glucose
Water
Ions
Amino acids
Oxygen

Water, CO_2 and other wastes. 90% of leaked fluid is reabsorbed.

RESULT: Net outward pressure
Water and solutes leave the capillary

RESULT: Net inward pressure
Water and solutes re-enter the capillary

Arteriolar end
Fluid forced out of capillaries

Arteriole

Lymph drainage

Bood flow

Venule

Lymph vessel with one-way valves

Venous end 90% of fluid reenters the capillaries

As described above, not all the fluid reenters the capillaries at the venous end of the capillary bed. This extra fluid is collected by the lymphatic vessels, a network of vessels alongside the blood vessels. Once the fluid enters the lymphatic vessels it is called lymph. Lymph is similar to tissue fluid but has more lymphocytes. The lymphatic vessels drain into the subclavian vein near the heart.

1. What is the purpose of the tissue fluid?

_____

_____

_____

2. Describe the features of capillaries that allow exchanges between the blood and other tissues:

_____

_____

_____

_____

3. Explain how hydrostatic (blood) pressure and oncotic pressure operate to cause fluid movement at:

(a) The arteriolar end of a capillary bed:

_____

_____

_____

_____

(b) The venous end of a capillary bed:

_____

_____

_____

_____

4. Describe the two ways in which tissue fluid is returned to the general circulation:

(a) _____

_____

_____

_____

(b) _____

_____

_____

_____

© 2015 **BIOZONE** International
ISBN: 978-1-927309-19-3
Photocopying Prohibited

151 The Human Heart

Key Idea: Humans have a four chambered heart divided into left and right halves. It acts as a double pump.

The heart is the centre of the human cardiovascular system. It is a hollow, muscular organ made up of four chambers (two **atria** and two **ventricles**) that alternately fill and empty of blood, acting as a double pump. The left side (systemic circuit) pumps blood to the body tissues and the right side (pulmonary circuit) pumps blood to the lungs. The heart lies between the lungs, to the left of the midline, and is surrounded by a double layered pericardium of connective tissue, which prevents over distension of the heart and anchors it within the central compartment of the thoracic cavity.

Human heart structure

(sectioned, anterior view)

Aorta carries oxygenated blood to the head and body

Vena cava receives deoxygenated blood from the head and body

Pulmonary artery carries deoxygenated blood to the lungs

Tricuspid valve prevents backflow of blood into right atrium

Chordae tendinae non-elastic strands supporting the valve flaps

Semi-lunar valve prevents the blood flow back into ventricle.

Bicuspid valve

RA

RV

LA

LV

Septum separates the ventricles

The heart is not a symmetrical organ. Although the quantity of blood pumped by each side of the heart is the same, the walls of the left ventricle are thicker and more muscular than those of the right ventricle. The difference affects the shape of the ventricular cavities, so the right ventricle is twisted over the left.

Key to abbreviations

RA Right atrium: receives deoxygenated blood via the vena cavae

RV Right ventricle: pumps deoxygenated blood to the lungs via the pulmonary artery

LA Left atrium: receives blood from the lungs via the pulmonary veins

LV Left ventricle: pumps oxygenated blood to the head and body via the aorta

Top view of a heart in section to show valves

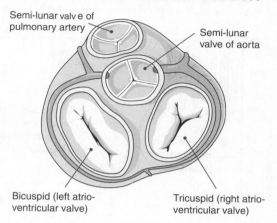

Semi-lunar valve of pulmonary artery

Semi-lunar valve of aorta

Bicuspid (left atrio-ventricular valve)

Tricuspid (right atrio-ventricular valve)

Anterior view of heart to show coronary arteries

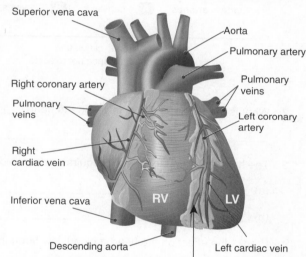

Superior vena cava

Aorta

Pulmonary artery

Pulmonary veins

Right coronary artery

Pulmonary veins

Left coronary artery

Right cardiac vein

Inferior vena cava

RV

LV

Descending aorta

Left cardiac vein

The high oxygen demands of the heart muscle are met by a dense capillary network branching from the coronary arteries. The coronary arteries (left and right) arise from the aorta and spread over the surface of the heart supplying the cardiac muscle with oxygenated blood. The left carries 70% of the coronary blood supply and the right the remaining 30%. Deoxygenated blood is collected by the cardiac veins and returned to the right atrium via a large coronary sinus.

1. In the schematic diagram of the heart, below, label the four chambers and the main vessels entering and leaving them. The arrows indicate the direction of blood flow. Use large coloured circles to mark the position of each of the four valves.

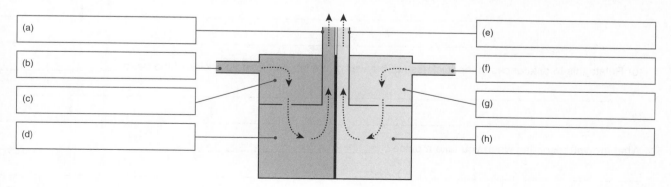

(a)

(b)

(c)

(d)

(e)

(f)

(g)

(h)

LINK **153** LINK **152** WEB **151** **KNOW**

Pressure changes and the asymmetry of the heart

The heart is not a symmetrical organ. The left ventricle and its associated arteries are thicker and more muscular than the corresponding structures on the right side. This asymmetry is related to the necessary pressure differences between the pulmonary (lung) and systemic (body) circulations (not to the distance over which the blood is pumped *per se*). The graph below shows changes in blood pressure in each of the major blood vessel types in the systemic and pulmonary circuits (the horizontal distance not to scale). The pulmonary circuit must operate at a much lower pressure than the systemic circuit to prevent fluid from accumulating in the alveoli of the lungs. The left side of the heart must develop enough "spare" pressure to enable increased blood flow to the muscles of the body and maintain kidney filtration rates without decreasing the blood supply to the brain.

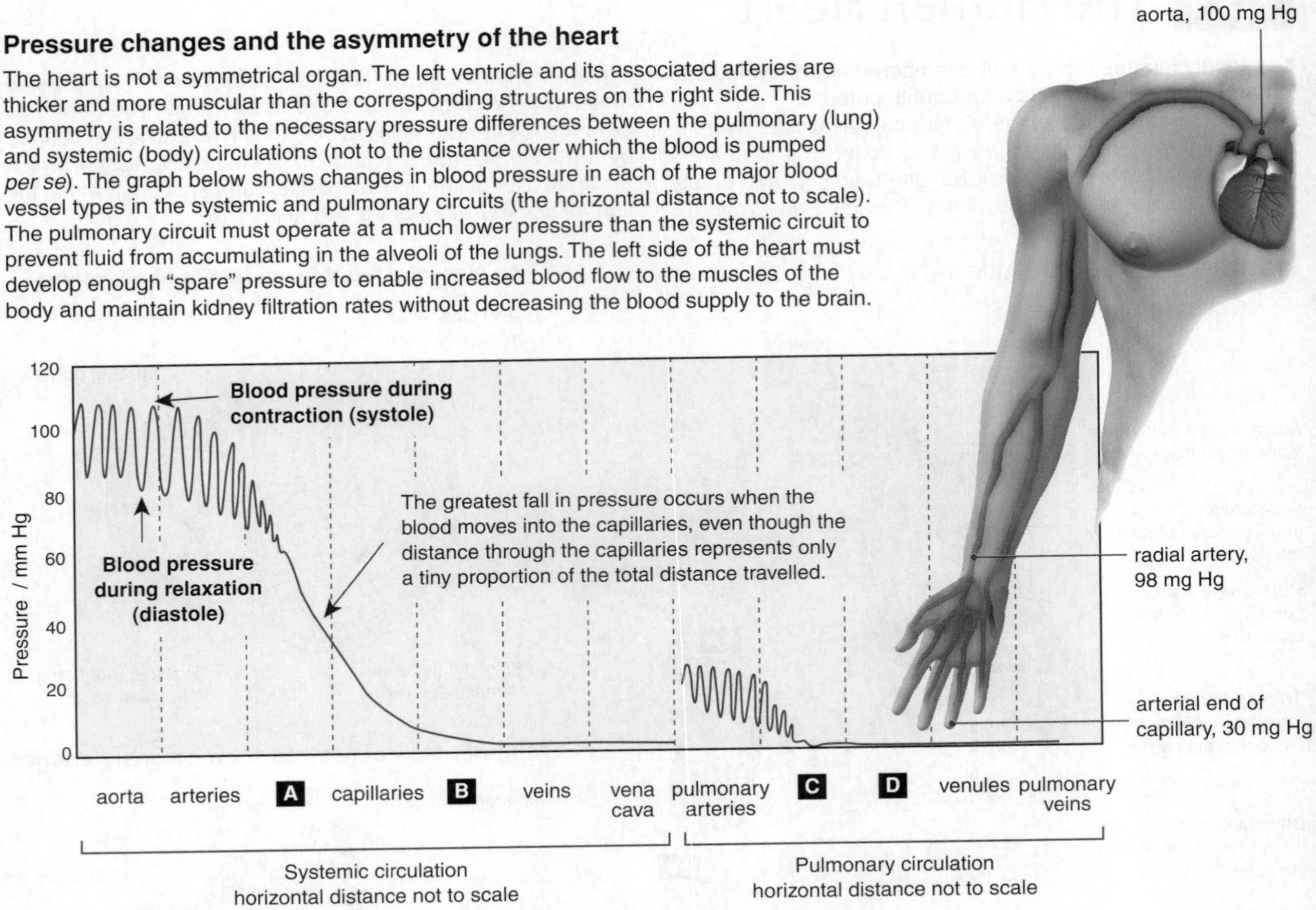

aorta, 100 mg Hg

Blood pressure during contraction (systole)

Blood pressure during relaxation (diastole)

The greatest fall in pressure occurs when the blood moves into the capillaries, even though the distance through the capillaries represents only a tiny proportion of the total distance travelled.

radial artery, 98 mg Hg

arterial end of capillary, 30 mg Hg

Pressure / mm Hg

aorta   arteries   **A**   capillaries   **B**   veins   vena cava   pulmonary arteries   **C**   **D**   venules pulmonary veins

Systemic circulation
horizontal distance not to scale

Pulmonary circulation
horizontal distance not to scale

2. What is the purpose of the valves in the heart? _____

_____

3. The heart is full of blood, yet it requires its own blood supply. Suggest two reasons why this is the case:

(a) _____

(b) _____

4. Predict the effect on the heart if blood flow through a coronary artery is restricted or blocked: _____

_____

_____

5. Identify the vessels corresponding to the letters **A-D** on the graph above:

A: _____ B: _____ C: _____ D: _____

6. (a) Why must the pulmonary circuit operate at a lower pressure than the systemic system?_____

_____

_____

(b) Relate this to differences in the thickness of the wall of the left and right ventricles of the heart: _____

_____

_____

7. What are you recording when you take a pulse? _____

_____

© 2015 **BIOZONE** International
ISBN: 978-1-927309-19-3
Photocopying Prohibited

152 The Cardiac Cycle

Key Idea: The cardiac cycle refers to the sequence of events of a heartbeat and involves three main stages: atrial systole, ventricular systole, and complete cardiac diastole.

The heart pumps with alternate contractions (**systole**) and relaxations (**diastole**). Heartbeat occurs in a cycle involving three stages: atrial systole, ventricular systole, and complete

cardiac diastole. Pressure changes in the heart's chambers generated by the cycle of contraction and relaxation are responsible for blood movement and cause the heart valves to open and close, preventing backflow of blood. The heartbeat occurs in response to electrical impulses, which can be recorded as a trace called an electrocardiogram.

The cardiac cycle

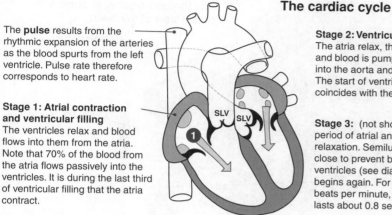

The **pulse** results from the rhythmic expansion of the arteries as the blood spurts from the left ventricle. Pulse rate therefore corresponds to heart rate.

Stage 1: Atrial contraction and ventricular filling
The ventricles relax and blood flows into them from the atria. Note that 70% of the blood from the atria flows passively into the ventricles. It is during the last third of ventricular filling that the atria contract.

Heart during ventricular filling

Stage 2: Ventricular contraction
The atria relax, the ventricles contract, and blood is pumped from the ventricles into the aorta and the pulmonary artery. The start of ventricular contraction coincides with the first heart sound.

Stage 3: (not shown) There is a short period of atrial and ventricular relaxation. Semilunar valves (**SLV**) close to prevent backflow into the ventricles (see diagram, left). The cycle begins again. For a heart beating at 75 beats per minute, one cardiac cycle lasts about 0.8 seconds.

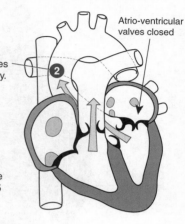

Atrio-ventricular valves closed

Heart during ventricular contraction

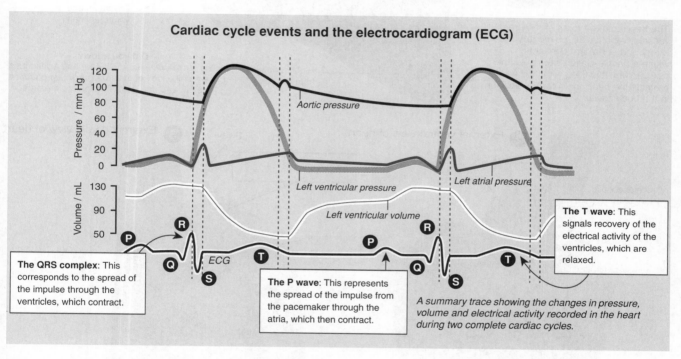

Cardiac cycle events and the electrocardiogram (ECG)

The QRS complex: This corresponds to the spread of the impulse through the ventricles, which contract.

The P wave: This represents the spread of the impulse from the pacemaker through the atria, which then contract.

The T wave: This signals recovery of the electrical activity of the ventricles, which are relaxed.

A summary trace showing the changes in pressure, volume and electrical activity recorded in the heart during two complete cardiac cycles.

1. On the ECG trace above:

    (a) When is the aortic pressure highest? _____

    (b) Which electrical event immediately precedes the increase in ventricular pressure? _____

    (c) What is happening when the pressure of the left ventricle is lowest? _____

2. Suggest the physiological reason for the period of electrical recovery experienced each cycle (the T wave):

    _____

3. Using the letters indicated, mark the points on trace above corresponding to each of the following:

    (a) E: Ejection of blood from the ventricle

    (b) BVC: Closing of the bicuspid valve

    (c) FV: Filling of the ventricle

    (d) BVO: Opening of the bicuspid valve

153 Dissecting a Mammalian Heart

Key Idea: Dissecting a sheep's heart allows hands-on exploration of a mammalian heart.

The dissection of a sheep's heart is a common practical activity and allows hands-on exploration of the appearance and structure of a mammalian heart. A diagram of a heart is an idealised representation of an organ that may look quite different in reality. You must learn to transfer what you know from a diagram to the interpretation of the real organ.

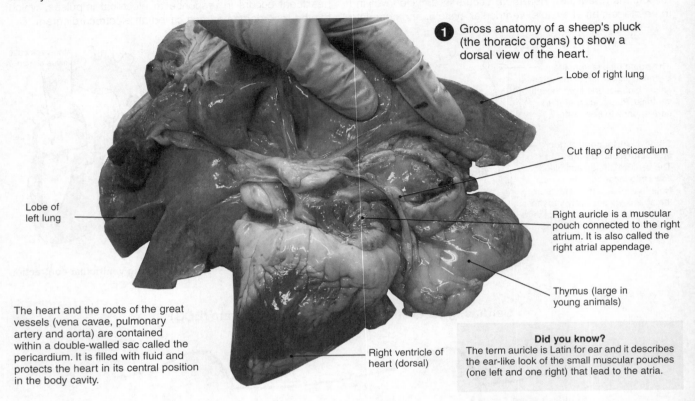

1 Gross anatomy of a sheep's pluck (the thoracic organs) to show a dorsal view of the heart.

Lobe of right lung

Cut flap of pericardium

Right auricle is a muscular pouch connected to the right atrium. It is also called the right atrial appendage.

Lobe of left lung

Thymus (large in young animals)

The heart and the roots of the great vessels (vena cavae, pulmonary artery and aorta) are contained within a double-walled sac called the pericardium. It is filled with fluid and protects the heart in its central position in the body cavity.

Right ventricle of heart (dorsal)

Did you know?
The term auricle is Latin for ear and it describes the ear-like look of the small muscular pouches (one left and one right) that lead to the atria.

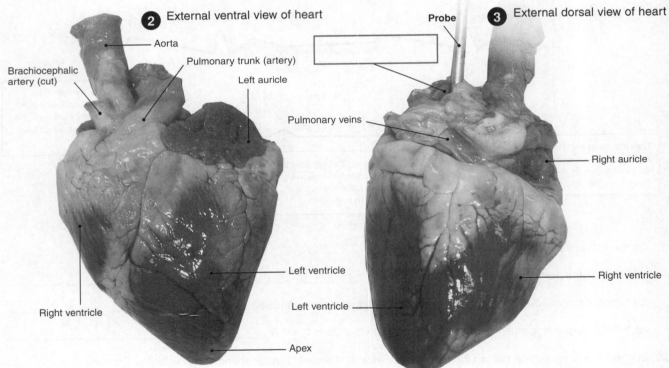

2 External ventral view of heart

Aorta

Brachiocephalic artery (cut)

Pulmonary trunk (artery)

Left auricle

Right ventricle

Left ventricle

Left ventricle

Apex

Probe

3 External dorsal view of heart

Pulmonary veins

Right auricle

Right ventricle

Note the main surface features of an isolated heart. The narrow pointed end forms the **apex** of the heart, while the wider end, where the blood vessels enter is the **base**. The ventral surface of the heart (above) is identified by a groove, the **interventricular sulcus**, which marks the division between the left and right ventricles.

1. Use coloured lines to indicate the interventricular sulcus and the base of the heart. Label the coronary arteries.

On the dorsal surface of the heart, above, locate the large thin-walled **vena cavae** and **pulmonary veins**. You may be able to distinguish between the anterior and posterior vessels. On the right side of the dorsal surface (as you look at the heart) at the base of the heart is the **right atrium**, with the **right ventricle** below it.

2. On this photograph, label the vessel indicated by the probe.

 © 2015 **BIOZONE** International
ISBN: 978-1-927309-19-3
Photocopying Prohibited

4 Dorsal view of heart

5 Shallow section, ventral view of heart

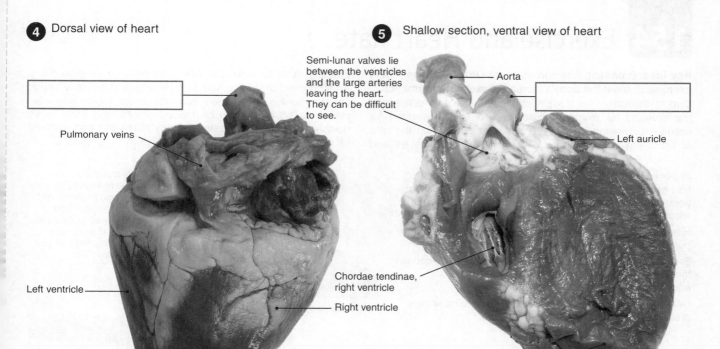

Semi-lunar valves lie between the ventricles and the large arteries leaving the heart. They can be difficult to see.

Pulmonary veins

Left ventricle

Chordae tendinae, right ventricle

Right ventricle

Aorta

Left auricle

Thick wall of left ventricle

3. On this **dorsal view**, label the vessel indicated. Palpate the heart and feel the difference in the thickness of the left and right ventricle walls.

4. This photograph shows a shallow section to expose the right ventricle. Label the vessel in the box indicated.

6 Frontal sections of heart to show chambers

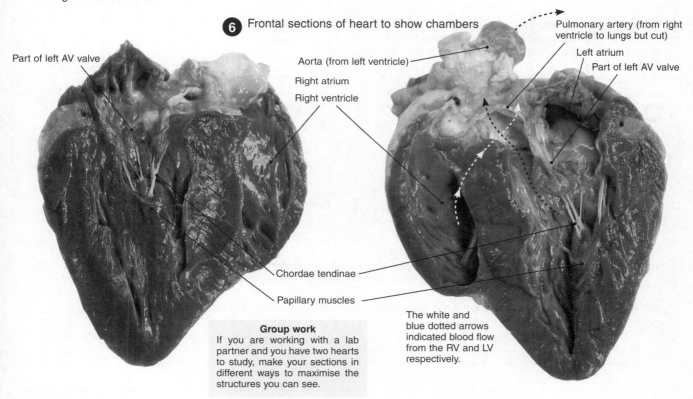

Part of left AV valve

Aorta (from left ventricle)

Right atrium

Right ventricle

Chordae tendinae

Papillary muscles

Pulmonary artery (from right ventricle to lungs but cut)

Left atrium

Part of left AV valve

The white and blue dotted arrows indicated blood flow from the RV and LV respectively.

Group work
If you are working with a lab partner and you have two hearts to study, make your sections in different ways to maximise the structures you can see.

If the heart is sectioned and the two halves opened, the valves of the heart can be seen. Each side of the heart has a one-way valve between the atrium and the ventricle known as the **atrioventricular valve**. They close during ventricular contraction to prevent back flow of the blood into the lower pressure atria.

The atrioventricular (AV) valves of the two sides of the heart are similar in structure except that the right AV valve has three cusps (tricuspid) while the left atrioventricular valve has two cusps (bicuspid or mitral valve). Connective tissue (**chordae tendineae**) run from the cusps to **papillary muscles** on the ventricular wall.

5. Judging by their position and structure, what do you suppose is the function of the chordae tendinae?

_____

_____

6. What feature shown here most clearly distinguishes the left and right ventricles?.

_____

_____

154 Exercise and Heart Rate

Key Idea: Breathing rate and heart rate both increase during exercise to meet the body's increased metabolic demands. During exercise, the body's metabolic rate increases and the demand for oxygen increases. Oxygen is required for cellular respiration and ATP production. Increasing the rate of breathing delivers more oxygen to working tissues and enables them to make the ATP they need to keep working. An increased breathing rate also increases the rate at which carbon dioxide is expelled from the body. Heart rate also increases so blood can be moved around the body more quickly. This allows for faster delivery of oxygen and removal of carbon dioxide.

In this practical, you will work in groups of three to see how exercise affects breathing and heart rate. Choose one person to carry out the exercise and one person each to record heart rate and breathing rate.

Heart rate (beats per minute) is obtained by measuring the pulse (right) for 15 seconds and multiplying by four.

Breathing rate (breaths per minute) is measured by counting the number of breaths taken in 15 seconds and multiplying it by four.

CAUTION: The person exercising should have no known pre-existing heart or respiratory conditions.

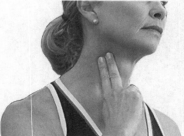

Measuring the carotid pulse

Gently press your index and middle fingers, not your thumb, against the carotid artery in the neck (just under the jaw) or the radial artery (on the wrist just under the thumb) until you feel a pulse.

Measuring the radial pulse

Procedure

Resting measurements
Have the person carrying out the exercise sit down on a chair for 5 minutes. They should try not to move. After 5 minutes of sitting, measure their heart rate and breathing rate. Record the resting data on the table (right).

Exercising measurements
Choose an exercise to perform. Some examples include step ups onto a chair, skipping rope, jumping jacks, and running in place.

Begin the exercise, and take measurements after 1, 2, 3, and 4 minutes of exercise. The person exercising should stop just long enough for the measurements to be taken. Record the results in the table.

Post exercise measurements
After the exercise period has finished, have the exerciser sit down in a chair. Take their measurements 1 and 5 minutes after finishing the exercise. Record the results on the table.

	Heart rate / beats minute^{-1}	Breathing rate / breaths minute^{-1}
Resting		
1 minute		
2 minutes		
3 minutes		
4 minutes		
1 minute after		
5 minutes after		

1. (a) Graph your results on separate piece of paper. You will need to make left and right vertical axes, one for heart rate and another for breathing rate. When you have finished answering the questions below, attach it to this page.

   (b) Analyse your graph and describe what happened to heart rate and breathing rate **during exercise**: _____

   _____

   _____

   _____

   _____

2. (a) Describe what happened to heart rate and breathing rate **after exercise**: _____

   _____

   _____

   (b) Why did this change occur? _____

   _____

LINK
PRAC 152

© 2015 **BIOZONE** International
ISBN: 978-1-927309-19-3
Photocopying Prohibited

155 Cardiovascular Disease

Key Idea: Cardiovascular disease refers to diseases affecting the heart and blood vessels.

Cardiovascular disease (CVD) refers to a wide range of diseases including coronary heart disease (CHD), atherosclerosis, **hypertension** (high blood pressure), peripheral vascular disease, stroke, and congenital heart conditions (those present at birth). Only a small proportion of the population (<1%) are born with heart abnormalities and most CVD develops as a result of lifestyle or environmental factors. Despite the fact that many of the risk factors are controllable, CVD is the single most common cause of death in the UK. In 2014, £15 billion was spent on treating CVD, and the cost may continue to rise. Deaths from CVD have been declining since the late 1970s, mainly due to education about the disease and its risk factors, and as a result of improvements in detection and treatment.

Types of cardiovascular disease

Atherosclerosis (hardening of the arteries) is caused by deposits of fats and cholesterol in the inner walls of the arteries. Blood flow becomes restricted and increases the risk of blood clots (thrombosis). Complications arising as a result of atherosclerosis include heart attack (infarction), gangrene, and stroke. A stroke is the rapid loss of brain function due to a disturbance in the blood supply to the brain, and may result in death if the damage is severe. Speech, or vision and movement on one side of the body is often affected.

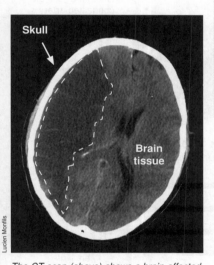

Skull

Brain tissue

Lucien Monfils

The CT scan (above) shows a brain affected by a severe cerebral infarction or ischaemic stroke. The loss of blood supply results in tissue death (outlined area). Blood clots resulting from atherosclerosis are a common cause of ischaemic stroke.

A normal heart

KEY
V Ventricle
A Atrium
Se Septum

Aortic aneurysm: A ballooning and weakening of the wall of the aorta.

Aneurysms usually result from generalised heart disease and high blood pressure.

Valve defects: Unusual heart sounds (murmurs) can result when a valve (often the mitral valve) does not close properly, allowing blood to bubble back into the atria. Valve defects may be congenital (present at birth) but they can also occur as a result of rheumatic fever.

Septal defects: These hole-in-the-heart congenital defects occur where the dividing wall (**septum**) between the left and right sides of the heart is not closed. These defects may occur between the atria or the ventricles, and are sometimes combined with valve problems.

Myocardial infarction *(heart attack):* Occurs when an area of the heart is deprived of blood supply resulting in tissue damage or death. It is the major cause of death in developed countries. Symptoms of infarction include a sudden onset of chest pain, breathlessness, nausea, and cold clammy skin. Damage to the heart may be so severe that it leads to heart failure and even death (myocardial infarction is fatal within 20 days in 40 to 50% of all cases).

Restricted supply of blood to heart muscle resulting in myocardial infarction

1. What is cardiovascular disease (CVD)? _____

_____

2. Distinguish between congenital and acquired CVD, including reference to risk factors in disease development:

_____

_____

_____

3. Explain why the high rates of cardiovascular disease are such a major public health concern: _____

_____

_____

LINK LINK LINK
158 **157** **156** **KNOW**

156 CVD Risk Factors

Key Idea: CVD risk factors are those factors that may increase the chances of developing cardiovascular disease. CVD risk factors increase the likelihood of a person developing CVD. Controllable risk factors can be modified by lifestyle changes, whereas uncontrollable risk factors, such as age, cannot be modified. A person with more risk factors has a greater likelihood of developing CVD, although total risk can minimised by reducing the number of controllable risk factors. Major controllable risk factors are smoking and the ratio of LDL:HDL cholesterol in the blood. About 13% of deaths from CVD are attributable to smoking. Smoking also acts synergistically with other risk factors to increase their impact.

Cholesterol and CVD

Cholesterol is transported in the blood within complex spherical particles called **lipoproteins**. One form (high density lipoprotein or HDL) helps remove cholesterol from the blood by transporting it to the liver. The other form (low density lipoprotein or LDL) deposits cholesterol in the walls of blood vessels. Abnormally high concentrations of LDL and lower concentrations of HDL are strongly associated with the development of atheroma. It is the **LDL:HDL ratio**, rather than total cholesterol itself, that provides the best indicator of risk for developing cardiovascular disease, and the risk profile is different for men and women (see below).

Ratio of LDL to HDL		
Risk	Men	Women
Very low (half mean risk)	1.0	1.5
Mean risk	3.6	3.2
Moderate risk (2X mean risk)	6.3	5.0
High (3X mean risk)	8.0	6.1

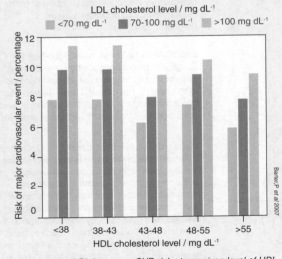

Above: A higher LDL increases CVD risk at any given level of HDL.

Smoking and CVD

Smoking is a significant risk factor for the development of all types of cardiovascular disease. The nicotine in cigarette smoke is a stimulant and increases both blood pressure and heart rate, constricting arteries and making the heart work harder. It also causes the body to mobilise fat stores, increasing the risk of **atheromas** (fatty plaques in the arteries). Constriction and blockage of the arteries by plaques increases the risk of stroke and myocardial infarction.

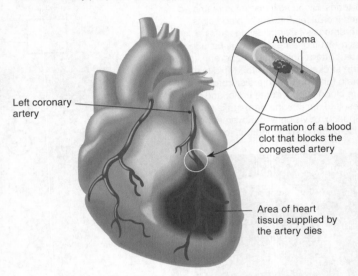

Relative risk of myocardial infarction (heart attack) by current tobacco exposure

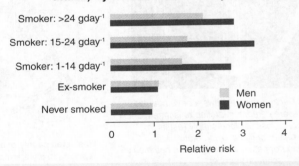

Obesity and CVD

Obesity has been clearly linked to various types of CVD, including coronary heart disease (CHD) as well as diabetes and hypertension. Excessive body weight puts an increased strain on the heart, which leads to increased blood pressure and enlargement of the heart.

The prevalence of obesity is increasing in the UK, despite there also being a general increase in levels of physical activity and healthier eating. For example, between 1980 and 1998 the prevalence of obesity in UK women more than doubled from 8% to 21%. A large cross-sectional study of UK women (left) showed that predicted 10 year risk of CHD (based on a number of measured indicators) was about the same for women with a body mass index (BMI) less than 20 but increased progressively after that (left).

Data: European Heart Journal (2001) **22**, 46-55 "Body mass index and metabolic risk factors for coronary heart disease in women."

LINK
157

KNOW

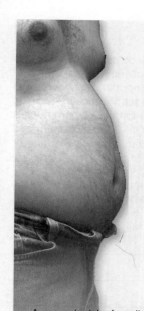

Cardiovascular disease: Who is at risk?

Controlled risk factors for cardiovascular disease

- High blood pressure
- Cigarette smoking
- High blood cholesterol
- High LDL:HDL ratio
- Obesity
- Type 2 diabetes mellitus
- High achiever personality
- Environmental stress
- Sedentary lifestyle

A person's risk of cardiovascular disease increases markedly with an increase in the number of risk factors. This is particularly the case for smoking, because smoking acts synergistically with other risk factors, particularly high blood pressure and high blood lipids. This means that any given risk factor has a proportionately greater effect in a smoker than in a non-smoker.

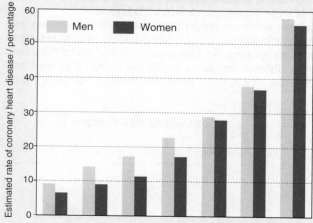

Estimated coronary heart disease rate according to various combinations of risk factors over 10 years (source: International Diabetes Foundation, 2001)

Legend: Men, Women

Y-axis: Estimated rate of coronary heart disease / percentage

X-axis: Risk factors

Systolic blood pressure / mm Hg	120	160	160	160	160	160	160
Cholesterol / mg 100 cm⁻³	220	220	259	259	259	259	259
HDL cholesterol / mg 100 cm⁻³	50	50	50	35	35	35	35
Diabetes	–	–	–	–	+	+	+
Cigarette smoking	–	–	–	–	–	+	+
Enlargement of left ventricle	–	–	–	–	–	–	+

1. (a) Distinguish between controllable and uncontrollable risk factors in the development of CVD: _____

_____

(b) Suggest why some of the controllable risk factors often occur together: _____

_____

_____

(c) Evaluate the evidence supporting the observation that patients with several risk factors are at higher risk of CVD:

_____

_____

_____

_____

2. (a) Explain the link between high LDL:HDL ratio and the risk of cardiovascular disease: _____

_____

_____

_____

(b) Explain why this ratio is more important to medical practitioners than total blood cholesterol *per se*: _____

_____

_____

3. (a) Describe the evidence for a link between obesity and risk of CHD as shown by the study of UK women (opposite):

_____

_____

(b) What is one strength of this study: _____

157 Reducing the Risk

Key Idea: Non-smokers, physically active people, and those who consume adequate amounts of fruit and vegetables are less likely to develop cardiovascular disease.

Physically active people and those that don't smoke are less likely to develop CVD. For adults, aerobic activity lasting at least thirty minutes, five time a week is required for maximum benefit. Children should be physically active for at least one hour a day, five times a week. In developed countries, over 20% of all heart disease and 10% of strokes are directly linked to physical inactivity. Eating at least five portions of fruit and vegetables a day is also important for decreasing the risk of CVD. Despite the increases in public education programmes, there has been little improvement in people's overall eating habits in the UK. Only 13% of men and 15% of women consume five or more portions of fruits or vegetables a day.

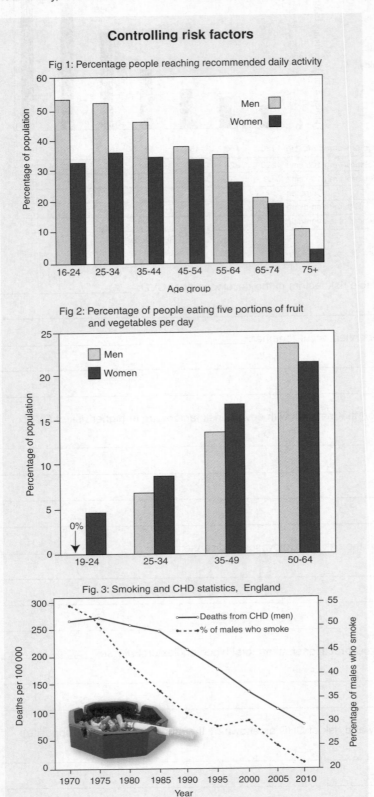

Controlling risk factors

Fig 1: Percentage people reaching recommended daily activity

Fig 2: Percentage of people eating five portions of fruit and vegetables per day

Fig. 3: Smoking and CHD statistics, England

Source: British Heart Foundation Statistics 2008

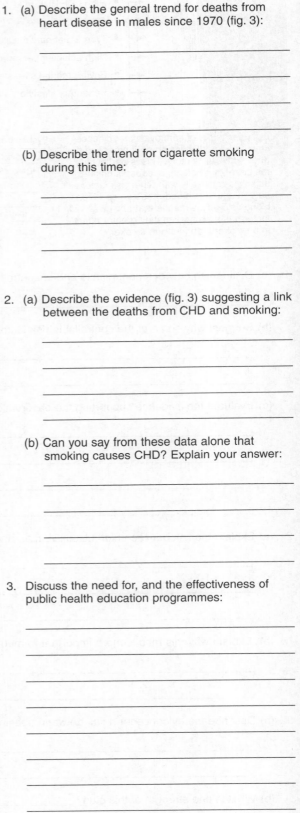

1. (a) Describe the general trend for deaths from heart disease in males since 1970 (fig. 3):

    (b) Describe the trend for cigarette smoking during this time:

2. (a) Describe the evidence (fig. 3) suggesting a link between the deaths from CHD and smoking:

    (b) Can you say from these data alone that smoking causes CHD? Explain your answer:

3. Discuss the need for, and the effectiveness of public health education programmes:

LINK
158

KNOW

© 2015 **BIOZONE** International
ISBN: 978-1-927309-19-3
Photocopying Prohibited

158 Evaluating the Risk

Key Idea: New information is emerging that may contradict some long held beliefs about CVD risk factors.

Investigating the effect of risk factors on health involves studying data for patterns. The most reliable studies involve a large group encompassing a range of people and lifestyles, and are controlled for factors that are not relevant to the variable being tested (nuisance factors). Results from these studies are often used to educate the public about healthy practices. However, over time new research may be released that contradicts current advice. For example, there have been a number of studies showing that high consumption of saturated fats increases the risk of heart disease while increased consumption of polyunsaturated fats decreases the risk of heart disease. However, studies carried out in the last few years suggests the link is not as straightforward as this (below). Recommendations about risk factors may change as more information is gathered about the long-term effects of certain foods or behaviours on risk of disease.

US studies show a positive correlation between eating red meat and incidence of heart disease, but studies from Europe and Australasia often do not. Cattle in the US are often corn fed whereas cattle in Europe and Australasia are grass fed. Could this be contributing to the inconsistent findings?

Saturated fat has been linked to heart disease, but a 2014 study* showed that a saturated fat in milk, margaric acid, may lower the risk of heart disease. The study was extensive, reviewing 72 studies and including 500 000 people. The authors suggested that guidelines on fatty acids and CVD could be reviewed.

*Association of Dietary, Circulating and Supplementary Fatty Acids with Coronary Risk

The same study (and others) showed no significant evidence that saturated fats increased heart disease. It did show a link between trans-fats and heart disease. Trans-fats are produced during the hydrogenation of vegetable oils to make them more solid.

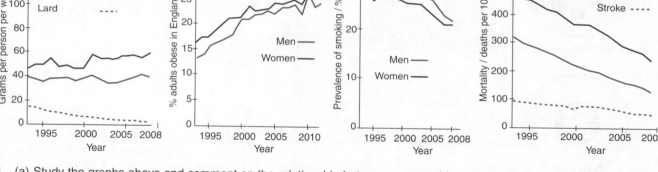

Consumption of fats, UK
Vegetable oil —
Butter —
Lard ----
(Grams per person per week vs Year: 1995, 2000, 2005, 2008)

Prevalence of obesity in England
Men —
Women —
(% adults obese in England vs Year: 1995, 2000, 2005, 2010)

Prevalence of smoking in UK
Men —
Women —
(Prevalence of smoking / % vs Year: 1995, 2000, 2005, 2008)

CVD mortality for men, UK
Cardiovascular disease —
Coronary heart disease —
Stroke ----
(Mortality / deaths per 100 000 vs Year: 1995, 2000, 2005, 2009)

1. (a) Study the graphs above and comment on the relationship between saturated fat consumption and mortality due to CVD in the UK (mortality, or death rate, shows a similar trend to incidence, or rate of occurrence):

(b) Identify three pieces of information that appear to contradict the link between saturated fats and heart disease:

2. (a) Obesity is a risk factor for CVD. Do the graphs above support this link? Explain your reasoning: _____

(b) Which risk factor is most closely correlated with mortality due to CVD? Explain your reasoning: _____

LINK 157   LINK 156   LINK 19   WEB 158   KNOW

159 Vascular Tissue in Plants

Key Idea: The xylem and phloem form the vascular tissue that moves fluids and minerals about the plant.

The vascular tissues (**xylem** and **phloem**) link all parts of the plant so that water, minerals, and manufactured food can be transported between different regions of the plant. The xylem and phloem are found together in vascular bundles. In dicotyledonous plants (below) the vascular bundles are located in a ring towards the outer edge of the stem. In monocotyledonous plants, the bundles are scattered randomly throughout the stem. The xylem transports water and minerals from the roots to the leaves, while the phloem transports sugars through the plant to where they are needed.

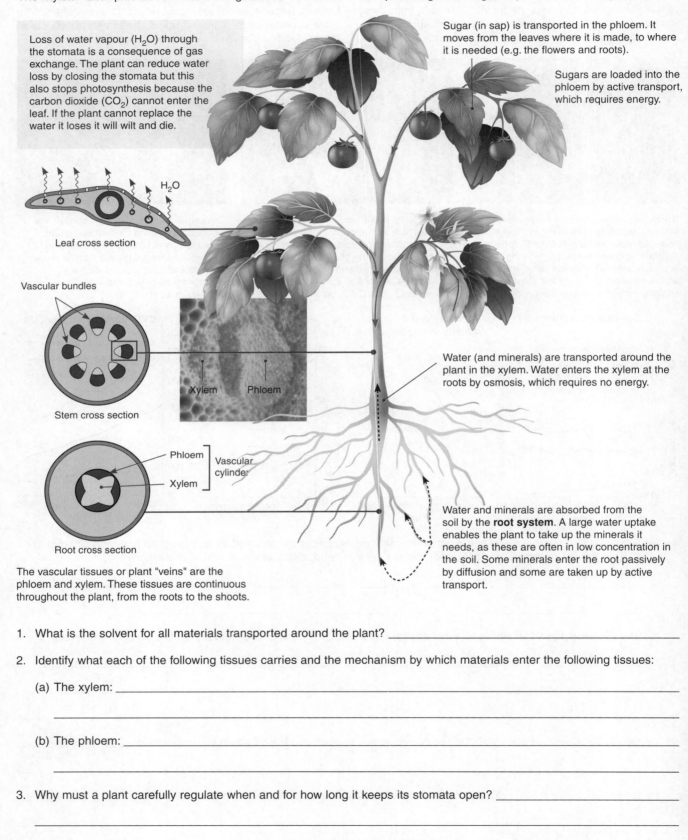

Loss of water vapour (H_2O) through the stomata is a consequence of gas exchange. The plant can reduce water loss by closing the stomata but this also stops photosynthesis because the carbon dioxide (CO_2) cannot enter the leaf. If the plant cannot replace the water it loses it will wilt and die.

Sugar (in sap) is transported in the phloem. It moves from the leaves where it is made, to where it is needed (e.g. the flowers and roots).

Sugars are loaded into the phloem by active transport, which requires energy.

H_2O

Leaf cross section

Vascular bundles

Xylem   Phloem

Stem cross section

Water (and minerals) are transported around the plant in the xylem. Water enters the xylem at the roots by osmosis, which requires no energy.

Phloem ⎤ Vascular
        ⎥ cylinder
Xylem ⎦

Root cross section

Water and minerals are absorbed from the soil by the **root system**. A large water uptake enables the plant to take up the minerals it needs, as these are often in low concentration in the soil. Some minerals enter the root passively by diffusion and some are taken up by active transport.

The vascular tissues or plant "veins" are the phloem and xylem. These tissues are continuous throughout the plant, from the roots to the shoots.

1. What is the solvent for all materials transported around the plant? _____

2. Identify what each of the following tissues carries and the mechanism by which materials enter the following tissues:

   (a) The xylem: _____

   _____

   (b) The phloem: _____

   _____

3. Why must a plant carefully regulate when and for how long it keeps its stomata open? _____

   _____

   _____

© 2015 **BIOZONE** International
ISBN: 978-1-927309-19-3
Photocopying Prohibited

160 Xylem and Phloem

Key Idea: In vascular plants, xylem transports water and minerals and phloem transports dissolved sugar.

Xylem and phloem are the main supporting tissue in plants. Both are complex tissues composed of a number of cell types. **Xylem** tissue is largely composed of large vessels, which have thickened and strengthened walls and conduct water. It also contains packing cells (parenchyma) and fibres, which support the tissue. Mature xylem is dead. **Phloem** tissue is composed of packing cells and supporting fibre cells, and two special cell types: **sieve tubes** and **companion cells**. Phloem transports dissolved sugars and is alive when mature.

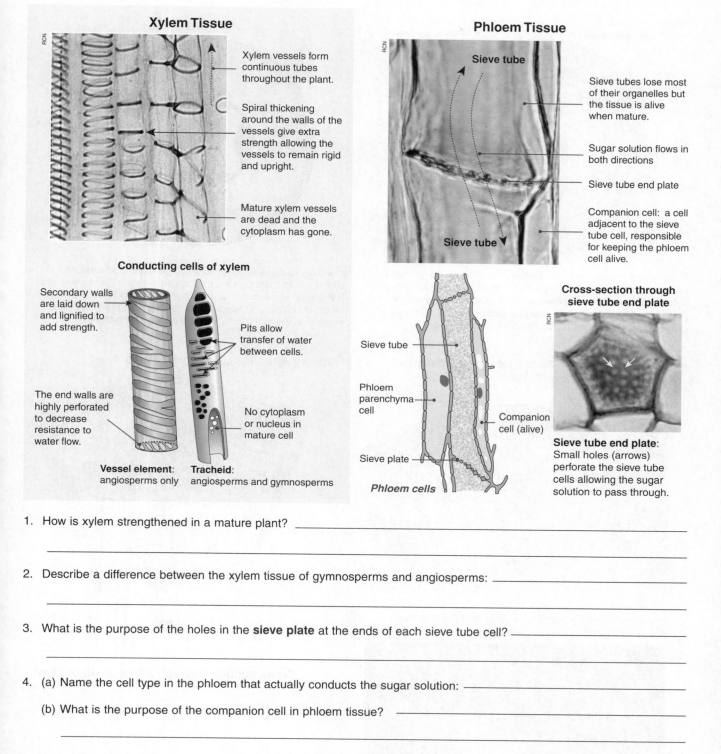

Xylem Tissue

- Xylem vessels form continuous tubes throughout the plant.
- Spiral thickening around the walls of the vessels give extra strength allowing the vessels to remain rigid and upright.
- Mature xylem vessels are dead and the cytoplasm has gone.

Conducting cells of xylem

- Secondary walls are laid down and lignified to add strength.
- Pits allow transfer of water between cells.
- The end walls are highly perforated to decrease resistance to water flow.
- No cytoplasm or nucleus in mature cell

Vessel element: angiosperms only
Tracheid: angiosperms and gymnosperms

Phloem Tissue

- Sieve tube
- Sieve tubes lose most of their organelles but the tissue is alive when mature.
- Sugar solution flows in both directions
- Sieve tube end plate
- Companion cell: a cell adjacent to the sieve tube cell, responsible for keeping the phloem cell alive.
- Sieve tube

Phloem cells
- Sieve tube
- Phloem parenchyma cell
- Companion cell (alive)
- Sieve plate

Cross-section through sieve tube end plate

Sieve tube end plate: Small holes (arrows) perforate the sieve tube cells allowing the sugar solution to pass through.

1. How is xylem strengthened in a mature plant? _____

_____

2. Describe a difference between the xylem tissue of gymnosperms and angiosperms: _____

_____

3. What is the purpose of the holes in the **sieve plate** at the ends of each sieve tube cell? _____

_____

4. (a) Name the cell type in the phloem that actually conducts the sugar solution: _____

   (b) What is the purpose of the companion cell in phloem tissue? _____

   _____

5. Describe the structural and functional differences between xylem and phloem: _____

_____

_____

_____

LINK WEB
161 160 KNOW

161 Identifying Xylem and Phloem

Key Idea: The vascular tissue in dicots can be identified by its appearance in sections viewed with a light microscope. The structure of the vascular tissue in dicotyledons (dicots) has a very regular arrangement with the xylem and phloem found close together. In the stem, the vascular tissue is distributed in a regular fashion near the outer edge of the stem. In the roots, the vascular tissue is found near the centre of the root.

Dicot stem structure

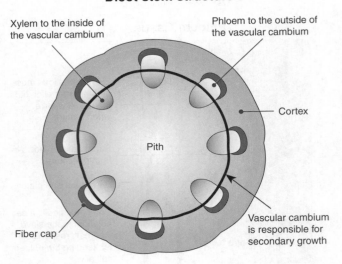

Xylem to the inside of the vascular cambium

Phloem to the outside of the vascular cambium

Cortex

Pith

Vascular cambium is responsible for secondary growth

Fiber cap

Dicot root structure

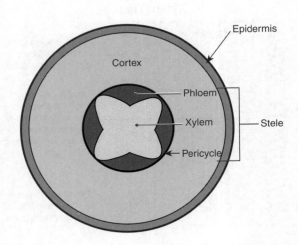

Epidermis

Cortex

Phloem

Xylem

Stele

Pericycle

In dicots, the vascular bundles (xylem and phloem) are arranged in an orderly fashion around the stem. Each vascular bundle contains **xylem** (to the inside) and **phloem** (to the outside). Between the phloem and the xylem is the **vascular cambium**. This is a layer of cells that divide to produce the thickening of the stem.

In a dicot root, the vascular tissue, (xylem and phloem) forms a central cylinder through the root called the stele. The large cortex is made up of parenchyma (packing) cells, which store starch and other substances. Air spaces between the cells are essential for aeration of the root tissue, which is non-photosynthetic.

1. In the micrograph below of a dicot stem identify the phloem (P) and xylem (X) tissue:

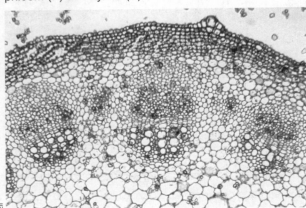

2. In the micrograph below of a dicot root identify the phloem (P) and xylem (X) tissue:

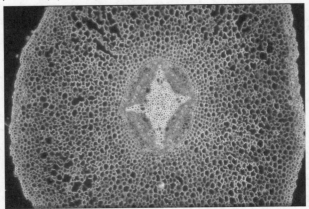

3. In the diagram below identify the labels A - F

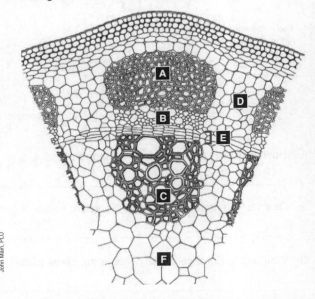

Cross section through a typical dicot stem

A. _____

B. _____

C. _____

D. _____

E. _____

F. _____

© 2015 **BIOZONE** International
ISBN: 978-1-927309-19-3
Photocopying Prohibited

162 Uptake at the Root

Key Idea: Water uptake by the root is a passive process. Mineral uptake can be passive or active.

Plants need to take up water and minerals constantly. They must compensate for the continuous loss of water from the leaves and provide the materials the plant needs to make food. The uptake of water and minerals is mostly restricted to the younger, most recently formed cells of the roots and the root hairs. Water uptake occurs by osmosis, whereas mineral ions enter the root by diffusion and active transport. Pathways for water movements through the plant are outlined below.

Water and mineral uptake by roots

Root hairs have a thin cuticle, so water enters the root easily

Cortex cells of root

Epidermal cell

Xylem

Stele (vascular cylinder). The outer layer of the stele, the pericycle, is next to the endodermis.

Root hair

Water moves by osmosis

Schematic cross-section through a dicot root

The endodermis is the central, innermost layer of the cortex. It is a single layer of cells with a waterproof band of suberin, called the **Casparian strip**, which encircles each cell.

Root hairs are extensions of the root epidermal cells and provide a large surface area for absorbing water and nutrients.

Paths for water movement through the plant

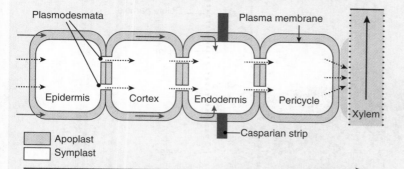

Plasmodesmata

Plasma membrane

Epidermis   Cortex   Endodermis   Pericycle

Xylem

Casparian strip

☐ Apoplast
☐ Symplast

Higher water potential
May be due to fully turgid cells, higher wall pressure, or lower concentration of dissolved substances

Lower water potential
May be due to less turgid cells, lower wall pressure, or higher concentration of dissolved substances

The uptake of water through the roots occurs by osmosis, i.e. the diffusion of water from a higher (less negative) to a lower (more negative) water potential. Most water travels through the **apoplast**, i.e. the spaces within the cellulose cell walls, the water-filled spaces of dead cells, and the hollow tubes of xylem vessels. A smaller amount moves through the **symplast** (the cytoplasm of cells). A very small amount travels through the plant vacuoles.

Some dissolved mineral ions enter the root passively with water. Minerals that are in very low concentration in the soil are taken up by active transport. At the waterproof Casparian strip, water and dissolved minerals must pass into the symplast, so the flow of materials into the stele can be regulated.

1. (a) What two mechanisms do plants use to absorb nutrients?

_____

_____

(b) Describe the two main pathways by which water moves through a plant:

_____

_____

_____

_____

2. Plants take up water constantly to compensate for losses due to transpiration. Describe a benefit of a large water uptake:

_____

_____

_____

_____

_____

3. (a) How does the Casparian strip affect the route water takes into the stele?

_____

_____

_____

_____

(b) Why might this feature be an advantage in terms of selective mineral uptake?

_____

_____

_____

_____

_____

_____

_____

_____

_____

_____

163 Transpiration

Key Idea: Water moves through the xylem primarily as a result of evaporation from the leaves and the cohesive and adhesive properties of water molecules.

Plants lose water all the time through their stomata as a consequence of gas exchange. Approximately 99% of the water a plant absorbs from the soil is lost by evaporation from the leaves and stem. This loss is called **transpiration** and the flow of water through the plant is called the **transpiration**

stream. Plants rely on a gradient in water potential (ψ) from the roots to the air to move water through their cells. Water flows passively from soil to air along a gradient of decreasing water potential. The gradient is the driving force for the movement of water up a plant. Transpiration has benefits to the plant because evaporative water loss is cooling and the transpiration stream helps the plant to take up minerals. Factors contributing to water movement are described below.

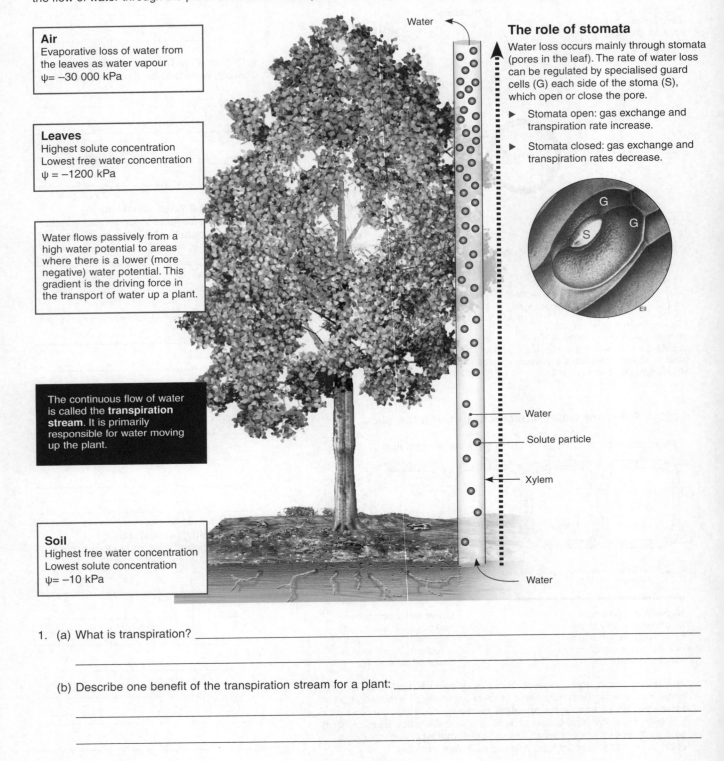

Air
Evaporative loss of water from the leaves as water vapour
$\psi = -30\ 000$ kPa

Leaves
Highest solute concentration
Lowest free water concentration
$\psi = -1200$ kPa

Water flows passively from a high water potential to areas where there is a lower (more negative) water potential. This gradient is the driving force in the transport of water up a plant.

The continuous flow of water is called the **transpiration stream**. It is primarily responsible for water moving up the plant.

Soil
Highest free water concentration
Lowest solute concentration
$\psi = -10$ kPa

Water

The role of stomata

Water loss occurs mainly through stomata (pores in the leaf). The rate of water loss can be regulated by specialised guard cells (G) each side of the stoma (S), which open or close the pore.

▶ Stomata open: gas exchange and transpiration rate increase.

▶ Stomata closed: gas exchange and transpiration rates decrease.

Water

Solute particle

Xylem

Water

1. (a) What is transpiration? _____

_____

(b) Describe one benefit of the transpiration stream for a plant: _____

_____

_____

_____

2. Why is transpiration an inevitable consequence of gas exchange? _____

_____

Processes involved in moving water through the xylem

1 Transpiration pull

Water is lost from the air spaces by evaporation through stomata and is replaced by water from the mesophyll cells. The constant loss of water to the air (and production of sugars) creates a lower (more negative) water potential in the leaves than in the cells further from the evaporation site. Water is pulled through the plant down a **decreasing gradient in water potential**.

2 Cohesion-tension

The transpiration pull is assisted by the special **cohesive** properties of water. Water molecules cling together as they are pulled through the plant. They also **adhere** to the walls of the xylem (**adhesion**). This creates one **unbroken column of water** through the plant. The upward pull on the cohesive sap creates a tension (a negative pressure). This helps water uptake and movement up the plant.

3 Root pressure

Water entering the stele from the soil creates a **root pressure**; a weak 'push' effect for the water's upward movement through the plant. Root pressure can force water droplets from some small plants under certain conditions (**guttation**), but generally it plays a minor part in the ascent of water.

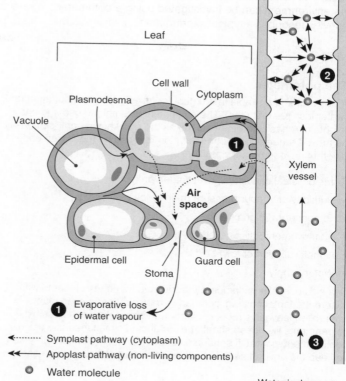

Water is drawn up the plant xylem

3. How does the plant regulate the amount of water lost from the leaves? _____

_____

4. (a) What would happen if too much water was lost from the leaves? _____

_____

   (b) When might this happen? _____

5. Describe the three processes that assist the transport of water from the roots of the plant upward:

   (a) _____

   _____

   _____

   (b) _____

   _____

   _____

   (c) _____

   _____

   _____

6. The maximum height water can move up the xylem by cohesion-tension alone is about 10 m. How then does water move up the height of a 40 m tall tree?

_____

_____

_____

164 Investigating Plant Transpiration

Key Idea: The relationship between the rate of transpiration and the environment can be investigated using a potometer. This activity describes a typical experiment to investigate the effect of different environmental conditions on transpiration rate using a potometer. You will present and analyse the results provided.

The potometer

A potometer is a simple instrument for investigating transpiration rate (water loss per unit time). The equipment is simple to use and easy to obtain. A basic potometer, such as the one shown right, can easily be moved around so that transpiration rate can be measured under different environmental conditions.

Some physical conditions investigated are:

- Humidity or vapour pressure (high or low)
- Temperature (high or low)
- Air movement (still or windy)
- Light level (high or low)
- Water supply

It is also possible to compare the transpiration rates of plants with different adaptations e.g. comparing transpiration rates in plants with rolled leaves vs rates in plants with broad leaves. If possible, experiments like these should be conducted simultaneously using replicate equipment. If conducted sequentially, care should be taken to keep the environmental conditions the same for all plants used.

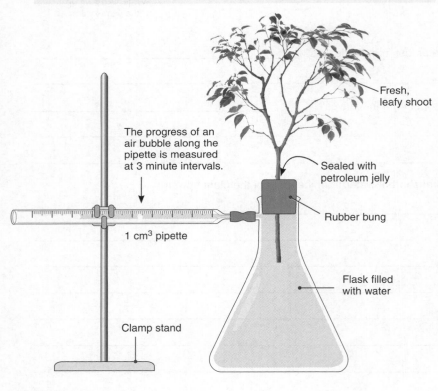

The progress of an air bubble along the pipette is measured at 3 minute intervals.

Fresh, leafy shoot

Sealed with petroleum jelly

Rubber bung

1 cm³ pipette

Flask filled with water

Clamp stand

The apparatus

This experiment investigated the influence of environmental conditions on plant transpiration rate. The experiment examined four conditions: room conditions (ambient), wind, bright light, and high humidity. After setting up the potometer, the apparatus was equilibrated for 10 minutes, and then the position of the air bubble in the pipette was recorded. This is the time 0 reading. The plant was then exposed to one of the environmental conditions. Students recorded the location of the air bubble every three minutes over a 30 minute period. The potometer readings for each environmental condition are presented in Table 1 (next page).

The aim

To investigate the effect of environmental conditions on the transpiration rate of plants.

Background

Plants lose water all the time by evaporation from the leaves and stem. This loss, mostly through pores in the leaf surfaces, is called **transpiration**. Despite the adaptations of plants to reduce water loss (e.g. waxy leaf cuticle), 99% of the water a plant absorbs from the soil is lost by evaporation. Environmental conditions affect transpiration rate by increasing or decreasing the gradient for diffusion of water molecules between the plant and its external environment.

Hypothesis

All the plants will lose water, but the greatest losses will be in hot or windy conditions.

A class was divided into four groups to study how four different environmental conditions (ambient, wind, bright light, and high humidity) affected transpiration rate. A **potometer** was used to measure transpiration rate (water loss per unit time). A basic potometer, such as the one shown left, can easily be moved around so that transpiration rate can be measured under different environmental conditions.

© 2015 **BIOZONE** International
ISBN: 978-1-927309-19-3
Photocopying Prohibited

Table 1. Potometer readings in cm³ water loss

Time / min Treatment	0	3	6	9	12	15	18	21	24	27	30
Ambient	0	0.002	0.005	0.008	0.012	0.017	0.022	0.028	0.032	0.036	0.042
Wind	0	0.025	0.054	0.088	0.112	0.142	0.175	0.208	0.246	0.283	0.325
High humidity	0	0.002	0.004	0.006	0.008	0.011	0.014	0.018	0.019	0.021	0.024
Bright light	0	0.021	0.042	0.070	0.091	0.112	0.141	0.158	0.183	0.218	0.239

1. (a) Plot the potometer data from Table 1 on the grid provided:

   (b) Identify the independent variable: _____

2. (a) Identify the control: _____

   (b) Explain the purpose of including an experimental control in an experiment: _____

   _____

   _____

   (c) Which factors increased water loss? _____

   (d) How does each environmental factor influence water loss? _____

   _____

   _____

   (e) Explain why the plant lost less water in humid conditions: _____

   _____

   _____

165 Translocation

Key Idea: Phloem transports the organic products of photosynthesis (sugars) through the plant in an active, energy-requiring process called translocation.

In angiosperms, the sugar moves through the sieve-tube members, which are arranged end-to-end and perforated with sieve plates. Apart from water, phloem sap comprises mainly sucrose. It may also contain minerals, hormones, and amino acids, in transit around the plant. Movement of sap in the phloem is from a **source** (a plant organ where sugar is made or mobilised) to a **sink** (a plant organ where sugar is stored or used). Loading sucrose into the phloem at a source involves energy expenditure; it is slowed or stopped by high temperatures or respiratory inhibitors. In some plants, unloading the sucrose at the sinks also requires energy, although in others, diffusion alone is sufficient to move sucrose from the phloem into the cells of the sink organ.

Phloem transport

Phloem sap moves from source to sink at rates as great as 100 m h^{-1}, which is too fast to be accounted for by cytoplasmic streaming. The most acceptable model for phloem movement is the **mass flow hypothesis** (also know as the pressure flow hypothesis). Phloem sap moves by bulk flow, which creates a pressure (hence the term "pressure-flow"). The key elements in this model are outlined below and right. For simplicity, the cells that lie between the source (and sink) cells and the phloem sieve-tube have been omitted.

1 Loading sugar into the phloem from a source (e.g. leaf cell) increases the solute concentration (decreases the water potential, ψ) inside the sieve-tube cells. This causes the sieve-tubes to take up water from the surrounding tissues by osmosis.

2 The water uptake creates a hydrostatic pressure that forces the sap to move along the tube, just as pressure pushes water through a hose.

3 The pressure gradient in the sieve tube is reinforced by the active unloading of sugar and consequent loss of water by osmosis at the sink (e.g. root cell).

4 Xylem recycles the water from sink to source.

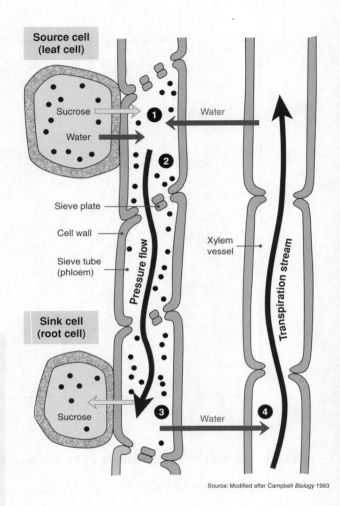

Source: Modified after Campbell *Biology* 1993

Measuring phloem flow
Aphids can act as natural phloem probes to measure phloem flow. The sucking mouthparts (stylet) of the insect penetrates the phloem sieve-tube cell. While the aphid feeds, it can be severed from its stylet, which remains in place and continues to exude sap. Using different aphids, the rate of flow of this sap can be measured at different locations on the plant.

1. (a) From what you know about osmosis, explain why water follows the sugar as it moves through the phloem:

_____

_____

_____

_____

(b) What is meant by '**source to sink**' flow in phloem transport?_____

_____

_____

2. Why does a plant need to move food around, particularly from the leaves to other regions? _____

_____

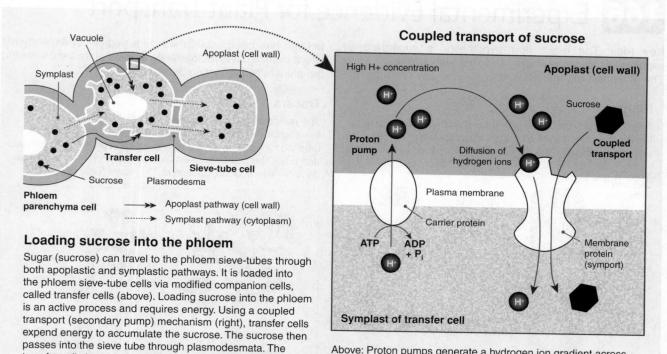

Loading sucrose into the phloem

Sugar (sucrose) can travel to the phloem sieve-tubes through both apoplastic and symplastic pathways. It is loaded into the phloem sieve-tube cells via modified companion cells, called transfer cells (above). Loading sucrose into the phloem is an active process and requires energy. Using a coupled transport (secondary pump) mechanism (right), transfer cells expend energy to accumulate the sucrose. The sucrose then passes into the sieve tube through plasmodesmata. The transfer cells have wall ingrowths that increase surface area for the transport of solutes. Using this mechanism, some plants can accumulate sucrose in the phloem to 2-3 times the concentration in the mesophyll.

Above: Proton pumps generate a hydrogen ion gradient across the membrane of the transfer cell. This process requires expenditure of energy. The gradient is then used to drive the transport of sucrose, by coupling the sucrose transport to the diffusion of hydrogen ions back into the cell.

3. In your own words, describe what is meant by the following:

(a) Translocation: _____

_____

(b) Pressure-flow movement of phloem: _____

_____

(c) Coupled transport of sucrose: _____

_____

4. Briefly explain how sucrose is transported into the phloem: _____

_____

_____

5. Explain the role of the companion (transfer) cell in the loading of sucrose into the phloem: _____

_____

_____

_____

6. (a) What does the flow of phloem sap from a severed aphid stylet indicate? _____

_____

(b) Where would you expect the flow rate to be greatest and why? _____

_____

(c) Why do you think aphid stylets are particularly useful for studying the rate of flow in phloem? _____

_____

_____

166 Experimental Evidence for Plant Transport

Key Idea: The mass flow hypothesis is supported by experiments involving ringing and autoradiographs.
The transport of materials including sugars through the

phloem has been established by a number of experiments which include using radioactively labelled atoms and severing the phloem tissue by ring barking a plant.

Ringing

A classic experiment in studying the flow of phloem sap is the removal of a ring of bark from the plant along with the underlying phloem. The experiment is described below:

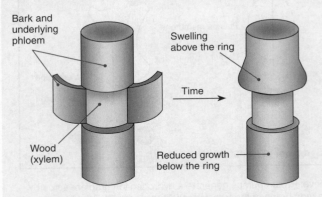

Bark and underlying phloem

Swelling above the ring

Time

Wood (xylem)

Reduced growth below the ring

Sap (from the phloem) oozes out of the wound above the ring showing the phloem is under pressure. Growth continues above the ring but is impeded below it, and leaves are unaffected, showing phloem originates in the leaves and moves down the plant.

Tracers

The radioactive carbon isotope ^{14}C has been used to investigate the site of sugar manufacture and transport. ^{14}C labelled CO_2 was supplied to one leaf of a plant for 20 minutes (left box). The plant was then used to make an autoradiograph on X-ray film and the location of ^{14}C noted (right box).

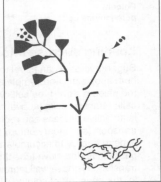

The autoradiograph shows evidence for translocation. Sugars are manufactured in the leaves and transported throughout the plant, including the stem roots, and fruit.

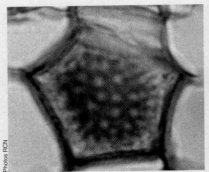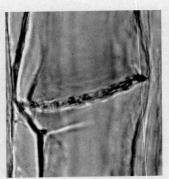

Photos RCN

Phloem sieve plate in TS and LS. The sieve plate is an apparent barrier to mass flow.

Mass flow hypothesis doesn't explain everything

Flow of material through the phloem appears to be bidirectional, and sugars and amino acids move at different rates (mass flow cannot account for the transport of substances in different directions or at different rates). In addition, sieve plates in the phloem represent a barrier (a mechanical resistance) to flow, yet they have not been lost during plant evolution.

1. What does the ringing experiment show about the phloem and the material in it? _____

_____

_____

2. What does the autoradiograph show about the movement of sugars? _____

_____

_____

3. Why does the apparent bi-directional flow in the phloem provide a case against the mass flow hypothesis?

_____

_____

4. Suggest why the presence of the sieve plate is often cited as evidence against the mass flow hypothesis:

_____

_____

© 2015 **BIOZONE** International
ISBN: 978-1-927309-19-3
Photocopying Prohibited

167 Chapter Review

Summarise what you know about this topic under the headings provided. You can draw diagrams or mind maps, or write short notes. Use the images and hints to help you and refer back to the introduction to check the points covered:

Surface area to volume ratio and gas exchange
HINT: Features of the gas exchange surface and mechanisms of increasing the efficiency of exchanges in different taxa.

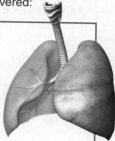

Digestion and absorption
HINT: Mechanisms for digesting and absorbing food.
The role of enzymes.

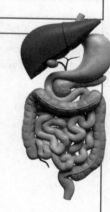

REVISE

Mass transport: animals

HINT: Describe the structure and function of the heart and blood vessels. Describe features of gas transport. Explain the nature and causes cardiovascular disease.

Mass transport: plants

HINT: Describe the structure and function of transport tissues in plants. What is the evidence for mass transport in plants?

168 KEY TERMS: Did You Get It?

1. (a) On the photo of the dissection of a fish's gills, label the following: *gills, operculum, branchial arch.*

   (b) Draw arrows on the photo to show the direction of water flow when the fish was in the water.

   (c) Explain how these gills are ventilated by the fish:

   _____

   _____

   _____

   _____

D. Kuru

2. The image below shows a cross section through a jasmine leaf. On the image label the following: *Palisade mesophyll cell, spongy mesophyll cell, upper epidermis, stomata, guard cell, vascular bundle (leaf vein), lower epidermis, air spaces.*

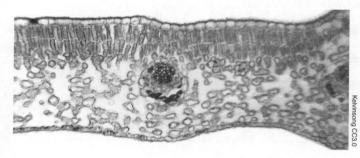

Kelvinsong CC3.0

3. Test your vocabulary by matching each term to its definition, as identified by its preceding letter code.

alveoli
_____

countercurrent flow
_____

expiration
_____

gas exchange
_____

gills
_____

haemoglobin
_____

inspiration
_____

lungs
_____

oxyhaemoglobin dissociation curve
_____

respiratory gas
_____

respiratory pigment
_____

spiracles
_____

stomata
_____

A A sigmoidal curve describing the oxygen-binding behaviour of haemoglobin at different oxygen tensions.

B A substance carried in blood that is able to bind oxygen for transport to cells. Examples include haemoglobin and haemocyanin.

C The exterior opening of the tracheae in arthropods.

D Pores in the epidermis of a leaf through which gases enter and leave the leaf tissue

E The exchange of oxygen and carbon dioxide across the respiratory membrane.

F The respiratory organs of many aquatic animals (although not aquatic mammals).

G Any gas that takes part in the respiratory process (usually just oxygen or carbon dioxide).

H The act of breathing out or removing air from the lungs.

I A term describing the flow of fluids and/or air in opposite directions so that diffusion gradients are maintained between the two media and exchanges between them are maximised.

J Internal gas exchange structures found in air breathing vertebrates.

K A large iron-containing protein that transports oxygen in the blood of vertebrates.

L Microscopic structures in the lungs of air-breathing vertebrates that form the terminus of the bronchioles. The site of gas exchange.

M The act of breathing in or filling the lungs with air.

TEST

4. (a) What type of blood vessel transports blood away from the heart? _____

(b) What type of blood vessel transports blood to the heart? _____

(c) What type of blood vessel enables exchanges between the blood and tissues? _____

5. (a) What is the name given to the contraction phase of the cardiac cycle? _____

(b) What is the name given to the relaxation phase of the cardiac cycle? _____

6. (a) What does the image (right) show: _____

(b) Circle the QRS complex.

(c) Circle the region corresponding to lowest ventricular pressure.

(d) Ventricular volume at this time is increasing/decreasing (delete one)

7. (a) What is the name given to the loss of water vapour from plant leaves and stems? _____

(b) What plant tissue is involved in this process? _____

(c) Is this tissue alive or dead? _____

(d) Does this process require energy? _____

8. (a) What does the image (right) show: _____

(b) In what tissue would you find it? _____

(c) Is this tissue alive or dead? _____

(d) What transport process is it associated with? _____

(e) What is being moved in this process? _____

9. Test your vocabulary by matching each term to its definition, as identified by its preceding letter code.

artery _____

atrium _____

blood _____

capillary _____

cardiac cycle _____

cohesion-tension hypothesis _____

heart _____

phloem _____

sink _____

source _____

vein _____

ventricle _____

xylem _____

A   Vascular tissue that conducts water and mineral salts from the roots to the rest of the plant. Dead in its functional state.

B   The sequence of events of a heartbeat, and involves three main stages: atrial systole, ventricular systole and complete cardiac diastole.

C   Circulatory fluid comprising numerous cell types, which transports respiratory gases, nutrients, and wastes.

D   Chamber of the heart that pumps blood into the arteries.

E   The smallest type of blood vessel, comprising only an endothelial layer, across which substances exchange between the blood and tissue fluid.

F   Muscular organ used to pump blood around the body

G   Tissue that conducts dissolved sugars in vascular plants. Comprises mostly sieve tubes and companion cells.

H   A plant organ where sugar is stored or used.

I   A plant organ where sugar is made or mobilised.

J   Chamber of the heart that receives blood from the body or lungs.

K   A large, thick-walled blood vessel that carries blood away from the heart.

L   Large blood vessel that returns blood to the heart.

M   The proposed mechanism for movement of water in the transpiration stream.

© 2015 BIOZONE International
ISBN: 978-1-927309-19-3
Photocopying Prohibited

Topic 4

Genetic information, variation, and relationships between organisms

4.1 DNA, genes, and chromosomes
Learning outcomes

Activity number

☐ 1 Describe the nature of the prokaryotic chromosome. — 169

☐ 2 Describe the structure and organisation of eukaryotic chromosomes, including the role of histone proteins in packaging DNA. — 170

☐ 3 Recognise that the mitochondria and chloroplasts of eukaryotic cells contain prokaryotic-like DNA and comment on the significance of this. — 170

☐ 4 Explain the terms gene and locus. Explain how a gene determines the sequence of amino acids in a polypeptide. Distinguish between exons and introns. — 170

☐ 5 Explain the features of the genetic code, including: — 172
  - The 4-letter alphabet and the 3-letter triplet code (codon) of base sequences.
  - The non-overlapping, linear nature of the code, which is read from start to finish in one direction. The specific punctuation codons and their significance.
  - The universal nature and degeneracy of the code.

4.2 DNA and protein synthesis
Learning outcomes

Activity number

☐ 6 Distinguish between the genome and the proteome. — 171

☐ 7 Recall the structure and roles of mRNA and tRNA. — 54

☐ 8 Describe transcription, including the role of RNA polymerase and the significance of the coding and template strands. Contrast transcription in prokaryotes and eukaryotes. Explain how and why the pre-mRNA is edited in eukaryotes. — 174 175

☐ 9 Describe translation (protein synthesis), including the role of tRNA, anticodons, and ATP, and the general structure and role of ribosomes. — 176 177

☐ 10 Use the genetic code to determine the amino acids encoded by different codons. — 172

☐ 11 Interpret data from experimental work investigating the role of nucleic acids. — 173

4.3 Sources of genetic diversity
Learning outcomes

Activity number

☐ 12 Explain what is meant by a gene mutation and recognise base deletions and base substitutions. Describe causes of gene mutations and explain the significance of code degeneracy. — 178

☐ 13 Explain what is meant by a and describe how they can arise as a result of non-disjunction during meiosis. — 183

☐ 14 Using a diagram, describe meiosis and its outcome, including the significance of crossing over and independent assortment. Contrast mitosis and meiosis. — 179 -182

☐ 15 Explain how the events in meiosis and sexual reproduction increase genetic variation within a species. — 179

☐ 16 Recognise the role of meiosis in the life cycles of different types of organisms. — 184

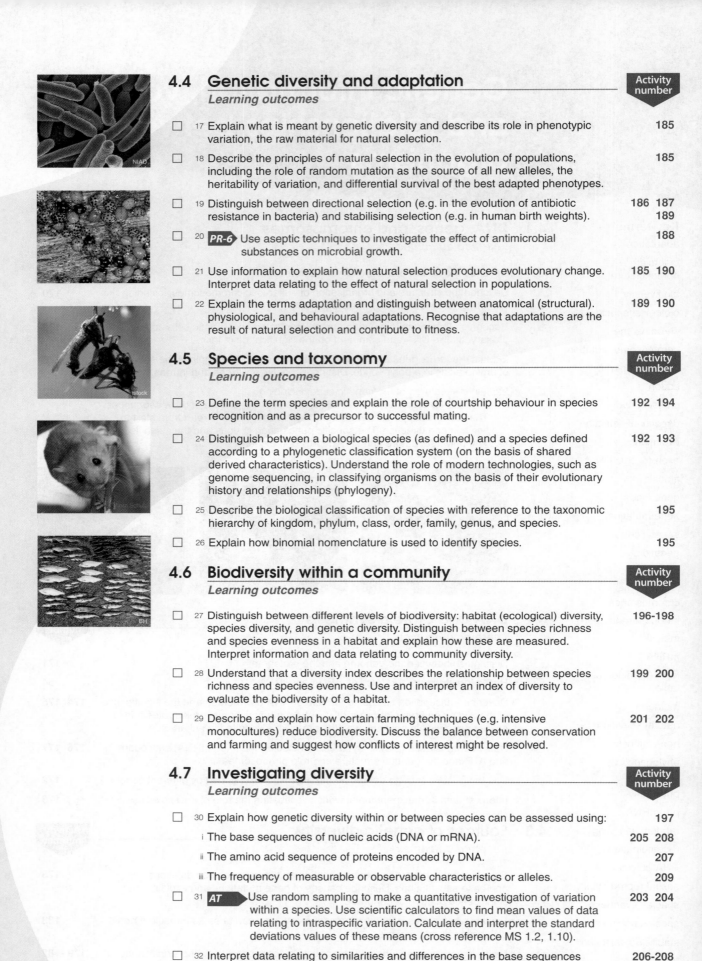

4.4 Genetic diversity and adaptation

Learning outcomes

Activity number

☐ 17 Explain what is meant by genetic diversity and describe its role in phenotypic variation, the raw material for natural selection.

185

☐ 18 Describe the principles of natural selection in the evolution of populations, including the role of random mutation as the source of all new alleles, the heritability of variation, and differential survival of the best adapted phenotypes.

185

☐ 19 Distinguish between directional selection (e.g. in the evolution of antibiotic resistance in bacteria) and stabilising selection (e.g. in human birth weights).

186 187
189

☐ 20 **PR-6** Use aseptic techniques to investigate the effect of antimicrobial substances on microbial growth.

188

☐ 21 Use information to explain how natural selection produces evolutionary change. Interpret data relating to the effect of natural selection in populations.

185 190

☐ 22 Explain the terms adaptation and distinguish between anatomical (structural). physiological, and behavioural adaptations. Recognise that adaptations are the result of natural selection and contribute to fitness.

189 190

4.5 Species and taxonomy

Learning outcomes

Activity number

☐ 23 Define the term species and explain the role of courtship behaviour in species recognition and as a precursor to successful mating.

192 194

☐ 24 Distinguish between a biological species (as defined) and a species defined according to a phylogenetic classification system (on the basis of shared derived characteristics). Understand the role of modern technologies, such as genome sequencing, in classifying organisms on the basis of their evolutionary history and relationships (phylogeny).

192 193

☐ 25 Describe the biological classification of species with reference to the taxonomic hierarchy of kingdom, phylum, class, order, family, genus, and species.

195

☐ 26 Explain how binomial nomenclature is used to identify species.

195

4.6 Biodiversity within a community

Learning outcomes

Activity number

☐ 27 Distinguish between different levels of biodiversity: habitat (ecological) diversity, species diversity, and genetic diversity. Distinguish between species richness and species evenness in a habitat and explain how these are measured. Interpret information and data relating to community diversity.

196-198

☐ 28 Understand that a diversity index describes the relationship between species richness and species evenness. Use and interpret an index of diversity to evaluate the biodiversity of a habitat.

199 200

☐ 29 Describe and explain how certain farming techniques (e.g. intensive monocultures) reduce biodiversity. Discuss the balance between conservation and farming and suggest how conflicts of interest might be resolved.

201 202

4.7 Investigating diversity

Learning outcomes

Activity number

☐ 30 Explain how genetic diversity within or between species can be assessed using:

197

i The base sequences of nucleic acids (DNA or mRNA).

205 208

ii The amino acid sequence of proteins encoded by DNA.

207

iii The frequency of measurable or observable characteristics or alleles.

209

☐ 31 **AT** Use random sampling to make a quantitative investigation of variation within a species. Use scientific calculators to find mean values of data relating to intraspecific variation. Calculate and interpret the standard deviations values of these means (cross reference MS 1.2, 1.10).

203 204

☐ 32 Interpret data relating to similarities and differences in the base sequences of DNA and in the amino acid sequences of proteins to suggest relationships between individuals in a species and between species.

206-208

☐ 33 Explain how gene technology has changed the way genetic diversity is investigated by allowing direct comparisons of DNA sequences.

208 209

169 Prokaryotic Chromosomes

Key Idea: Prokaryote DNA is packaged as one single chromosome that is not associated with protein.

DNA is a universal carrier of genetic information but it is packaged differently in prokaryotic and eukaryotic cells. Unlike eukaryotic chromosomes, the prokaryotic chromosome is not enclosed in a nuclear membrane and is not associated with protein. It is a single circular (rather than linear) molecule of double stranded DNA, attached to the plasma membrane and located in a nucleoid region, which is in direct contact with the cytoplasm. As well as the bacterial chromosome, bacteria often contain small circular, double-stranded DNA molecules called plasmids. Plasmids are independent of the main bacterial chromosome and usually contain 5-100 genes that are not crucial to cell survival under normal conditions.

The prokaryotic chromosome and plasmid DNA

The single circular chromosome is attached to the plasma membrane and not complexed with proteins as in eukaryotes. Proteins associated with the plasma membrane are responsible for DNA replication and segregating the new chromosome to a daughter cell in cell division.

Plasmids (small circular auxiliary DNA strands) occur in the cytoplasm. Plasmids replicate independently of the main chromosome and can move between cells by **conjugation**.

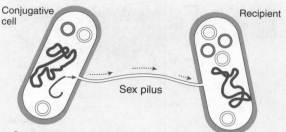

Sex pilus

Conjugation in bacteria
Special conjugative plasmids contain transfer genes, which enable **conjugation** and the transfer of genetic information between bacterial cells. The transfer occurs via special sex pili, which form a bridge-like structure between the donor and the recipient.

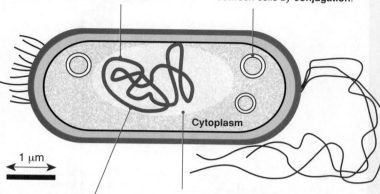

Cytoplasm

1 μm

Most bacteria have a single, circular chromosome. This makes them haploid for most genes, unless copies are located on extra-chromosomal plasmids.

The chromosomal DNA is located in a **nucleoid region** (pale area in this image). It is not enclosed in a membrane. In actively growing cells, the nucleoid may take up as much as 20% of the cell's volume.

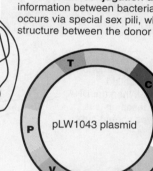

pLW1043 plasmid

Genes for
C Conjugative ability
T Trimethoprim resistance
V Vancomycin resistance
D Disinfectant resistance
S Streptomycin resistance
P Penicillin resistance

One gene-one protein?

In contrast to eukaryotes, prokaryotic DNA consists almost entirely of protein coding genes and their regulatory sequences. It was the study of prokaryotic genomes that gave rise to the one gene-one protein hypothesis, which still largely holds true for bacteria.

Plasmids often carry genes that encode beneficial traits, including antibiotic resistance and the ability to use new substrates. The ability of bacteria to exchange plasmids carrying beneficial extrachromosomal genes has contributed to the spread of antibiotic resistance. The pLW1043 plasmid (above) from the superbug *Staphylococcus aureus* (MRSA) carries several genes for antibiotic resistance, acquired progressively over time.

1. Describe three important ways in which prokaryote and eukaryote chromosomes differ:

(a) _____

_____

(b) _____

_____

(c) _____

_____

2. Explain the consequences to protein synthesis of the prokaryotic chromosome being free in the cytoplasm:

_____

_____

3. Most of the bacterial genome comprises protein coding genes and their regulatory sequences. What is the consequence of this to the relative sizes of bacterial and eukaryotic genomes:

_____

_____

© 2015 **BIOZONE** International
ISBN: 978-1-927309-19-3
Photocopying Prohibited

LINK   LINK   WEB

187 **69** **169** **KNOW**

170 Eukaryotic Chromosome Structure

Key Idea: Eukaryotic DNA is located in the cell nucleus. A DNA molecule is very long. It must be wound up to fit into the cell's nucleus.
Eukaryotes package their DNA as discrete linear chromosomes. The number of chromosomes varies from species to species. The way the DNA is packaged changes during the life cycle of the cell, but classic chromosome structures (below) appear during metaphase of mitosis.

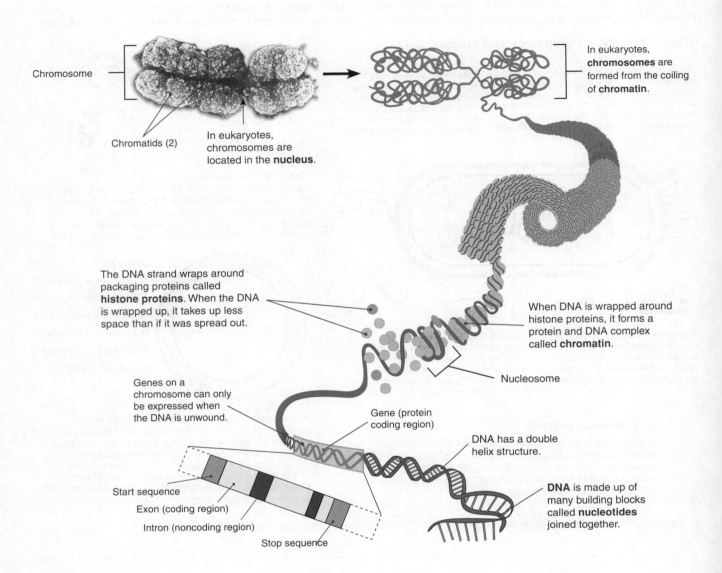

Chromosome

Chromatids (2)

In eukaryotes, chromosomes are located in the **nucleus**.

In eukaryotes, **chromosomes** are formed from the coiling of **chromatin**.

The DNA strand wraps around packaging proteins called **histone proteins**. When the DNA is wrapped up, it takes up less space than if it was spread out.

When DNA is wrapped around histone proteins, it forms a protein and DNA complex called **chromatin**.

Nucleosome

Genes on a chromosome can only be expressed when the DNA is unwound.

Gene (protein coding region)

DNA has a double helix structure.

Start sequence

Exon (coding region)

Intron (noncoding region)

Stop sequence

DNA is made up of many building blocks called **nucleotides** joined together.

Non-coding regions

Only about 2% of the DNA in humans codes for proteins. Much of the rest codes for RNA (e.g. tRNA) or has a regulatory function, e.g. the centromere or telomeres. In general, the genomes of more complex organisms contain much more of this so-called "non protein-coding" DNA. Even within protein coding sequences, parts of the DNA are excised from the primary transcript to create the mRNA that codes for the protein to be translated.

Exons and introns

Most protein-coding genes in eukaryotic DNA are not continuous. The protein-coding regions (**exons**) are interrupted by non-protein-coding regions called **introns**. Introns are edited out of the protein-coding sequence prior to translation (protein synthesis). After processing, the introns may go on to serve a regulatory function.

To help you remember, **ex**ons are **ex**pressed, and **in**trons are **in**-between the protein-coding regions.

The bladderwort, *Utricularia gibba*, has just 3% non-coding DNA.

98% of the DNA in humans is non-coding DNA.

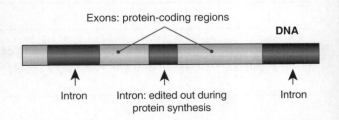

Exons: protein-coding regions

DNA

Intron

Intron: edited out during protein synthesis

Intron

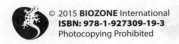

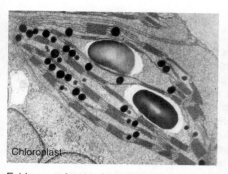
Chloroplast

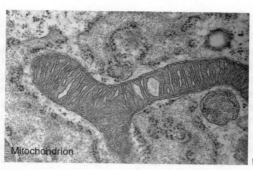
Mitochondrion

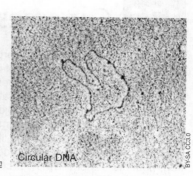
Circular DNA

Evidence points to chloroplasts and mitochondria being prokaryotic in origin, acquired when a pre-eukaryotic cell engulfed another prokaryote, to form a mutually beneficial endosymbiosis. In the case of mitochondria, the cell type was probably a purple bacterium capable of generating ATP using an electron transport system. In the case of chloroplasts, the likely endosymbiont was a photosynthetic cyanobacterium. Evidence includes the fact that both chloroplasts and mitochondria contain their own DNA, separate from the nuclear DNA of the cell. Chloroplast DNA is between 120 000 - 150 000 bp long, while mitochondrial DNA can vary between species from about 15 000 bp to 2.5 million bp.

The DNA of mitochondria and chloroplasts is circular (not linear as in the nucleus) and is replicated independently of the nuclear DNA. As in prokaryotes, it is not associated with proteins. Each mitochondrion contains ~2–10 mtDNA copies.

1. Where is the DNA located in eukaryotes? _____

2. Why does DNA need to be packaged up to fit inside a cell nucleus? _____
   _____

3. How do histone proteins help in the coiling of DNA? _____
   _____
   _____
   _____

4. Explain the significance of the following terms used to describe the structure of chromosomes:

   (a) DNA: _____
   _____

   (b) Chromatin: _____
   _____

   (c) Nucleosome: _____
   _____

   (d) Chromatid: _____
   _____

5. What is the difference between an exon and an intron? _____
   _____
   _____
   _____

6. Describe three lines of evidence supporting a prokaryotic origin for mitochondria and chloroplasts: _____
   _____
   _____
   _____
   _____
   _____
   _____

171 Genomes

Key Idea: The genome is an organism's complete set of genetic material, including all of its genes. The proteome is the full range of proteins expressed by the genome at a certain time. Both show wide variation between species.

The aim of most genome projects is to determine the DNA sequence of the organism's entire genome. Many different species have now had their genomes sequenced including the honeybee, nematode worm, African clawed frog, pufferfish, zebra fish, rice, cow, dog, and rat. Genome sizes and the number of genes per genome vary, and are not necessarily correlated with the size and structural complexity of the organism. Once completed, genome sequences are analysed by computer to identify genes. Finding the total number of proteins in a genome is more difficult, as many genes can produce more than one variation of mRNA. One way of estimating the number of proteins is to identify the different mRNAs in a cell. The activity below provides information on genome size and the number of known proteins produced by the organism. This is most likely less than the possible number of polypeptides produced.

*Mb = megabase pairs or 1,000,000 bp

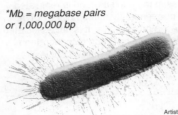

Artist's impression

Bacterium
(*Escherichia coli*)

Genome size: 4.6 Mb*
Number of genes: 4403
Number of proteins (proteome): 4595

E. coli has been used as a laboratory organism for over 70 years. Various strains of *E. coli* are responsible for several human diseases.

Yeast
(*Saccharomyces cerevisiae*)

Genome size: 13 Mb
Number of genes: 6000
Number of proteins: 6718

The first eukaryotic genome to be completely sequenced. Yeast is used as a model organism to study human cancer.

Human
(*Homo sapiens*)

Genome size: 3000 Mb
Number of genes: < 22 500
Number of proteins: 72 233

The completion of the human genome has allowed advances in medical research, especially in cancer research.

Rice
(*Oryza sativa*)

Genome size: 466 Mb (indica) and 420 Mb (japonica)
Number of genes: 46 000
Number of proteins: 63 167

A food staple for much of the world's population. The importance of rice as a world food crop made sequencing it a high priority.

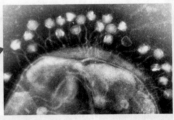

Mouse
(*Mus musculus*)

Genome size: 2500 Mb
Number of genes: 30 000
Number of proteins: 45 188

New drugs destined for human use are often tested on mice because more than 90% of their proteins show similarities to human proteins.

Fruit fly
(*Drosophila melanogaster*)

Genome size: 150 Mb
Number of genes: 14 000
Number of proteins: 20 049

Drosophila has been used extensively for genetic studies for many years. About 50% of all fly proteins show similarities to mammalian proteins.

Japanese canopy plant
(*Paris japonica*)

Genome size: 149 000 Mb
Number of proteins: Unknown

This rare native Japanese plant has the largest genome sequenced so far (15% larger than any previous estimate for a eukaryote). Plants with very large genomes reproduce and grow slowly.

T2 phage

Genome size: 160 000 bp
Number of genes: Approx. 300
Number of proteins: Approx 300

T2 phage is one of a group of related T-even phages that infect bacteria. Analysis of these phages indicates a small core genome with variations being the result of genetic transfers during evolution.

1. For each organism below, calculate how much smaller or larger the genome is than the human genome:

   (a) Japanese canopy plant: _____

   (b) *E. coli*: _____

   (c) T2 phage: _____

2. Plants with very large genome sizes are at higher risk of extinction. Can you suggest why? _____

   _____

WEB   LINK

KNOW 171 205

© 2015 **BIOZONE** International
ISBN: 978-1-927309-19-3
Photocopying Prohibited

172 The Genetic Code

Key Idea: The genetic code is the set of rules by which the genetic information in DNA or mRNA is translated into proteins. The genetic information for the assembly of amino acids is stored as three-base sequence. These three letter codes on mRNA are called **codons**. Each codon represents one of 20 amino acids used to make proteins. The code is effectively universal, being the same in all living things (with a few minor exceptions). The genetic code is summarised in a mRNA-amino acid table, which identifies the amino acid encoded by each mRNA codon. The code is **degenerate**, meaning there may be more than one codon for each amino acid. Most of this degeneracy is in the third nucleotide of a codon.

Amino acid		Codons that code for this amino acid	No.	Amino acid		Codons that code for this amino acid	No.
Ala	Alanine	GCU, GCC, GCA, GCG	4	**Leu**	Leucine		
Arg	Arginine			**Lys**	Lysine		
Asn	Asparagine			**Met**	Methionine		
Asp	Aspartic acid			**Phe**	Phenylalanine		
Cys	Cysteine			**Pro**	Proline		
Gln	Glutamine			**Ser**	Serine		
Glu	Glutamic acid			**Thr**	Threonine		
Gly	Glycine			**Trp**	Tryptophan		
His	Histidine			**Tyr**	Tyrosine		
Ile	Isoleucine			**Val**	Valine		

1. Use the **mRNA-amino acid table** (below) to list in the table above all the **codons** that code for each of the amino acids and the number of different codons that can code for each amino acid (the first amino acid has been done for you).

2. (a) How many amino acids could be coded for if a codon consisted of just two bases?_____

   (b) Why is this number of bases inadequate to code for the 20 amino acids required to make proteins?

   _____

   _____

3. Describe the consequence of the degeneracy of the genetic code to the likely effect of a change to one base in a triplet:

   _____

   _____

mRNA-amino acid table

How to read the table: The table on the right is used to 'decode' the genetic code as a sequence of amino acids in a polypeptide chain, from a given mRNA sequence. To work out which amino acid is coded for by a codon (triplet of bases) look for the first letter of the codon in the row label on the left hand side. Then look for the column that intersects the same row from above that matches the second base. Finally, locate the third base in the codon by looking along the row from the right hand end that matches your codon.

Example: Determine **CAG**

C on the left row,
A on the top column,
G on the right row
CAG is Gln (**glutamine**)

Read second letter here
Read first letter here
Read third letter here

Second letter

First letter		U	C	A	G	Third letter
U		UUU Phe	UCU Ser	UAU Tyr	UGU Cys	U
		UUC Phe	UCC Ser	UAC Tyr	UGC Cys	C
		UUA Leu	UCA Ser	UAA STOP	UGA STOP	A
		UUG Leu	UCG Ser	UAG STOP	UGG Trp	G
C		CUU Leu	CCU Pro	CAU His	CGU Arg	U
		CUC Leu	CCC Pro	CAC His	CGC Arg	C
		CUA Leu	CCA Pro	CAA Gln	CGA Arg	A
		CUG Leu	CCG Pro	CAG Gln	CGG Arg	G
A		AUU Ile	ACU Thr	AAU Asn	AGU Ser	U
		AUC Ile	ACC Thr	AAC Asn	AGC Ser	C
		AUA Ile	ACA Thr	AAA Lys	AGA Arg	A
		AUG Met	ACG Thr	AAG Lys	AGG Arg	G
G		GUU Val	GCU Ala	GAU Asp	GGU Gly	U
		GUC Val	GCC Ala	GAC Asp	GGC Gly	C
		GUA Val	GCA Ala	GAA Glu	GGA Gly	A
		GUG Val	GCG Ala	GAG Glu	GGG Gly	G

© 2015 **BIOZONE** International
ISBN: 978-1-927309-19-3
Photocopying Prohibited

173 DNA Carries the Code

Key Idea: A series of experiments in the 1940s and 1950s confirmed that it was DNA that carried the genetic information.

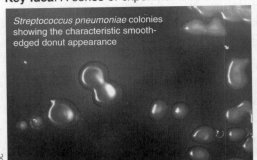

Streptococcus pneumoniae colonies showing the characteristic smooth-edged donut appearance

Scientists had known about DNA since the end of the 19th century, but its role in storing information remained unknown until the 1940s, and its structure remained a mystery for another decade after that. In 1928, experiments by British scientist Frederick Griffith gave the first indications that DNA was responsible for passing on information. Griffith had been working with two strains of the bacteria *Streptococcus pneumoniae*. Only one strain (the pathogenic strain) caused pneumonia and it was easily identified because it formed colonies with smooth edges. The other, benign strain formed colonies with rough edges. When mice were injected with the pathogenic strain they developed pneumonia and died. The mice injected with the benign strain did not. Mice injected with the heat-killed pathogenic strain did not develop pneumonia either. This showed that the disease was not caused by a chemical associated with the bacteria, or a response by the body to the bacteria, it was the bacterial cells themselves. In a second experiment, Griffith mixed the benign strain with the heat-killed pathogenic strain and injected it into healthy mice. To his surprise, the mice developed pneumonia. When bacteria from the mice were recovered and cultured they produced colonies identical to the pathogenic strain. Somehow the harmless bacteria had acquired information from the dead pathogenic strain. Griffith called this process **transformation**.

In 1944, American scientists, led by Oswald Avery, continued with Griffith's experiments. They made an extract from the heat-killed pathogenic strain and treated it with chemicals to destroy any lipids, carbohydrates, or proteins. This was mixed with the benign strain and transformation still occurred. This established that no proteins, lipids, or carbohydrates were responsible for the transformation. When another identical extract was treated with chemicals that break down DNA, the transformation did not take place - the benign strain failed to acquire the information required to cause pneumonia. From this it was deduced that DNA was the unit that was carrying the information from one bacteria to another.

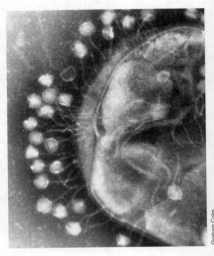

Another experiment in 1952 by Alfred Hershey and Martha Chase, confirmed what the other two experiments had shown. Hershey and Chase worked with viruses, which were known to have DNA and to transfer information to their host. However, there was debate over whether the information was transferred by the DNA or by the protein coat of the virus. Hershey and Chase used radioactive sulfur and radioactive phosphorus to mark different parts of the virus. The sulfur was incorporated into the protein coat while the phosphorus was incorporated into the viral DNA. The viruses were then mixed with bacteria and the infected bacteria analysed. The bacteria were found to contain radioactive phosphorus but not radioactive sulfur, showing that the virus had indeed passed information to its host by injecting its own DNA.

1. How did Griffith confirm that it was the bacteria causing the pneumonia and not something else?

_____

_____

_____

2. Why were sulfur and phosphorus used in Hershey's experiment? _____

_____

_____

_____

3. Why is it important to conduct two different experiments (e.g. Avery's and Hershey's) when investigating a hypothesis?

_____

_____

_____

_____

© 2015 **BIOZONE** International
ISBN: 978-1-927309-19-3
Photocopying Prohibited

174 Genes to Proteins

Key Idea: Genes are sections of DNA that code for proteins. Genes are expressed when they are transcribed into messenger RNA (mRNA) and then translated into a protein. **Gene expression** is the process of rewriting a gene into a protein. It involves **transcription** of the DNA into mRNA and **translation** of the mRNA into protein. A gene is bounded by a start (promoter) region, upstream of the gene, and a

terminator region, downstream of the gene. These regions control transcription by telling RNA polymerase where to start and stop transcription of the gene. The information flow for gene to protein is shown below. Nucleotides are read in groups of three called triplets. The equivalent on the mRNA molecule is the codon. Some codons have special control functions (start and stop) in the making of a protein.

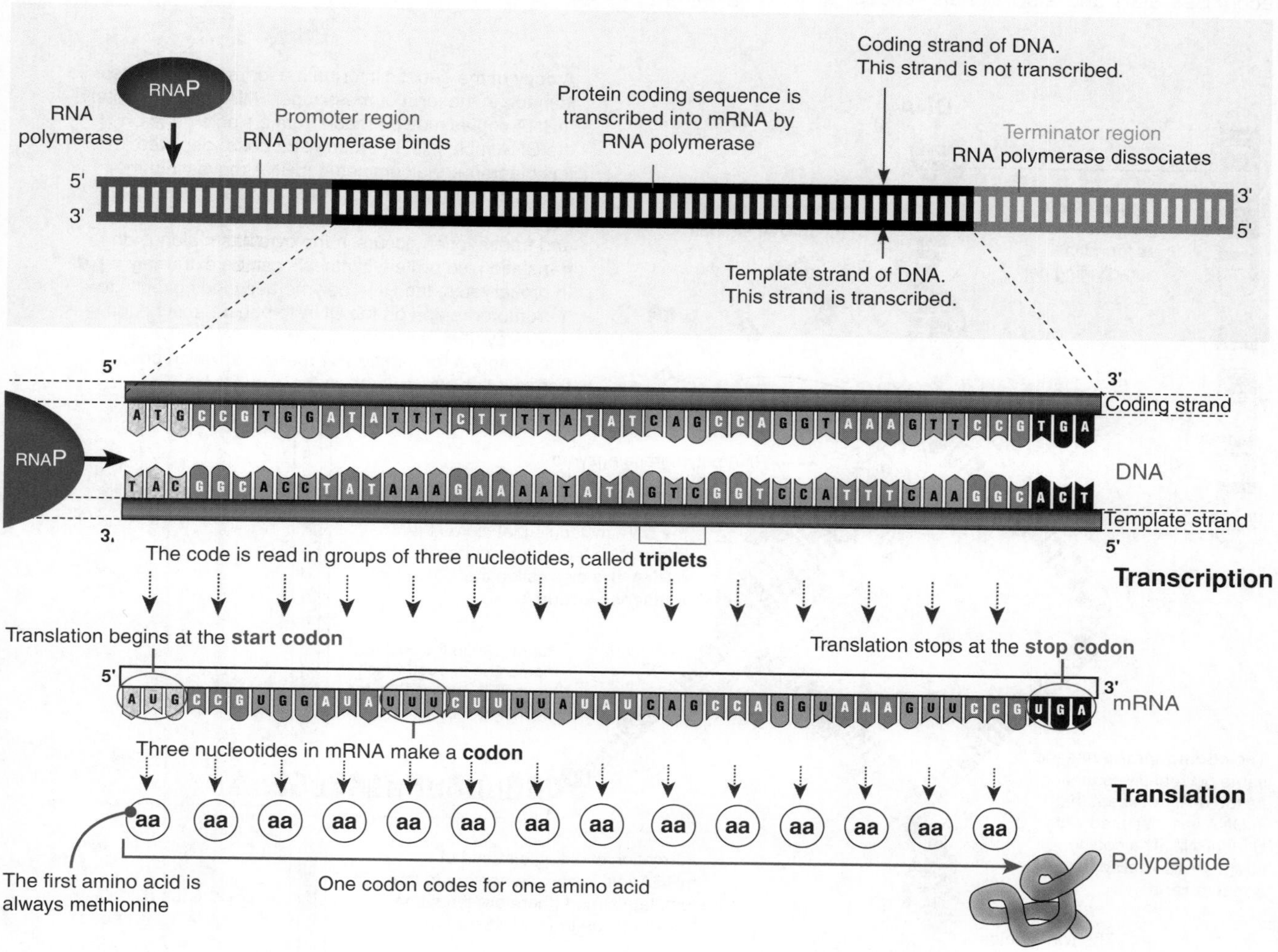

1. (a) The three base code on DNA is called: _____

   (b) The three base code on mRNA is called: _____

2. (a) What is a **gene**? _____

   _____

   (b) What molecule transcribes the gene? _____

   (c) What is the role of the promoter and terminator regions? _____

   _____

3. What does the term **gene expression** mean? _____

   _____

4. Recall the anti-parallel nature of DNA, with the strands orientated in opposite directions. Explain its significance:

   _____

   _____

175 Transcription

Key Idea: Transcription is the first step of gene expression. A segment of DNA is transcribed (rewritten) into mRNA. In eukaryotes, transcription takes place in the nucleus.

The enzyme that directly controls transcription is RNA polymerase, which makes a strand of mRNA using the single strand of DNA (the **template strand**) as a template. The enzyme transcribes a gene length of DNA at a time and recognises start and stop signals (codes) at the beginning and end of the gene. Only RNA polymerase is involved in mRNA synthesis as it unwinds the DNA as well. It is common to find several RNA polymerase enzyme molecules on the same gene at any one time, allowing a high rate of mRNA synthesis to occur. In eukaryotes, non-coding sections called **introns** must first be removed and the remaining **exons** spliced together to form mature mRNA before the mRNA can be translated into a protein.

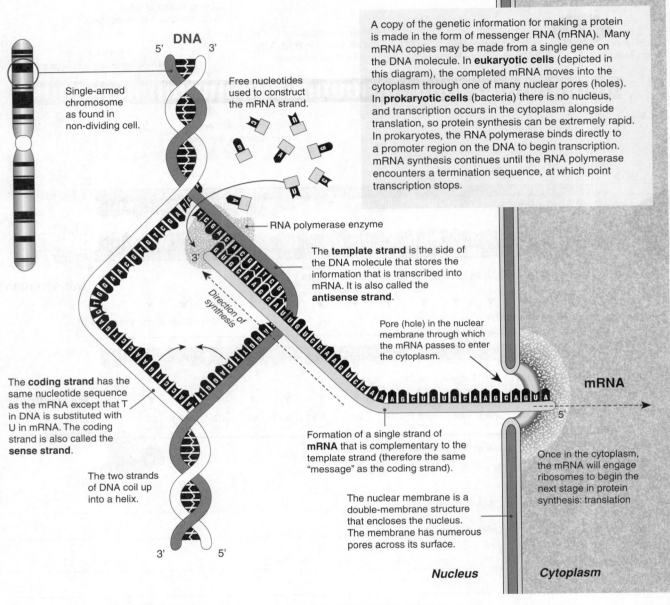

DNA

Single-armed chromosome as found in non-dividing cell.

Free nucleotides used to construct the mRNA strand.

A copy of the genetic information for making a protein is made in the form of messenger RNA (mRNA). Many mRNA copies may be made from a single gene on the DNA molecule. **In eukaryotic cells** (depicted in this diagram), the completed mRNA moves into the cytoplasm through one of many nuclear pores (holes). **In prokaryotic cells** (bacteria) there is no nucleus, and transcription occurs in the cytoplasm alongside translation, so protein synthesis can be extremely rapid. In prokaryotes, the RNA polymerase binds directly to a promoter region on the DNA to begin transcription. mRNA synthesis continues until the RNA polymerase encounters a termination sequence, at which point transcription stops.

RNA polymerase enzyme

The **template strand** is the side of the DNA molecule that stores the information that is transcribed into mRNA. It is also called the **antisense strand**.

Direction of synthesis

The **coding strand** has the same nucleotide sequence as the mRNA except that T in DNA is substituted with U in mRNA. The coding strand is also called the **sense strand**.

The two strands of DNA coil up into a helix.

Pore (hole) in the nuclear membrane through which the mRNA passes to enter the cytoplasm.

mRNA

Formation of a single strand of **mRNA** that is complementary to the template strand (therefore the same "message" as the coding strand).

The nuclear membrane is a double-membrane structure that encloses the nucleus. The membrane has numerous pores across its surface.

Once in the cytoplasm, the mRNA will engage ribosomes to begin the next stage in protein synthesis: translation

Nucleus

Cytoplasm

A lampbrush chromosome. Lampbrush chromosomes form in immature egg cells (oocytes) when a large amount of transcription is taking place.

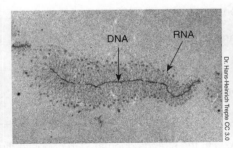

Dr. Hans-Heinrich Trepte CC 3.0

The image above shows ribosomal RNA molecules being transcribed from a short piece of DNA. The DNA can be seen as the dark line in the centre.

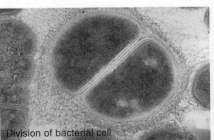

Division of bacterial cell

Because prokaryotic DNA is in contact with the cytoplasm transcription and translation can occur simultaneously.

WEB 175   LINK 170   LINK 174

KNOW

Splicing mRNA in eukaryotes

1 Double stranded DNA of a gene from a eukaryotic organism (e.g. human) containing introns.

DNA   *Intron*   *Intron*   *Intron*   *Intron*   *Intron*

} Double stranded molecule of genomic DNA

Exon   *Exon Exon*   *Exon*   *Exon*   *Exon*

Transcription

2 As a normal part of the cell process of gene expression, transcription creates a **primary RNA** molecule.

Primary RNA

Introns are removed → **Introns**

3 The introns are removed by enzymes to form a mature mRNA (now excluding the introns) that codes for the making of a single protein.

Exons are joined together ↓

mature mRNA

1. Identify three differences between transcription in eukaryotes and prokaryotes:

   (a) _____

   (b) _____

   (c) _____

2. Explain why gene expression in prokaryotes can occur many times faster than in a eukaryote: _____

   _____

   _____

3. Which strand of DNA is transcribed into mRNA? _____

4. The mRNA is complementary to the DNA strand in question 2 above. What does complementary mean in this case?

   _____

   _____

   _____

5. Explain the role of messenger RNA (mRNA) in protein synthesis: _____

   _____

   _____

6. The genetic code contains punctuation codons to mark the starting and finishing points of the code for synthesis of polypeptide chains and proteins. Consult the mRNA–amino acid table earlier in this workbook and state the codes for:

   (a) Start codon: (b) Stop (termination) codons:

7. For the following triplets on the DNA, determine the **codon** sequence for the mRNA that would be synthesised:

   (a) Triplets on the DNA: T A C   T A G   C C G   C G A   T T T

       Codons on the mRNA: _____

   (b) Triplets on the DNA: T A C   A A G   C C T   A T A   A A A

       Codons on the mRNA: _____

8. How is mature mRNA different from primary mRNA? _____

   _____

   _____

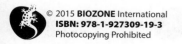

176 Translation

Key Idea: Translation is the second step of gene expression. It occurs in the cytoplasm, where ribosomes read the mRNA code and decode it to synthesise protein.

In eukaryotes, translation occurs in the cytoplasm associated with free ribosomes or ribosomes on the rough endoplasmic reticulum. The diagram below shows how a mRNA molecule can be 'serviced' by many ribosomes at the same time. The role of the tRNA molecules is to bring in the individual amino acids. The anticodon of each tRNA must make a perfect complementary match with the mRNA codon before the amino acid is released. Once released, the amino acid is added to the growing polypeptide chain by enzymes.

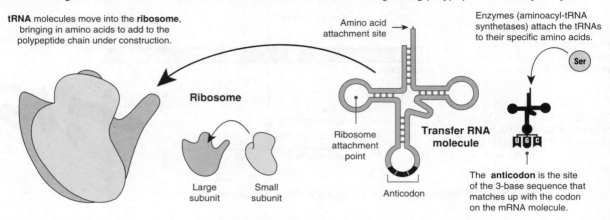

tRNA molecules move into the **ribosome**, bringing in amino acids to add to the polypeptide chain under construction.

Ribosome

Large subunit   Small subunit

Amino acid attachment site

Enzymes (aminoacyl-tRNA synthetases) attach the tRNAs to their specific amino acids.

Ser

Ribosome attachment point

Transfer RNA molecule

Anticodon

The **anticodon** is the site of the 3-base sequence that matches up with the codon on the mRNA molecule.

Ribosomes are made up of a complex of ribosomal RNA (rRNA) and proteins. They exist as two separate sub-units (above) until they are attracted to a binding site on the mRNA molecule, when they join together. Ribosomes have binding sites that attract transfer RNA (**tRNA**) molecules loaded with amino acids. The tRNA molecules are about 80 nucleotides in length and are made under the direction of genes in the chromosomes. There is a different tRNA molecule for each of the different possible anticodons (see the diagram below) and, because of the degeneracy of the genetic code, there may be up to six different tRNAs carrying the same amino acid.

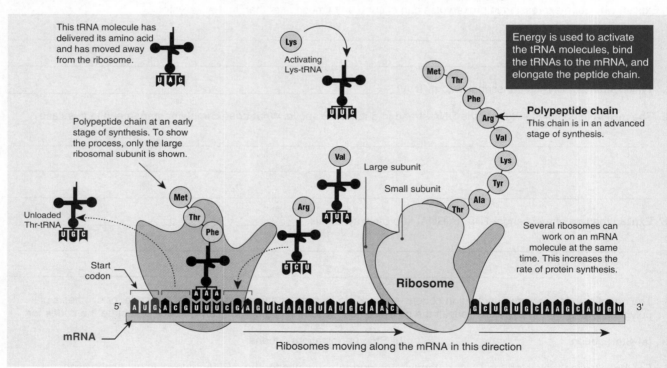

This tRNA molecule has delivered its amino acid and has moved away from the ribosome.

UAC

Lys

Activating Lys-tRNA

UUC

Energy is used to activate the tRNA molecules, bind the tRNAs to the mRNA, and elongate the peptide chain.

Met Thr Phe Arg

Polypeptide chain
This chain is in an advanced stage of synthesis.

Val Lys Tyr Ala Thr

Polypeptide chain at an early stage of synthesis. To show the process, only the large ribosomal subunit is shown.

Val

AUA

Large subunit

Small subunit

Unloaded Thr-tRNA

UGC

Met Thr Phe

Arg

GCU

Start codon

Ribosome

Several ribosomes can work on an mRNA molecule at the same time. This increases the rate of protein synthesis.

5′ AUGACGUUUCGAGUCAAGUAUGCAAC ... GCUGUGCAAGCAUGU 3′

mRNA

Ribosomes moving along the mRNA in this direction

1. For the following codons on the mRNA, determine the **anticodons** for each tRNA that would deliver the amino acids:

   Codons on the mRNA: U A C   U A G   C C G   C G A   U U U

   Anticodons on the tRNAs: _____

2. There are many different types of tRNA molecules, each with a different anticodon (HINT: see the mRNA table).

   (a) How many different tRNA types are there, each with a unique anticodon? _____

   (b) Explain your answer: _____

   _____

© 2015 **BIOZONE** International
ISBN: 978-1-927309-19-3
Photocopying Prohibited

177 Protein Synthesis Summary

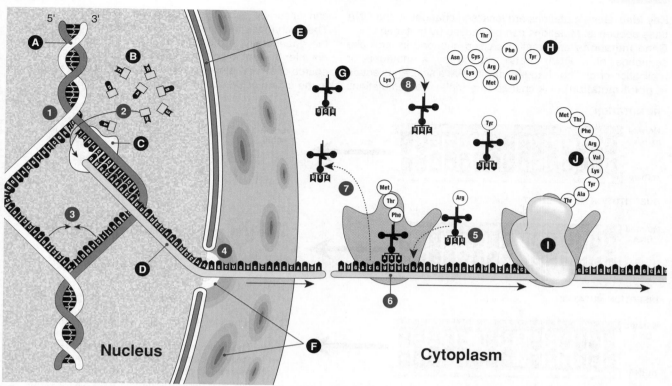

Nucleus

Cytoplasm

The diagram above shows an overview of the process of protein synthesis. It is a combination of the diagrams from the previous two pages. Each of the major steps in the process are numbered, while structures are labelled with letters.

1. Briefly describe each of the numbered processes in the diagram above:

   (a) Process 1: _____

   (b) Process 2: _____

   (c) Process 3: _____

   (d) Process 4: _____

   (e) Process 5: _____

   (f) Process 6: _____

   (g) Process 7: _____

   (h) Process 8: _____

2. Identify each of the structures marked with a letter and write their names below in the spaces provided:

   (a) Structure A: _____   (f) Structure F: _____

   (b) Structure B: _____   (g) Structure G: _____

   (c) Structure C: _____   (h) Structure H: _____

   (d) Structure D: _____   (i) Structure I: _____

   (e) Structure E: _____   (j) Structure J: _____

3. Describe two factors that would determine whether or not a particular protein is produced in the cell:

   (a) _____

   _____

   (b) _____

   _____

LINK   LINK   WEB
176 **175** **177** **TEST**

178 Gene Mutations and Mutagens

Key Idea: Gene mutations are localised changes to the DNA base sequence. Mutations can be caused by mutagens.

Gene mutations are small, localised changes in the base sequence of a DNA strand caused by a mutagen or replication error. The changes may involve a single nucleotide (a **point mutation**) or a change to a triplet. Point mutations can occur by substitution, insertion, or deletion of bases. These changes alter the mRNA transcribed but, because of the degeneracy in the genetic code, a point mutation may not alter the amino acid sequence. Mutations are the ultimate source of all new alleles, although those that cause a change in the amino acid sequence are usually harmful.

NO MUTATION

Normal DNA AAAATGCTTCTCCAA
mRNA UUUUACGAAGAGGUU

Amino acids: Phe — Tyr — Glu — Glu — Val

Amino acid sequence forms a normal polypeptide chain.

SUBSTITUTION MUTATION T instead of C

Mutated DNA AAAATGTTTCTCCAA
mRNA UUUUACAAAGAGGUU

Amino acids: Phe — Tyr — Lys — Glu — Val

Polypeptide chain with wrong amino acid.

INSERTION MUTATION Insertion of C

Mutated DNA AAAATGCCTTCTCCA
mRNA UUUUACGGAAGAGGU

Amino acids: Phe — Tyr — Gly — Arg — Gly

The insertion creates a large scale movement (called a **frame shift**) resulting in a completely new sequence of amino acids. The resulting protein is unlikely to have any biological activity.

DELETION MUTATION Deletion of C

Mutated DNA AAAATGTTCTCCAAG
mRNA UUUUACAAGAGGUUC

Amino acids: Phe — Tyr — Lys — Arg — Phe

Large scale movement resulting in a completely new sequence of amino acids. The resulting protein is unlikely to have any biological activity.

1. Explain what is meant by a **frame shift mutation**: _____

2. Some gene mutations are more disruptive to an organism than others.

   (a) Identify which type of gene mutations are the most damaging to an organism: _____

   (b) Explain why they are the most disruptive: _____

   (c) Describe what type of gene mutation is least likely to cause a change in protein structure and explain your answer:

3. In the following DNA sequence, replace the G of the **second codon** with an A to create a new mutant DNA, then determine the new mRNA sequence, and the amino acid sequence. Refer to the mRNA-amino acid table to identify the amino acids coded in each case.

   (a) Original DNA: AAA   AT[G]   TTT   CTC   CAA   GAT

   Mutated DNA: _____

   mRNA: _____

   Amino acids: _____

   (b) Identify the amino acid coded by codon 2 (ATG) in the original DNA: _____

   (c) Explain the effect of the mutation: _____

© 2015 **BIOZONE** International
ISBN: 978-1-927309-19-3
Photocopying Prohibited

Gametic and somatic mutations

Only mutations taking place in the cells that produce gametes are inherited. It is these mutations that are important in evolution as a source of new alleles (gene variants) upon which natural selection can act. If mutations occur in a body (somatic) cell after the organism has begun to develop beyond the zygote stage, they may give rise to a chimaera (an organism with a mix of genetically different cells).

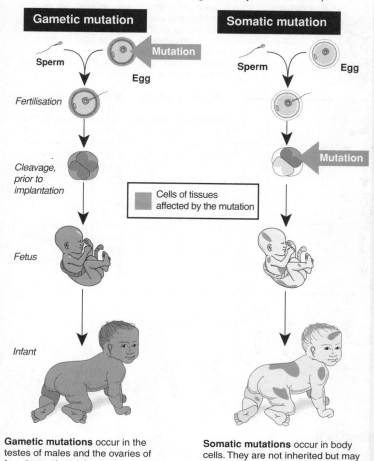

Gametic mutation

Sperm

Mutation

Egg

Fertilisation

Cleavage, prior to implantation

Cells of tissues affected by the mutation

Fetus

Infant

Somatic mutation

Sperm   Egg

Mutation

Gametic mutations occur in the testes of males and the ovaries of females and are inherited.

Somatic mutations occur in body cells. They are not inherited but may affect the person during their lifetime.

Mutagens

The natural rate of mutation in a gene is normally very low, but this rate can be increased by environmental factors such as ionising radiation and mutagenic chemicals (e.g. benzene). Any factor that causes or increases the rate of mutation is called a mutagen.

Ionising radiation

Ionising radiation includes γ - rays , X - rays, and ultraviolet radiation. The high energy radiation can disrupt bonds in the DNA causing breaks or incorrect bonding. Excessive exposure to ultraviolet radiation causes skin cancer.

Poisons and irritants

Many chemicals have mutagenic effects, resulting in various cancers. These are commonly called carcinogens and include tobacco tar, organic solvents, and dioxins. Dioxins are a common and highly toxic carcinogen.

Viruses

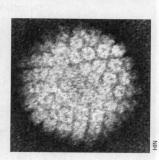

Some viruses integrate into the human chromosome, upsetting genes and triggering cancers. Examples include hepatitis B virus (liver cancer), HIV (Kaposi's sarcoma), and HPV (left) which is linked to cervical cancer.

4. Explain how **somatic mutations** differ from **gametic mutations** and comment on the significance of the difference:

_____

_____

_____

5. Describe examples of factors that induce mutations under the following headings:

(a) Radiation: _____

_____

_____

(b) Chemical agents: _____

_____

_____

6. Explain how **mutagens** cause mutations: _____

_____

_____

179 Meiosis

Key Idea: Meiosis is a special type of cell division. It produces sex cells (gametes) for the purpose of sexual reproduction. Meiosis involves a single chromosomal duplication followed by two successive nuclear divisions, and results in a halving of the diploid chromosome number. Meiosis occurs in the sex organs of plants and animals. If genetic mistakes (**gene** and **chromosome mutations**) occur here, they will be passed on to the offspring (they will be inherited).

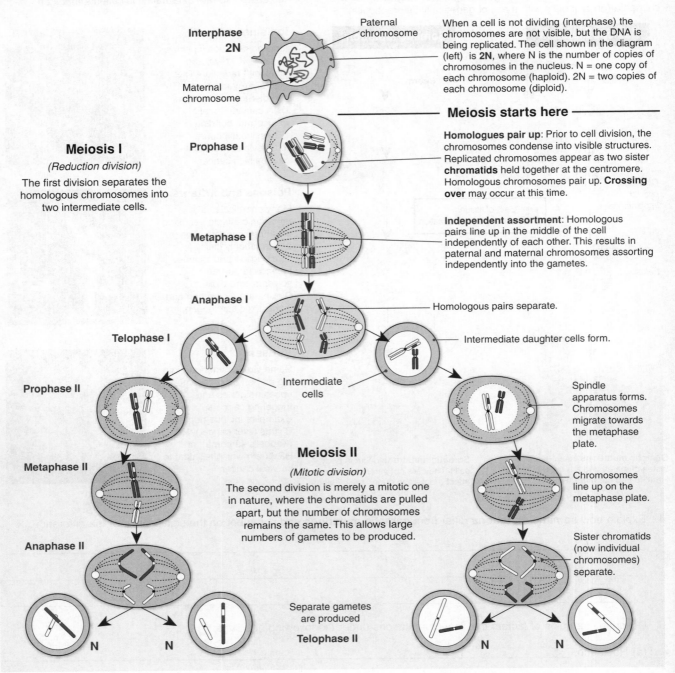

Interphase 2N

Paternal chromosome

Maternal chromosome

When a cell is not dividing (interphase) the chromosomes are not visible, but the DNA is being replicated. The cell shown in the diagram (left) is **2N**, where N is the number of copies of chromosomes in the nucleus. N = one copy of each chromosome (haploid). 2N = two copies of each chromosome (diploid).

—— **Meiosis starts here** ——

Meiosis I

(Reduction division)

The first division separates the homologous chromosomes into two intermediate cells.

Prophase I

Homologues pair up: Prior to cell division, the chromosomes condense into visible structures. Replicated chromosomes appear as two sister **chromatids** held together at the centromere. Homologous chromosomes pair up. **Crossing over** may occur at this time.

Metaphase I

Independent assortment: Homologous pairs line up in the middle of the cell independently of each other. This results in paternal and maternal chromosomes assorting independently into the gametes.

Anaphase I — Homologous pairs separate.

Telophase I

— Intermediate daughter cells form.

Intermediate cells

Prophase II

Spindle apparatus forms. Chromosomes migrate towards the metaphase plate.

Meiosis II

(Mitotic division)

The second division is merely a mitotic one in nature, where the chromatids are pulled apart, but the number of chromosomes remains the same. This allows large numbers of gametes to be produced.

Metaphase II

Chromosomes line up on the metaphase plate.

Anaphase II

Sister chromatids (now individual chromosomes) separate.

Separate gametes are produced

Telophase II

N   N   N   N

1. Describe the behaviour of the chromosomes in the first division of meiosis: _____

_____

_____

_____

2. Describe the behaviour of the chromosomes in the second division of meiosis: _____

_____

WEB 179 LINK 181 LINK 182

© 2015 **BIOZONE** International
ISBN: 978-1-927309-19-3
Photocopying Prohibited

Crossing over and recombination

Prophase I of meiosis

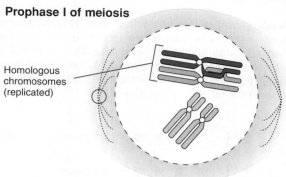

Homologous chromosomes (replicated)

Crossing over refers to the mutual exchange of pieces of chromosome (and their genes) between the **homologous** chromosomes. It can occur only during prophase in the first division of meiosis. Recombination as a result of crossing over is an important mechanism to increase genetic variability in the offspring and has the general effect of allowing genes to move independently of each other through the generations in a way that allows concentration of beneficial alleles.

In prophase I homologous chromosomes pair up to form **bivalents**. This process is called **synapsis**. While they are paired, the non-sister chromatids of homologous pairs may become tangled and segments may be exchanged in a process called **crossing over**. The crossing over occurs at points called chiasmata.

Crossing over results in the **recombination** of alleles, producing greater variation in the offspring than would otherwise occur.

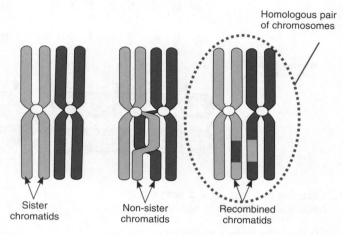

Homologous pair of chromosomes

Sister chromatids

Non-sister chromatids

Recombined chromatids

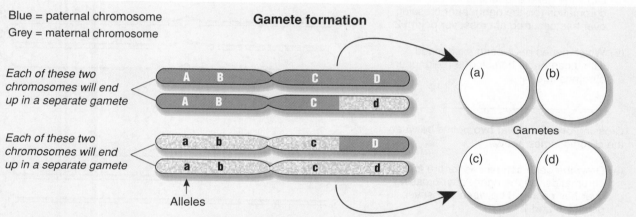

Blue = paternal chromosome
Grey = maternal chromosome

Gamete formation

Each of these two chromosomes will end up in a separate gamete

A B C D
A B C d

Each of these two chromosomes will end up in a separate gamete

a b c D
a b c d

Alleles

(a) (b)

Gametes

(c) (d)

The homologous chromosomes above have completed a crossing over event. Recombination have resulted in four different allele combinations instead the two that would appear if there was no crossing over.

3. (a) When does DNA replication occur? _____

   (b) What is the difference between a chromosome and a chromatid: _____

   _____

4. (a) Distinguish between a haploid and a diploid cell: _____

   _____

   _____

   (b) Circle the **haploid** cells in the diagram on the previous page

5. Complete the diagram above (a) - (d) by drawing the gametes formed:

6. (a) How does crossing over alter the genotype of the gametes produced by meiosis? _____

   _____

   (b) What is the consequence of this? _____

   _____

180 Crossing Over Problems

Key Idea: Crossing over can occur in multiple places in chromosomes, producing a huge amount of genetic variation. The diagram below shows a pair of homologous chromosomes about to undergo chiasma formation during the first cell division in the process of meiosis. There are known crossover points along the length of the chromatids (same on all four chromatids shown in the diagram). In the prepared spaces below, draw the gene sequences after crossing over has occurred on three unrelated and separate occasions (it would be useful to use different coloured pens to represent the genes from the two different chromosomes). See the diagrams on the previous page as a guide.

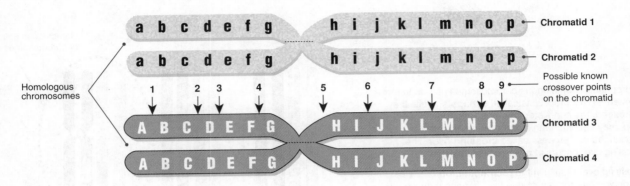

1. Crossing over occurs at a **single** point between the chromosomes above.

   (a) Draw the gene sequences for the four chromatids (on the right), after crossing over has occurred at crossover point: **2**

   (b) Which genes have been exchanged with those on its homologue (neighbour chromosome)?

   _____

2. Crossing over occurs at **two** points between the chromosomes above.

   (a) Draw the gene sequences for the four chromatids (on the right), after crossing over has occurred between crossover points: **6** and **7**.

   (b) Which genes have been exchanged with those on its homologue (neighbour chromosome)?

   _____

3. Crossing over occurs at **four** points between the chromosomes above.

   (a) Draw the gene sequences for the four chromatids (on the right), after crossing over has occurred between crossover points: **1** and **3**, and **5** and **7**.

   (b) Which genes have been exchanged with those on its homologue (neighbour chromosome)?

   _____

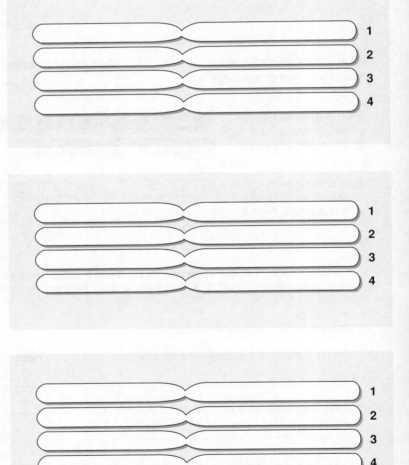

4. What would be the genetic consequences if there was no crossing over between chromatids during meiosis?

_____

_____

KNOW

181 Modelling Meiosis

Key Idea: We can simulate crossing over, gamete production, and the inheritance of alleles during meiosis using ice-block sticks to represent chromosomes.

This practical activity simulates the production of gametes (sperm and eggs) by meiosis and shows you how crossing over increases genetic variability. This is demonstrated by studying how two of your own alleles are inherited by the child produced at the completion of the activity. Completing this activity will help you to visualise and understand meiosis. It will take 25-45 minutes.

Background

Each of your somatic cells contain 46 chromosomes. You received 23 chromosomes from your mother (**maternal chromosomes**), and 23 chromosomes from your father (**paternal chromosomes**). Therefore, you have 23 homologous (same) pairs. For simplicity, the number of chromosomes studied in this exercise has been reduced to four (two homologous pairs). To study the effect of crossing over on genetic variability, you will look at the inheritance of two of your own traits: the ability to **tongue roll** and **handedness**.

Chromosome #	Phenotype	Genotype
10	Tongue roller	TT, Tt
10	Non-tongue roller	tt
2	Right handed	RR, Rr
2	Left handed	rr

Record your phenotype and genotype for each trait in the table (right).
NOTE: If you have a dominant trait, you will not know if you are heterozygous or homozygous for that trait, so you can choose either genotype for this activity.

BEFORE YOU START THE SIMULATION: Partner up with a classmate. Your gametes will combine with theirs (fertilisation) at the end of the activity to produce a child. Decide who will be the female, and who will be the male. You will need to work with this person again at step 6.

1. Collect four ice-blocks sticks. These represent four chromosomes. Colour two sticks blue or mark them with a P. These are the paternal chromosomes. The plain sticks are the maternal chromosomes. Write your initial on each of the four sticks. Label each chromosome with their chromosome number (right).

   Label four sticky dots with the alleles for each of your phenotypic traits, and stick it onto the appropriate chromosome. For example, if you are heterozygous for tongue rolling, the sticky dots with have the alleles **T** and **t**, and they will be placed on chromosome 10. If you are left handed, the alleles will be **r** and **r** and be placed on chromosome 2 (right).

2. Randomly drop the chromosomes onto a table. This represents a cell in either the testes or ovaries. **Duplicate** your chromosomes (to simulate DNA replication) by adding four more identical ice-block sticks to the table (below). This represents **interphase**.

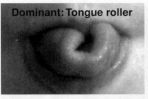

Dominant: Tongue roller

Dominant: Right hand

Recessive: Non-roller

Recessive: Left hand

Trait	Phenotype	Genotype
Handedness		
Tongue rolling		

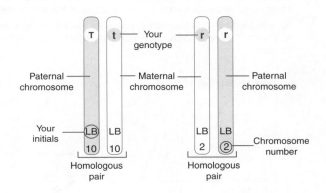

3. Simulate **prophase I** by lining the duplicated chromosome pair with their homologous pair (below). For each chromosome number, you will have four sticks touching side-by-side (A). At this stage **crossing over** occurs. Simulate this by swapping sticky dots from adjoining homologs (B).

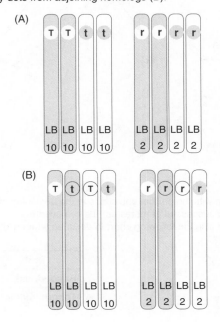

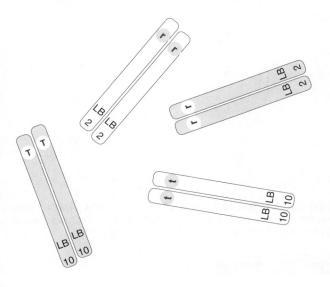

4. Randomly align the homologous chromosome pairs to simulate alignment on the metaphase plate (as occurs in **metaphase I**). Simulate **anaphase I** by separating chromosome pairs. For each group of four sticks, two are pulled to each pole.

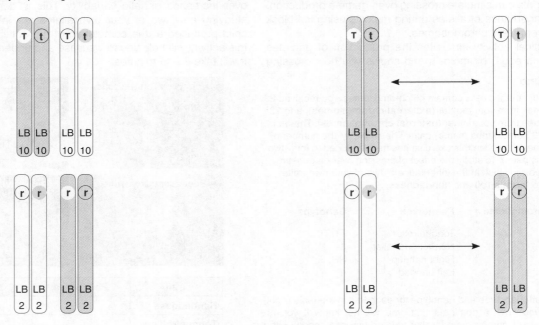

5. **Telophase I:** Two intermediate cells are formed. If you have been random in the previous step, each intermediate cell will contain a mixture of maternal and paternal chromosomes. This is the end of **meiosis 1**.

Now that meiosis 1 is completed, your cells need to undergo **meiosis 2.** Carry out prophase II, metaphase II, anaphase II, and telophase II. Remember, there is no crossing over in meiosis II. At the end of the process each intermediate cell will have produced two haploid gametes (below).

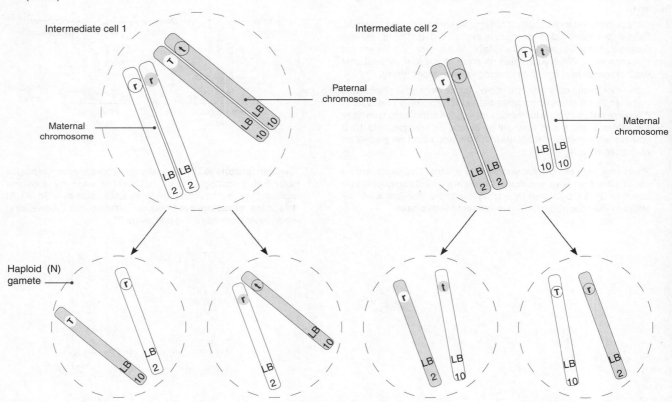

6. Pair up with the partner you chose at the beginning of the exercise to carry out **fertilisation**. Randomly select one sperm and one egg cell. The unsuccessful gametes can be removed from the table. Combine the chromosomes of the successful gametes. You have created a child! Fill in the following chart to describe your child's genotype and phenotype for tongue rolling and handedness.

Trait	Phenotype	Genotype
Handedness		
Tongue rolling		

182 Mitosis vs Meiosis

Key Idea: Mitosis produces two daughter cells genetically identical to the parent cell. Meiosis produces four daughter cells that contain half the genetic information of the parent cell. Cell division is fundamental to all life, as cells arise only by the division of existing cells. All types of cell division begin with replication of the cell's DNA. In eukaryotes, this is followed by division of the nucleus. There are two forms of nuclear division: **mitosis** and **meiosis**, and they have quite different purposes and outcomes. Mitosis is the simpler of the two and produces two identical daughter cells from each parent cell. Mitosis is responsible for growth and repair processes in multicellular organisms and reproduction in single-celled and asexual eukaryotes. Meiosis involves a **reduction division** in which haploid gametes are produced for the purposes of sexual reproduction. Fusion of haploid gametes in fertilisation restores the diploid cell number in the **zygote**.

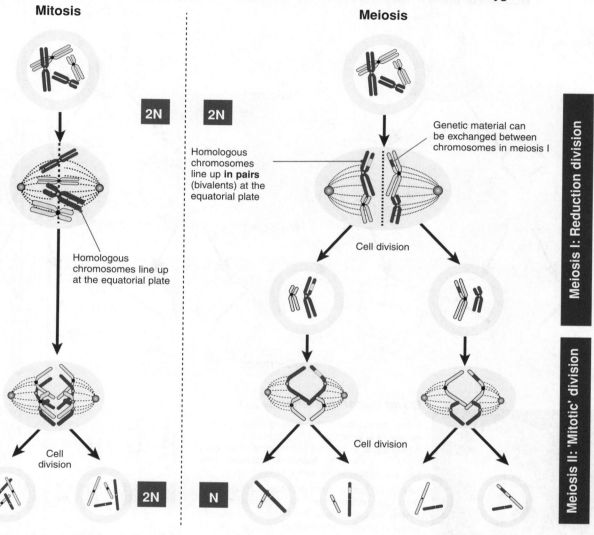

1. Explain how mitosis conserves chromosome number while meiosis reduces the number from diploid to haploid:

_____

_____

_____

2. Describe a fundamental difference between the first and second divisions of meiosis: _____

_____

_____

3. How does meiosis introduce genetic variability into gametes and offspring (following gamete fusion in fertilisation)?

_____

_____

_____

183 Non-Disjunction in Meiosis

Key Idea: Non-disjunction during meiosis results in incorrect apportioning of chromosomes to the gametes.

In meiosis, chromosomes are usually distributed the daughter cells without error. Occasionally, homologous chromosomes fail to separate properly in meiosis I, or sister chromatids fail to separate in meiosis II. In these cases, one gamete receives two of the same type of chromosome and the other gamete receives no copy. This error is known as **non-disjunction** and it results in abnormal numbers of chromosomes in the gametes. The union of an aberrant and a normal gamete at fertilisation produces offspring with an abnormal chromosome number. This condition is known as aneuploidy.

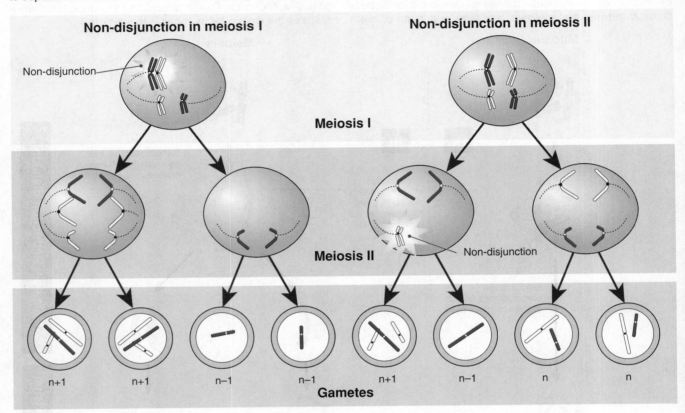

Down Syndrome (Trisomy 21)

Down syndrome is the most common of the human aneuploidies. The incidence rate in humans is about 1 in 800 births for women aged 30 to 31 years, with a **maternal age effect** (the rate increases rapidly with maternal age).

Nearly all cases (approximately 95%) result from **non-disjunction** of chromosome 21 during **meiosis**. When this happens, a gamete (most commonly the oocyte) ends up with 24 rather than 23 chromosomes, and fertilisation produces a trisomic offspring.

Left: Down syndrome phenotype.

Right: A karyogram for an individual with trisomy 21. The chromosomes are circled.

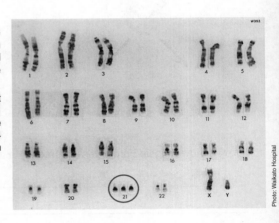

Photo: Waikato Hospital

1. Describe the consequences of non-disjunction during meiosis: _____

_____

_____

2. Explain why non-disjunction in meiosis I results in a higher proportion of faulty gametes than non-disjunction in meiosis II:

_____

_____

3. What is the maternal age effect and what are its consequences? _____

_____

KNOW

© 2015 **BIOZONE** International
ISBN: 978-1-927309-19-3
Photocopying Prohibited

184 Meiosis and Life Cycles

Key Idea: Plants, animals, and fungi all use different strategies for the production of gametes and zygotes.

Meiosis is the point in the life cycle of sexually reproducing organisms when genetic material is recombined to produce new variation. Where meiosis occurs in the life cycle varies according to the type of organism. Most fungi and some algae have a **zygotic life cycle**, in which formation of the zygote by fusion of haploid cells is followed immediately by meiosis. Animals follow a **gametic life cycle**, whereas plants follow a **sporic life cycle** (compared below).

Gametic life cycle (animals)

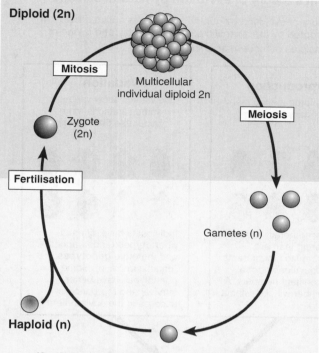

Key feature: meiosis produces haploid gametes

Sporic life cycle (plants)

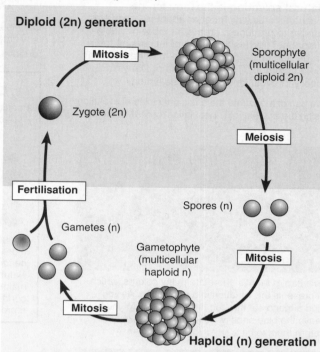

Key feature: meiosis produces haploid spores

In gametic meiosis (above) the haploid gametes are formed by meiosis in a diploid individual and fuse together to form another diploid individual. This type of life cycle is characteristic of animals.

Zygotic life cycle

Zygotic meiosis occurs in fungi. The diploid zygote is shortlived and immediately undergoes meiosis to produce haploid individuals. These produce haploid gametes, which fuse to form the zygote.

In sporic meiosis, the diploid individual (called the sporophyte) produces haploid spores as a result of meiosis. The spores develop into a multicellular haploid individual (called the gametophyte). The gametophyte generation then produces gametes which fuse to form the zygote (2N). This type of life cycle is known as the alternation of generations. In some plants, the haploid generation develops as free-living multicellular individual (e.g. ferns) while in others, the haploid generation remains small (e.g. angiosperms and gymnosperms).

1. (a) - (e) Complete the fern life cycle by adding the correct labels from: fertilisation, meiosis, mitosis N, 2N:

2. What is the gametophyte in a fern?

   _____

3. What does meiosis produce in a plant life cycle?

   _____

4. In animals where does meiosis occur in the life cycle?

   _____

   _____

   _____

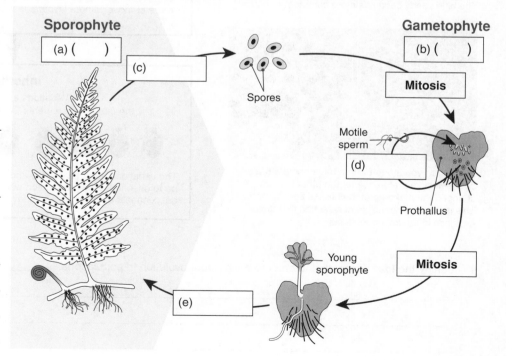

LINK
89

KNOW

185 Mechanism of Natural Selection

Key Idea: Natural selection is the mechanism by which organisms that are better adapted to their environment survive to produce a greater number of offspring.

Evolution is the change in inherited characteristics in a population over generations. Evolution is the consequence of interaction between four factors: (1) The potential for populations to increase in numbers, (2) Genetic variation as a result of mutation and sexual reproduction, (3) competition for resources, and (4) proliferation of individuals with better survival and reproduction.

Natural selection is the term for the mechanism by which better adapted organisms survive to produce a greater number of viable offspring. This has the effect of increasing their proportion in the population so that they become more common. This is the basis of Darwin's theory of evolution by natural selection.

We can demonstrate the basic principles of evolution using the analogy of a 'population' of M&M's candy.

#1

In a bag of M&M's, there are many colours, which represents the variation in a population. As you and a friend eat through the bag of candy, you both leave the blue ones, which you both dislike, and return them to bag.

#2

The blue candy becomes more common...

#3

Eventually, you are left with a bag of blue M&M's. Your selective preference for the other colours changed the make-up of the M&M's population. This is the basic principle of selection that drives evolution in natural populations.

Darwin's theory of evolution by natural selection

Darwin's theory of evolution by natural selection is outlined below. It is widely accepted by the scientific community today and is one of founding principles of modern science.

Overproduction
Populations produce too many young: many must die

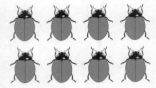

Populations generally produce more offspring than are needed to replace the parents. Natural populations normally maintain constant numbers. A certain number will die without reproducing.

Variation
Individuals show variation: some variations more favourable than others

Individuals have different **phenotypes** (appearances) and therefore **genotypes** (genetic makeup). Some phenotypes have better survival and reproductive success in the environment.

Natural selection
Natural selection favours the individuals best suited to the prevailing environment (the environment at the time)

Individuals in the population compete for limited resources. Those with favourable variations will be more likely to survive. Relatively more of those without favourable variations will die.

Inherited
Variations are inherited: the best suited variants leave more offspring

The variations (both favourable and unfavourable) are passed on to offspring. Each generation will contain proportionally more descendants of individuals with favourable characters.

1. Identify the four factors that interact to bring about evolution in populations: _____

_____

_____

_____

© 2015 **BIOZONE** International
ISBN: **978-1-927309-19-3**
Photocopying Prohibited

Variation, selection, and population change

Natural populations, like the ladybug population above, show genetic variation. This is a result of **mutation** (which creates new alleles) and sexual reproduction (which produces new combinations of alleles). Some variants are more suited to the environment of the time than others. These variants will leave more offspring, as described for the hypothetical population (right).

1. Variation through mutation and sexual reproduction:
In a population of brown beetles, mutations independently produce red colouration and 2 spot marking on the wings. The individuals in the population compete for limited resources.

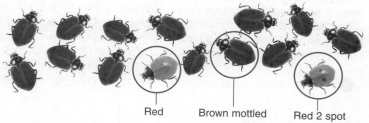

Red   Brown mottled   Red 2 spot

2. Selective predation:
Brown mottled beetles are eaten by birds but red ones are avoided.

3. Change in the genetics of the population:
Red beetles have better survival and fitness and become more numerous with each generation. Brown beetles have poor fitness and become rare.

2. What produces the genetic variation in populations? _____

3. Define evolution: _____
_____

4. Explain how the genetic make-up of a population can change over time: _____
_____
_____
_____
_____
_____
_____
_____

5. Complete the table below by calculating the percentage of beetles in the example above right.

Beetle population	% Brown beetles	% Red beetles	% Red beetles with spots
1			
2			
3			

186 Types of Natural Selection

Key Idea: Natural selection acts on phenotypes and can favour for the most common phenotype or cause a shift in the most common phenotype in one or more directions.

Natural selection operates on the phenotypes of individuals, produced by their particular combinations of alleles. It results in the differential survival of some genotypes (and their phenotypes) over others. Over time, natural selection may lead

to a permanent change in the genetic makeup of a population. Natural selection is always linked to phenotypic suitability in the prevailing environment so it is a dynamic process. It may favour existing phenotypes or shift the phenotypic median, as is shown in the diagrams below. The top row of diagrams below represents the population phenotypic spread before selection, and the bottom row the spread afterwards.

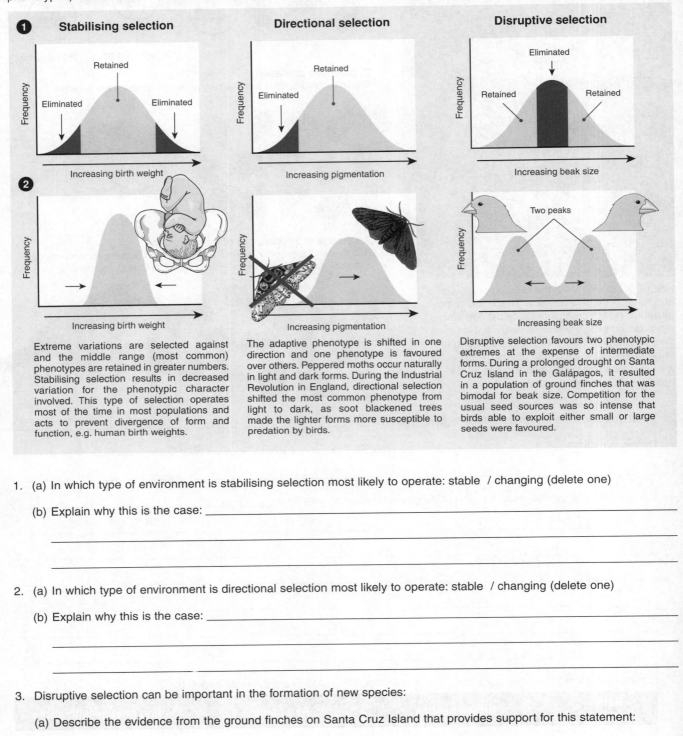

Extreme variations are selected against and the middle range (most common) phenotypes are retained in greater numbers. Stabilising selection results in decreased variation for the phenotypic character involved. This type of selection operates most of the time in most populations and acts to prevent divergence of form and function, e.g. human birth weights.

The adaptive phenotype is shifted in one direction and one phenotype is favoured over others. Peppered moths occur naturally in light and dark forms. During the Industrial Revolution in England, directional selection shifted the most common phenotype from light to dark, as soot blackened trees made the lighter forms more susceptible to predation by birds.

Disruptive selection favours two phenotypic extremes at the expense of intermediate forms. During a prolonged drought on Santa Cruz Island in the Galápagos, it resulted in a population of ground finches that was bimodal for beak size. Competition for the usual seed sources was so intense that birds able to exploit either small or large seeds were favoured.

1. (a) In which type of environment is stabilising selection most likely to operate: stable / changing (delete one)

   (b) Explain why this is the case: _____

   _____

   _____

2. (a) In which type of environment is directional selection most likely to operate: stable / changing (delete one)

   (b) Explain why this is the case: _____

   _____

   _____

3. Disruptive selection can be important in the formation of new species:

   (a) Describe the evidence from the ground finches on Santa Cruz Island that provides support for this statement:

   _____

   _____

   (b) Predict the consequences of the end of the drought and an increased abundance of medium size seeds as food:

   _____

© 2015 **BIOZONE** International
ISBN: 978-1-927309-19-3
Photocopying Prohibited

187 The Evolution of Antibiotic Resistance

Key Idea: Current widespread use of antibiotics has created a selective environment for the proliferation of antibiotic resistance in bacterial populations.

Antibiotic resistance arises when a genetic change allows bacteria to tolerate levels of antibiotic that would normally inhibit growth. This resistance may arise spontaneously, through mutation or copying error, or by transfer of genetic material between microbes. Genomic analyses from 30 000 year old permafrost sediments show that the genes for antibiotic resistance are not new. They have long been present in the bacterial genome, predating the modern selective pressure of antibiotic use. In the current selective environment, these genes have proliferated and antibiotic resistance has spread. For example, methicillin resistant strains of *Staphylococcus aureus* (MRSA) have acquired genes for resistance to all penicillins. Such strains are called superbugs.

The evolution of drug resistance in bacteria

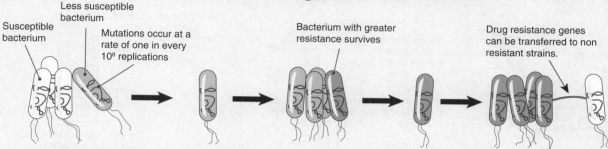

Any population, including bacterial populations, includes variants with unusual traits, in this case reduced sensitivity to an antibiotic. These variants arise as a result of mutations in the bacterial chromosome.

When a person takes an antibiotic, only the most susceptible bacteria will die. The more resistant cells remain alive and continue dividing. Note that the antibiotic does not create the resistance; it provides the environment in which selection for resistance can take place.

If the amount of antibiotic delivered is too low, or the course of antibiotics is not completed, a population of resistant bacteria develops. Within this population too, there will be variation in susceptibility. Some will survive higher antibiotic levels than others.

A highly resistant population has evolved. The resistant cells can exchange genetic material with other bacteria (via horizontal gene transmission), passing on the genes for resistance. The antibiotic initially used against this bacterial strain will now be ineffective.

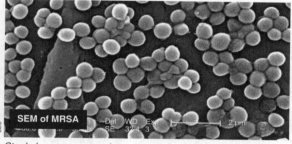

SEM of MRSA

Staphylococcus aureus is a common bacterium responsible for skin infections in humans. MRSA is a strain that has evolved resistance to penicillin and related antibiotics. MRSA is troublesome in hospital-associated infections because patients with open wounds, invasive devices (e.g. catheters), or poor immunity are at greater risk for infection than the general public.

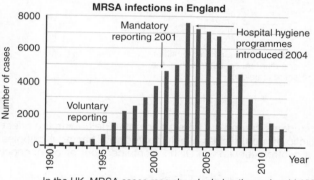

In the UK, MRSA cases rose sharply during the early-mid 1990s, but are now declining as a result of mandatory reporting and the implementation of stringent hospital hygiene programmes.

1. What does **antibiotic resistance** mean? _____

_____

2. (a) How does antibiotic resistance arise in a bacterial population? _____

_____

   (b) Describe two ways in which antibiotic resistance can become widespread: _____

_____

_____

_____

3. With reference to MRSA, describe the implications to humans of widespread antibiotic resistance: _____

_____

_____

LINK 188   LINK 169   WEB 187   KNOW

188 Measuring Antibiotic Sensitivity

Key Idea: Aseptic technique is required to reduce chances of contamination and ensure the effectiveness of an antibiotic is properly tested and quantified.

The effectiveness of antibiotics against a microbe can be tested by spreading agar plates with the microbe in question and placing discs impregnated with antibiotic on the agar.

The type of nutrient agar (growth medium) used depends on the particular microbe involved. Samples from patients with a bacterial infection are often tested to identify the most appropriate antibiotic and the most effective dose rate. This reduces the time they will need to be on the drug and reduces the chance of antibiotic resistance arising and spreading.

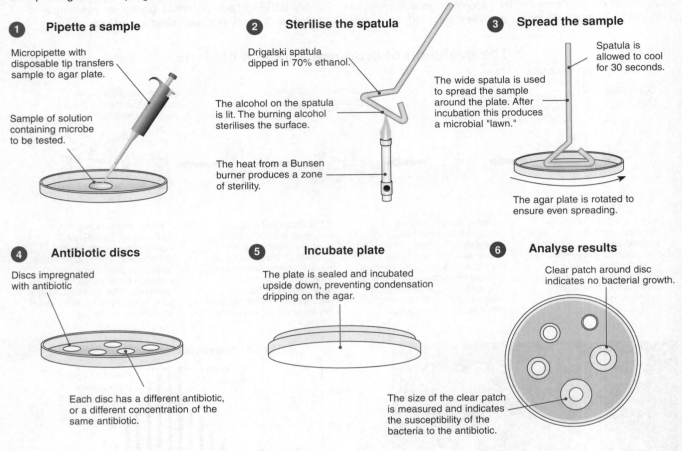

1 **Pipette a sample**

Micropipette with disposable tip transfers sample to agar plate.

Sample of solution containing microbe to be tested.

2 **Sterilise the spatula**

Drigalski spatula dipped in 70% ethanol.

The alcohol on the spatula is lit. The burning alcohol sterilises the surface.

The heat from a Bunsen burner produces a zone of sterility.

3 **Spread the sample**

Spatula is allowed to cool for 30 seconds.

The wide spatula is used to spread the sample around the plate. After incubation this produces a microbial "lawn."

The agar plate is rotated to ensure even spreading.

4 **Antibiotic discs**

Discs impregnated with antibiotic

Each disc has a different antibiotic, or a different concentration of the same antibiotic.

5 **Incubate plate**

The plate is sealed and incubated upside down, preventing condensation dripping on the agar.

6 **Analyse results**

Clear patch around disc indicates no bacterial growth.

The size of the clear patch is measured and indicates the susceptibility of the bacteria to the antibiotic.

1. Two students carried out an experiment to determine the effect of antibiotics on bacteria. They placed discs saturated with antibiotic on petri dishes evenly coated with bacterial colonies. Dish 1 contained four different antibiotics labelled A to D and a control labelled CL. Dish 2 contained four different concentrations of a single antibiotic and a control labelled CL.

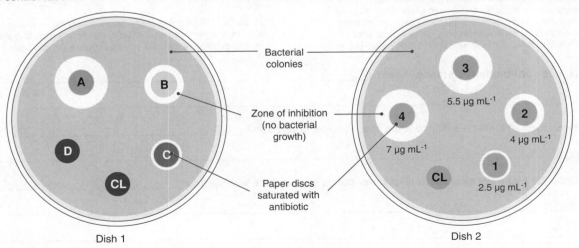

Bacterial colonies

Zone of inhibition (no bacterial growth)

Paper discs saturated with antibiotic

Dish 1

3 — 5.5 µg mL^{-1}
2 — 4 µg mL^{-1}
4 — 7 µg mL^{-1}
1 — 2.5 µg mL^{-1}

Dish 2

(a) Which was the most effective antibiotic on Dish 1? _____

(b) Which was the most effective concentration on Dish 2? _____

(c) Explain your choice in question 1(b): _____

_____

189 Selection for Human Birth Weight

Key Idea: Stabilising selection operates to keep human birth weight within relatively narrow constraints.

Selection pressures operate on populations in such a way as to reduce mortality. As with other traits, human birth weight is a product of natural selection. In a study of human birth weights it is possible to observe the effect of selection pressures operating to constrain human birth weight within certain limits. This is a good example of **stabilising selection**. This activity explores the selection pressures acting on the birth weight of humans. Carry out the steps below:

Step 1: Collect the birth weights from 100 birth notices from your local newspaper (or 50 if you are having difficulty getting enough; this should involve looking back through the last 2-3 weeks of birth notices). If you cannot obtain birth weights in your local newspaper, a set of 100 sample birth weights is provided in the Model Answers booklet.

Step 2: Group the weights into each of the 12 weight classes (of 0.5 kg increments). Determine what percentage (of the total sample) fall into each weight class (e.g. 17 babies weigh 2.5-3.0 kg out of the 100 sampled = 17%)

Step 3: Graph these in the form of a histogram for the 12 weight classes (use the graphing grid provided right). Be sure to use the scale provided on the left vertical (y) axis.

Step 4: Create a second graph by plotting percentage mortality of newborn babies in relation to their birth weight. Use the scale on the right y axis and data provided (below).

Step 5: Draw a line of 'best fit' through these points.

Mortality of newborn babies related to birth weight

Weight / kg	Mortality / %
1.0	80
1.5	30
2.0	12
2.5	4
3.0	3
3.5	2
4.0	3
4.5	7
5.0	15

Source: Biology: The Unity & Diversity of Life (4th ed) by Starr and Taggart

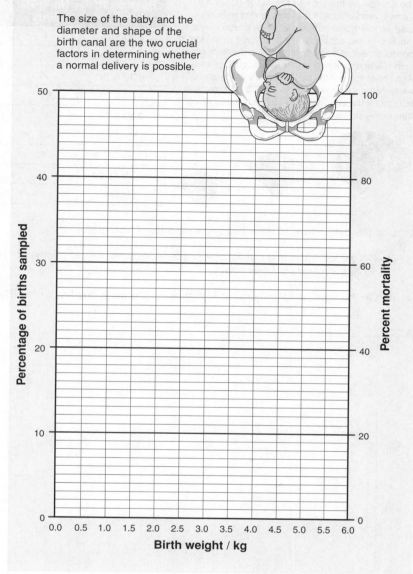

The size of the baby and the diameter and shape of the birth canal are the two crucial factors in determining whether a normal delivery is possible.

1. Describe the shape of the histogram for birth weights: _____

2. What is the optimum birth weight in terms of the lowest newborn mortality? _____

3. Describe the relationship between newborn mortality and birth weight: _____

_____

4. Describe the selection pressures that are operating to control the range of birth weight: _____

_____

_____

5. How might have modern medical intervention during pregnancy and childbirth altered these selection pressures?

_____

_____

LINK   WEB
186   189   DATA

190 Observing Natural Selection

Key Idea: The effect of directional selection on a population can be verified by making measurements of phenotypic traits. Natural selection acts on the phenotypes in a population. An individual with a phenotype that increases its ability to survive and reproduce will leave more offspring, increasing the proportion of that phenotype's genes in the next generation. When environments change, selection can favour a shift in phenotype to create a new phenotypic mean. Many population studies have shown natural selection can cause phenotypic (and therefore genotypic) change relatively quickly.

The finches on the Galápagos island (Darwin's finches) are famous in that they are commonly used as examples of how evolution produces new species. In this activity you will analyse data from the measurement of beak depths of the medium ground finch (*Geospiza fortis*) on the island of Daphne Major near the centre of the Galápagos Islands. The measurements were taken in 1976 before a major drought hit the island and in 1978 after the drought (survivors and survivors' offspring).

Beak depth / mm	No. 1976 birds	No. 1978 survivors	Beak depth of offspring / mm	Number of birds
7.30-7.79	1	0	7.30-7.79	2
7.80-8.29	12	1	7.80-8.29	2
8.30-8.79	30	3	8.30-8.79	5
8.80-9.29	47	3	8.80-9.29	21
9.30-9.79	45	6	9.30-9.79	34
9.80-10.29	40	9	9.80-10.29	37
10.30-10.79	25	10	10.30-10.79	19
10.80-11.29	3	1	10-80-11.29	15
11.30+	0	0	11.30+	2

1. Use the data above to draw two separate sets of histograms:

   (a) On the left hand grid draw side-by-side histograms for the number of 1976 birds per beak depth and the number of 1978 survivors per beak depth.

   (b) On the right hand grid draw a histogram of the beak depths of the offspring of the 1978 survivors.

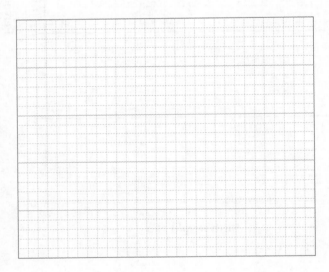
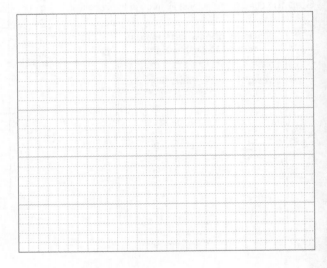

2. What type of selection is operating here? _____

3. (a) Mark the approximate mean beak depth on the graphs of the 1976 beak depths and the 1978 offspring.

   (b) How much has the average moved from 1976 to 1978? _____

   (c) Is beak depth heritable? What does this mean for the process of natural selection in the finches?

   _____

   _____

4. The 1976 drought resulted in plants dying back and not producing seed. Based on the graphs, what can you say about competition between the birds for the remaining seeds, i.e. in what order were the seeds probably used up?

   _____

   _____

191 Adaptation and Fitness

Key Idea: Adaptations are inherited traits that have evolved and are maintained by natural selection. They have a functional role in an organism's life and enhance an individual's fitness. An **adaptation** (or adaptive feature) is any heritable trait that equips an organism to its functional position in the environment (its niche). These traits may be structural, physiological, or behavioural and reflect ancestry as well as adaptation.

Adaptation is important in an evolutionary sense because adaptive features promote fitness. **Fitness** is a measure of an organism's ability to maximise the numbers of offspring surviving to reproductive age. Genetic adaptation must not be confused with physiological adjustment (acclimatisation), which refers to an organism's ability to adjust during its lifetime to changing environmental conditions.

Ear length in rabbits and hares

The external ears of many mammals are used as important organs to assist in thermoregulation (controlling loss and gain of body heat). The ears of rabbits and hares native to hot, dry climates, such as the jack rabbit of south-western USA and northern Mexico, are relatively very large. The Arctic hare lives in the tundra zone of Alaska, northern Canada and Greenland, and has ears that are relatively short. This reduction in the size of the extremities (ears, limbs, and noses) is typical of cold adapted species.

Arctic hare: *Lepus arcticus*

Black-tail jackrabbit: *Lepus californicus*

Body size in relation to climate

Regulation of body temperature requires a large amount of energy and mammals exhibit a variety of structural and physiological adaptations to increase the effectiveness of this process. Heat production in any endotherm depends on body volume (heat generating metabolism), whereas the rate of heat loss depends on surface area. Increasing body size minimises heat loss to the environment by reducing the surface area to volume ratio. Animals in colder regions therefore tend to be larger overall than those living in hot climates. This relationship is well documented in many mammalian species. Cold adapted species also tend to have more compact bodies and shorter extremities than related species in warmer climates.

Fennec fox

Arctic fox

The **fennec fox** of the Sahara illustrates the adaptations typical of mammals living in hot climates: a small body size and lightweight fur, and long ears, legs, and nose. These features facilitate heat dissipation and reduce heat gain.

The Arctic fox shows the physical characteristics typical of cold adapted mammals: a stocky, compact body shape with small ears, short legs and nose, and dense fur. These features reduce heat loss to the environment.

Number of horns in rhinoceroses

Not all differences between species can be convincingly interpreted as adaptations to particular environments. Rhinoceroses charge rival males and predators, and the horn(s), when combined with the head-down posture, add effectiveness to this behaviour. Horns are obviously adaptive, but it is not clear if having one (Indian rhino) or two (black rhino) horns is related to the functionality in the environment or a reflection of evolution from a small hornless ancestor.

African black rhino

Great Indian rhino

1. Distinguish between adaptation and acclimatisation: _____

_____

_____

2. Explain the nature of the relationship between the length of extremities (such as limbs and ears) and climate:

_____

_____

3. Explain the adaptive value of a compact body with a relatively small surface area in a colder climate:

_____

_____

LINK   WEB
190   191   KNOW

Snow bunting
(Plectrophenax nivalis)

The snow bunting is a small ground feeding bird that lives and breeds in the Arctic and sub-Arctic islands. Although migratory, snow buntings do not move to traditional winter homes but prefer winter habitats that resemble their Arctic breeding grounds, such as bleak shores or open fields of northern Britain and the eastern United States. Snow buntings have the unique ability to molt very rapidly after breeding. During the warmer months, the buntings are a brown colour, changing to white in winter (right). They must complete this colour change quickly, so that they have a new set of feathers before the onset of winter and before migration. In order to achieve this, snow buntings lose as many as four or five of their main flight wing feathers at once, as opposed to most birds, which lose only one or two.

Very few small birds breed in the Arctic, because most small birds lose more heat than larger ones. In addition, birds that breed in the brief Arctic summer must migrate before the onset of winter, often travelling over large expanses of water. Large, long winged birds are better able to do this. However, the snow bunting is superbly adapted to survive in the extreme cold of the Arctic region.

Less heat is lost from white plumage compared to dark plumage.

White feathers are hollow and filled with air, which acts as an insulator. In the dark-coloured feathers the internal spaces are filled with pigmented cells.

Snow buntings, on average, lay one or two more eggs than equivalent species further south. They are able to rear more young because the continuous daylight and the abundance of insects at high latitudes enables them to feed their chicks around the clock.

During snow storms or periods of high wind, snow buntings will burrow into snowdrifts for shelter.

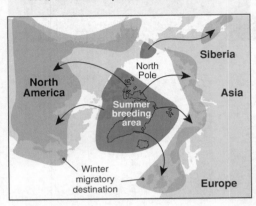

Habitat and ecology: Widespread throughout Arctic and sub-Arctic Islands. Active throughout the day and night, resting for only 2-3 hours in any 24 hour period. Snow buntings may migrate up to 6000 km but are always found at high latitudes. **Reproduction and behaviour**: The nest, which is concealed amongst stones, is made from dead grass, moss, and lichen. The male bird feeds his mate during the incubation period and helps to feed the young.

4. Describe a structural, physiological, and behavioural adaptation of the **snow bunting**, explaining how each adaptation assists survival:

   (a) Structural adaptation: _____

   _____

   _____

   (b) Physiological adaptation: _____

   _____

   _____

   (c) Behavioural adaptation: _____

   _____

   _____

5. Examples of adaptations are listed below. Identify them as predominantly structural, physiological, and/or behavioural:

   (a) Relationship of body size and shape to latitude (tropical or Arctic): _____

   (b) The production of concentrated urine in desert dwelling mammals: _____

   (c) The summer and winter migratory patterns in birds and mammals: _____

   (d) The C4 photosynthetic pathway and CAM metabolism of plants: _____

   (e) The thick leaves and sunken stomata of desert plants: _____

   (f) Hibernation or torpor in small mammals over winter: _____

   (g) Basking in lizards and snakes: _____

192 The Biological Species Concept

Key Idea: There is difficulty in using the biological species concept to define some species as many apparently separate species can interbreed to produce fertile offspring.

One of the most well recognised definitions of a biological species is as "*a group of actually or potentially interbreeding natural populations that is reproductively isolated from other* *such groups*" (Ernst Mayr). However, the concept of a species is not always simple to apply. The concept is difficult to apply to fossil species and to asexual organisms. The occurrence of cryptic species and closely related species that interbreed to produce fertile hybrids (e.g. species of *Canis*), indicate that the boundaries of a species gene pool can be unclear.

Geographical distribution of selected *Canis* species

The global distribution of most of the species of Canis (dogs and wolves) is shown on the map, right. The grey wolf inhabits the forests of North America, northern Europe, and Siberia. The red wolf and Mexican wolf (original distributions shown) were once distributed more widely, but are now extinct in the wild except for reintroduction efforts. In contrast, the coyote has expanded its original range and is now found throughout North and Central America. The range of the three jackal species overlap in the open savannah of Eastern Africa. The dingo is distributed throughout the Australian continent. Distribution of the domesticated dog is global as a result of the spread of human culture. The dog has been able to interbreed with all other members of the genus listed here to form fertile hybrids.

Interbreeding between *Canis* species

The Canis species illustrate problems with the traditional species concept. The domesticated dog is able to breed with other members of the same genus to produce fertile hybrids. Red wolves, grey wolves, Mexican wolves, and coyotes are all capable of interbreeding to produce fertile hybrids. Red wolves are very rare, and it is possible that hybridisation with coyotes has been a factor in their decline. By contrast, the ranges of the three distinct species of jackal overlap in the Serengeti of Eastern Africa. These animals are highly territorial, but simply ignore members of the other jackal species and no interbreeding takes place.

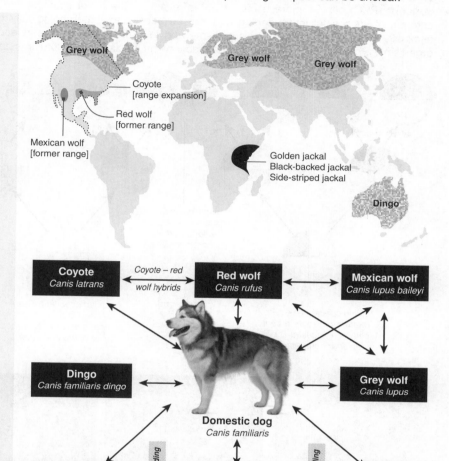

1. What type of barrier prevents interbreeding between the three jackal species? _____

2. Describe the barrier preventing interbreeding between the dingo and other *Canis* species (apart from the dog):

_____

3. Describe a possible contributing factor to the occurrence of interbreeding between the coyote and red wolf:

_____

4. The grey wolf is a widely distributed species. Explain why the North American and the northern European and Siberian populations are considered to be the same species:

_____

_____

_____

5. Explain what you understand by the term species, identifying examples where the definition is problematic:

_____

_____

_____

LINK 195   LINK 193   WEB 192   KNOW

193 The Phylogenetic Species Concept

Key Idea: Phylogenetic species are determined on the basis of shared derived characteristics.

Although the biological species concept (BSC) is useful, there are many situations in which it is difficult to apply, e.g. for asexual populations (including bacteria) or extinct organisms. In such situations, the **phylogenetic species concept** (PSC) can be more useful. It not is reliant on the criterion of successful interbreeding and can be applied to asexually or sexually reproducing organisms and to extinct organisms. Phylogenetic species are defined on the basis

of their shared evolutionary ancestry, which is determined on the basis of **shared derived characteristics**. These may be morphological, especially for higher taxonomic ranks, or biochemical (e.g. DNA differences). The PSC defines a species as the smallest group that all share a derived character state. While the PSC solves some difficulties, it creates others. For example, the ability to distinguish genetically distinct but morphologically identical cryptic species on the basis of DNA analyses can lead to a proliferation of existing species that is not helpful in establishing a phylogeny.

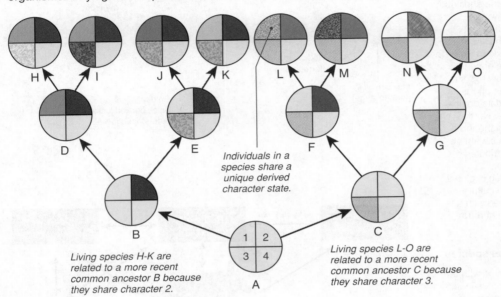

Individuals in a species share a unique derived character state.

Living species H-K are related to a more recent common ancestor B because they share character 2.

Living species L-O are related to a more recent common ancestor C because they share character 3.

This simplified phylogenetic tree traces four characters among 15 species (8 present and 7 ancestral). The 8 modern species (H-O) share a character (4) derived from a distant common ancestor (A). The primitive character unites all 8 species, but the branching of the tree is based on characters derived from the ancestral ones. Classification on the basis of shared derived characters defines the species as the smallest group that can be distinguished by a unique combination of characters. If large numbers of characters are included in the analysis, it is easy to see how this method results in a proliferation of species. Under the PSC model, there are no subspecies; either a population is a phylogenetic species or it is not taxonomically distinguishable.

Tree sparrows (*P. montanus*) are ~10% smaller than the similar house sparrow but the two species hybridise freely.

House sparrows (*P. domesticus*) are widespread with many intermediate "subspecies" of unknown status.

Mallards are infamous for their ability to hybridise freely with a large number of other duck "species".

True sparrows all belong to the genus *Passer*. There are a large number of species distinguished on the basis of song, plumage, and size. A vestigial dorsal outer primary feather and an extra bone in the tongue are ancestral characters. Many populations are not good biological species in that they hybridise freely to produce fertile offspring. A similar situation exists within the genus *Anas* of dabbling ducks (which includes the mallards). Many birds are best described using the PSC rather than the BSC.

1. (a) Explain the basis by which species are assigned under the PSC: _____

_____

_____

(b) Describe one problem with the use of the PSC: _____

_____

(c) Describe situations where the use of the PSC might be more appropriate than the BSC: _____

_____

_____

2. Suggest how genetic techniques could be used to elucidate the phylogeny of a cluster of related phylogenetic species:

_____

_____

© 2015 BIOZONE International
ISBN: 978-1-927309-19-3
Photocopying Prohibited

194 Behaviour and Species Recognition

Key Idea: Animals exhibit species-specific behaviours that improve their chances of successful reproduction.

Many of the behaviours observed in animals are associated with reproduction, reflecting the importance of this event in an individual's life cycle. Many types of behaviour are aimed at facilitating successful reproduction. These include **courtship behaviours**, which may involve attracting a mate to a particular breeding site. Courtship behaviours are aimed at reducing conflict between the sexes and are often stereotyped or **ritualised**. They rely on sign stimuli to elicit specific responses in potential mates. Other reproductive behaviours are associated with assessing the receptivity of a mate, defending mates against competitors, and rearing the young. Behavioural differences between species are a type of reproductive isolating mechanism to help preserve the uniqueness of a species gene pool.

Courtship and species recognition

Accurate species recognition when choosing a mate is vital for successful reproduction and species survival. Failure to choose a mate of the same species would result in reproductive failure or hybrid offspring which are infertile or unable to survive. Birds exhibit a wide range of species-specific courtship displays to identify potential mates of the same species who are physiologically ready to reproduce. They may use simple visual or auditory stimuli, or complex stimuli involving several modes of communication specific to the species.

Peacock courtship (left) involves a visually elaborate tail display to attract female attention. The male raises and fans his tail to display the bright colours and eye-spot patterns. Peahens tend to mate with peacocks displaying the best quality tail display which includes the quantity, size and distribution of eye-spots.

Bird song is an important behavioural isolation method for many species including eastern and western meadowlarks. Despite the fact that they look very similar and share the same habitat, they have remained as two separate species. Differences between the songs of the two species enables them to recognise individuals of their own species and mate only with them. This maintains the species isolation.

Eastern meadowlark

Some species use chemical cues as mating signals and to determine mate choice. The crested auklet (left) secretes aldehydes which smell like tangerines. Birds rub their bills in the scented nape of a partner during courtship. This "ruff-sniff" behaviour allows mate evaluation based on chemical potency. A potential partner might be seen as fitter and more attractive if it produces more aldehydes, because the chemical repels ectoparasites.

Courtship behaviour aids successful mating

Courtship behaviour occurs as a prelude to mating. One of its functions is to synchronise the behaviours of the male and female so that mating can occur, and to override attack or escape behaviour. Here, a male greater frigatebird calls, spreads its wings, and inflates its throat pouch to court a female.

In many bird and arthropod species, the male will provide an offering, such as food, to the female. These **rituals** reduce aggression in the male and promote appeasement behaviour by the female. For some **monogamous** species, e.g. the blue-footed boobies (left), the pairing begins a long term breeding partnership.

Although courtship rituals may be complex, they are very stereotyped and not easily misinterpreted. Males display, usually through exaggerated physical posturing, and the females then select their mates. Courtship displays are species specific and may include ritualised behaviour such as dancing, feeding, and nest-building.

1. (a) Why might courtship behaviour be necessary prior to mating? _____
_____

(b) Why is courtship behaviour often ritualised, with stereotyped displays? _____
_____
_____

2. What is the role of courtship behaviour in species recognition? _____
_____
_____
_____
_____

LINK
192 **KNOW**

195 Classification Systems

Key Idea: Organisms are named and assigned to taxa based on their shared characteristics and evolutionary relationships. Organisms are categorised into a hierarchical system of taxonomic groups (taxa) based on features they share that distinguish them from other taxa. The fundamental unit of classification is the **species**, and each member of a species is assigned a unique two part (binomial) name that identifies it. Classification systems are nested, so that with increasing taxonomic rank, related taxa at one hierarchical level are combined into more inclusive taxa at the next higher level.

Naming an organism

Most organisms have a common name as well a scientific name. Common names may change from place to place as people from different areas name organisms differently based on both language and custom. Scientifically, every organism is given a classification that reflects its known lineage (i.e. its evolutionary history). The last two (and most specific) parts of that lineage are the **genus** and **species** names. Together these are called the scientific name and every species has its own. This two-part naming system is called **binomial nomenclature**. When typed the name is always *italicised*. If handwritten, it should be <u>underlined</u>.

The animal *Rangifer tarandus* is known as the caribou in North America, but as the reindeer in Europe. The scientific name is unambiguous.

1. The table below shows part of the classification for humans using the seven major levels of classification. For this question, use the example of the classification of the European hedgehog on the next page, as a guide.

   (a) Complete the list of the taxonomic groupings on the left hand side of the table below:

	Taxonomic Group	Human Classification
1.		
2.		
3.		
4.		
5.	Family	Hominidae
6.		
7.		

   (b) Complete the classification for humans (*Homo sapiens*) on the table above.

2. Construct an acronym or mnemonic to help you remember the principal taxonomic groupings (KPCOFGS):

   _____

   _____

3. (a) What is the two part naming system for classifying organisms called?_____

   (b) What are the two parts of the name? _____

4. What are the advantages of a scientific name (as opposed to a common name)? _____

   _____

   _____

5. What disadvantages can you see that might arise from classification based solely on the appearance of an organism?

   _____

   _____

   _____

   _____

© 2015 **BIOZONE** International
ISBN: 978-1-927309-19-3
Photocopying Prohibited

Classification of the European Hedgehog

The classification for the **European hedgehog** is described below to show the levels that can be used in classifying an organism. Not all possible subdivisions have been shown here (categories as **sub-family** often appear). The only natural category is the **species**, which may be separated into **sub-species**, based on molecular and morphological data.

Kingdom: **Animalia**
Animals; one of five kingdoms

Phylum: **Chordata**
Animals with a notochord (supporting rod of cells along the upper surface)
tunicates, salps, lancelets, and vertebrates

23 other phyla

Sub-phylum: **Vertebrata**
Animals with backbones
fish, amphibians, reptiles, birds, mammals

Class: **Mammalia**
Animals that suckle their young on milk from mammary glands
placentals, marsupials, monotremes

Infra-class: **Eutheria or Placentals**
Mammals whose young develop for some time in the female's reproductive tract gaining nourishment from a placenta
placental mammals

Order: **Eulipotyphla**
The insectivore-type mammals. Once part of the now abandoned order Insectivora, the order also includes shrews, moles, desmans, and solenodons.

20 other orders

Family: **Erinaceidae**
Comprises two subfamilies: the true or spiny hedgehogs and the moonrats (gymnures). Representatives in the family include the Ethiopian hedgehog, desert hedgehog, and the moonrats. The molecular evidence supports the Eulipotyphla being a monophyletic group (a common ancestor and all its descendants) but other classifications are common, e.g. sometimes the order is given as Erinaceomorpha with Erinaceidae as its only family.

4 other families

Genus: *Erinaceus*
One of twelve genera in this family. The genus *Erinaceus* includes four species.

11 other genera

Species: *europaeus*
The European hedgehog. Among the largest of the spiny hedgehogs. Characterised by a dense covering of spines on the back, the presence of a big toe (hallus) and 36 teeth.

3 other species

The advent of DNA sequencing and other molecular techniques for classification has resulted in the reclassification of many species. There is now considerable debate over the classification of species at almost all levels of classification. The now-defunct order, Insectivora, is one example. This order included a range of mammals with unspecialised features. The order was abandoned in 1956 but persisted (and still persists) in many textbooks. Over the years, families were moved out, merged, split apart again and reformed in other ways based on new evidence or interpretations. Do not be surprised if you see more than one classification for hedgehogs (or any other organism for that matter).

European hedgehog
Erinaceus europaeus

196 Biodiversity

Key Idea: Biodiversity is the sum of all biotic variation from the level of genes to ecosystems. All organisms within an ecosystem contribute to its functioning, but keystone species have a disproportionate effect on ecosystem functioning.

Biodiversity is defined as the sum of all biotic variation from the level of genes to ecosystems. Species diversity describes species richness (the number of species), genetic diversity is the diversity of genes within a species, and ecosystem diversity (of which habitat diversity is a part) refers to the diversity at the ecosystem level. Total biodiversity is threatened by the loss of just one of these components. While every species plays a role in ecosystem function, **keystone species** have a disproportionate effect on ecosystem stability because of their pivotal role in some aspect of ecosystem functioning, e.g. as predators or in nutrient cycling. The loss of a keystone species can result in rapid ecosystem change.

Habitat diversity

Habitat diversity (the presence of many different types of habitat) is important for maintaining biodiversity. Specific habitats are occupied by different organisms and, in general, the greater the number of habitats, the greater the species diversity. Within habitats, microhabitats (smaller areas with specific characteristics) further increase biodiversity. For example, in a stream habitat, microhabitats exist under the rocks, in riffles, in pools, and in vegetation at the stream edges. Some common English habitats are shown (right).

Habitat protection is important to maintain species biodiversity. Habitat loss is one of the biggest threats to biodiversity and is the most common cause of extinction. Examples of habitat destruction include clear cutting forests for logging and agriculture, ploughing natural meadows to make way for agriculture, draining wetland and peatlands, and creating dams that alter river flows.

Coastal sand dunes, Wales

Stream, Peak district

Bluebell woodland

Meadow, Yorkshire

Measuring biodiversity

Biodiversity is quantified for a variety of reasons, e.g. to assess the success of conservation work or to measure the impact of human activity.

One measure of biodiversity is to simply count all the species present (the **species richness**). Species richness (S) is directly related to the number of species in a sampled area. It is a crude measure of the homogeneity of a community but it does not give any information about the relative abundance of particular species and so is relatively meaningless by itself. Thus a sample area with 500 daisies and 3 dandelions has the same species richness as a sample area with 200 daisies and 300 dandelions.

Species evenness measures the proportion of individuals of each species in an area (the relative abundance). Species evenness is highest when the proportions of all species are the same and decreases as the proportions of species become less similar.

Sample of freshwater invertebrates in a stream			
Common name	Site 1 / $n\,m^{-2}$	Site 2 / $n\,m^{-2}$	Site 3 / $n\,m^{-2}$
Freshwater shrimp	67	20	5
Freshwater mite	4	15	1
Flat mayfly	23	21	0
Bighead stonefly	12	18	2
Blackfly	78	40	100
Bloodworm	21	22	43

Data for species richness and species evenness can be obtained by sampling, e.g. using quadrats. In the example above, three sites in a stream were sampled using quadrats and the species and number of individuals per m^2 recorded for each site. Using Site 1 as an example, species richness is 6, since $S = n$. Measures of species evenness are an integral component of biodiversity indices, such as Simpson's Index of biodiversity, but can also be estimated from the numbers of individuals of each species. In terms of species evenness, site 2 > site 1 > site 3.

High species richness

Low species richness

Stephen Moore

1. Distinguish between species diversity and genetic diversity and explain the importance of both of these to our definition of total biological diversity:

_____

_____

_____

_____

© 2015 **BIOZONE** International
ISBN: 978-1-927309-19-3
Photocopying Prohibited

Keystone species in Europe and the UK

Grey wolf

European beaver

Scots pine

Grey or timber wolves (*Canis lupus*) are a keystone predator and were once widespread through North America, Europe, and Eurasia. Historically they have been eliminated because of their perceived threat to humans and livestock, and now occupy only a fraction of their former range. As a top predator, the wolf is a keystone species. When they are absent, populations of their prey (e.g. red deer) increase to the point that they adversely affect other flora and fauna.

The European beaver (*Caster fiber*) was originally distributed throughout most of Europe and northern Asia but populations have been decimated as a result of hunting and habitat loss. Where they occur, beavers are critical to ecosystem function and a number of species depend partly or entirely on beaver ponds for survival. Their tree-felling activity is akin to a natural coppicing process and promotes vigorous regrowth, while historically they helped the spread of alder (a water-loving species) in Britain.

Scots pine (*Pinus sylvestris*) is the most widely distributed conifer in the world. In the Scots pine forests in Scotland, this species occupies a unique position, both because of the absence of other native conifers and because it directly or indirectly supports so many other species. Among those dependent on Scots pine for survival are blaeberries, wood ants, pine martens, and a number of bird species including the capercaillie (wood grouse) and the UK's only endemic bird, the Scottish crossbill.

2. Why is habitat diversity important to maintaining species biodiversity? _____
_____
_____

3. (a) Distinguish between the two measures of biodiversity: species richness and species evenness: _____
_____
_____
_____

(b) Why is it is important to incorporate both these measures when considering species conservation? _____
_____
_____

4. Why are keystone species are so important to ecosystem function? _____
_____
_____
_____

5. On a separate sheet of paper, discuss the biological features of the grey wolf, European beaver, and Scots pine that contribute to their position as a keystone species. Attach the sheet to this workbook.

197 Sampling Populations

Key Idea: A population's characteristics may be inferred from data collected by sampling. Random sampling methods are preferred as they provide unbiased data.

In most ecological studies, it is not possible to measure or count all the members of a population. Instead, information is obtained through sampling in a manner that provides a fair (unbiased) representation of the organisms present and their distribution. This is usually achieved through **random**

sampling, a technique in which each individual has the same probability of being selected at any stage during the sampling process. Sometimes researchers collect information by **non-random sampling**, a process that does not give all the individuals in the population an equal chance of being selected. While faster and cheaper to carry out than random sampling, non-random sampling may not give a true representation of the population.

Sampling strategies

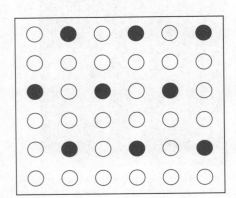

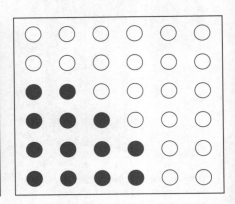

Systematic sampling

Samples from a larger population are selected according to a random starting point and a fixed, periodic sampling interval. For the example above, the sampling period is every fourth individual. Systematic sampling is a random sampling method, provided the periodic interval is determined beforehand and the starting point is random.

Example: Selecting individuals from a patient list.

Stratified sampling

Stratified sampling divides the population into subgroups before sampling. The strata should be mutually exclusive, and individuals must be assigned to only one stratum. Stratified sampling is used to highlight a specific subgroup within the population. Individuals are then randomly sampled from the strata to study.

Example: Dividing the population into males and females.

Opportunistic sampling

A non-random sampling technique in which subjects are selected because of they are easily accessible to the researcher. Opportunistic sampling excludes a large proportion of the population and is usually not representative of the population. It is sometimes used in pilot studies to gather data quickly and with little cost.

Example: Selecting 13 people at a cafe where you are having lunch.

1. Why do we sample populations? _____

_____

_____

2. Why is random sampling preferable to non-random sampling? _____

_____

3. (a) Why can stratified sampling be considered a random sampling method? _____

_____

(b) Describe a situation where its use might be appropriate? _____

_____

4. A student wants to investigate the incidence of asthma in their school. Describe how they might select samples from the school population using:

(a) Systematic sampling: _____

_____

(b) Stratified sampling: _____

_____

(c) Opportunistic sampling: _____

_____

WEB   LINK   LINK

KNOW 197 198 200

© 2015 **BIOZONE** International
ISBN: 978-1-927309-19-3
Photocopying Prohibited

198 Interpreting Samples

Key Idea: If sample data are collected without bias and in sufficient quantity, even a simple analysis can provide useful information about the composition of a community and the possible physical factors influencing this.

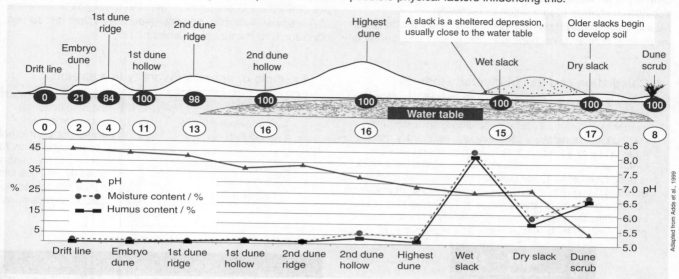

1. The beach dune profile (top) shows transect sampling points at fixed morphological features (e.g. dune ridges). The blue ovals on the dune profile represent the percentage vegetation cover at each sampling point. The white ovals record the number of plant species. Some physical data for each sampling site are presented in the graph below the profile.

   (a) What is the trend in pH from drift line to dune scrub? _____

   (b) Suggest why moisture and humus content increase along the transect? _____

   _____

   _____

   _____

2. The figure below shows changes in vegetation cover along a 2 m vertical transect up the trunk of an oak tree. Changes in the physical factors light, humidity, and temperature along the same transect were also recorded.

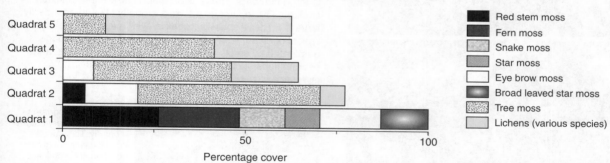

QUADRAT	1	2	3	4	5
Height / m	0.4	0.8	1.2	1.6	2.0
Light / arbitrary units	40	56	68	72	72
Humidity / percent	99	88	80	76	78
Temperature / °C	12.1	12.2	13	14.3	14.2

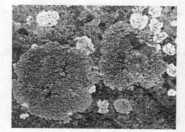

   (a) At which height were mosses most diverse and abundant? _____

   (b) What plant type predominates at 2.0 m height? _____

   (c) What can you deduce about the habitat preferences of most mosses and lichens from this study? _____

   _____

LINK
200 DATA

199 Diversity Indices

Key Idea: Diversity indices allow a quantitative analysis of diversity of an ecosystem and can be used as an indicator of ecosystem change (degradation or recovery).

Measures of biodiversity are commonly used as the basis for making conservation decisions, identifying environmental

degradation, or monitoring ecosystem recovery. Species diversity indices may be used to quantify biodiversity and are often used in conjunction with the presence or absence of particular indicator species (species typical of certain conditions) to monitor ecosystem health.

Calculation and use of diversity indices

Diversity can be quantified using a diversity index. Diversity indices account for both species richness and species evenness and can be useful in identifying environmental degradation (or recovery). Most indices of diversity are easy to use and they are widely used in ecological work. One example, which is a derivation of the Simpson's Index, is described below. Other indices produce values ranging between 0 and almost 1. These are more easily interpreted because of the more limited range of values but no single index offers the 'best' measure of diversity. They are chosen on the basis of their suitability to different situations.

$$d = \frac{N(N-1)}{\sum n(n-1)}$$

This formula is called Simpson's index for finite populations

d = Diversity index
N = Total number of individuals (of all species) in the sample
n = Number of individuals of each species in the sample

Example of species diversity in a stream

Species	n
A (backswimmer)	12
B (stonefly larva)	7
C (silver water beetle)	2
D (caddisfly larva)	6
E (water spider)	5
F (mayfly larva)	8
$\sum n = 40$	

The table left records the results from a survey of stream invertebrates. It is not necessary to know the species to calculate a diversity index as long as the different species can be distinguished.

Calculation of d using the formula (left) is:

$$d = \frac{40 \times 39}{(12 \times 11) + (7 \times 6) + (2 \times 1) + (6 \times 5) + (5 \times 4) + (8 \times 7)} = \frac{1560}{282} = 5.53$$

A value of 5.53 can only really be evaluated relative to a previous state or another community. Communities with a wide range of species produce a higher score than communities dominated by larger numbers of only a few species.

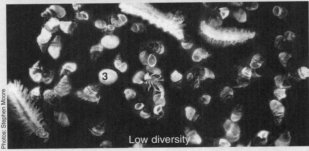

High diversity

Low diversity

Photos: Stephen Moore

Using diversity indices and the role of indicator species

To be properly interpreted, indices are usually evaluated with reference to earlier measurement or a standard ecosystem measure. The photographs left show samples from two stream communities, a high diversity community with a large number of macroinvertebate species (top) and a low diversity community (lower photograph) with fewer species in large numbers. These photographs also show indicator species. The top image shows a stonefly (1) and an alderfly larva (2). These species (together with mayfly larvae) are typical of clean, well oxygenated water. The lower image is dominated by snails (3), which are tolerant of a wide range of conditions, included degraded environments.

Photo: C Johnson-Walker, c 3.0

The aptly named rat-tail maggot is the larva of the drone fly. This species is an indicator of gross pollution. Its prominent feature is a long snorkel-like breathing siphon.

1. (a) An area of forest floor was sampled and six invertebrate species were recorded, with counts of 7, 10, 11, 2, 4, and 3 individuals. Using Simpson's index for finite populations, calculate d for this community:

   d = _____ d = _____

   (b) The same study also sampled near the margin of the forest and the same six invertebrates were recorded, with counts of 16, 4, 1, 3, 4, and 2 individuals. Use Simpson's index for finite populations, calculate d for this community:

   d = _____ d = _____

   (c) Comment on the diversity of these communities relative to each other: _____

   _____

   _____

© 2015 **BIOZONE** International
ISBN: 978-1-927309-19-3
Photocopying Prohibited

200 Investigating Biodiversity

Key Idea: Sampling must be carefully planned in order to obtain meaningful results.

Careful planning is needed before sampling to ensure sound, unbiased data are obtained. If your sampling technique, assumptions, sample size, or sample unit are inadequate, your results will not provide a true representation of the community under study. The Simpson's index of diversity can be used to compare species diversity at two different sites.

Observation

Walking through a conifer plantation, a student observed that there seemed to be only a few different invertebrate species in the forest leaf litter. She wondered if more invertebrate species would be found in a nearby oak woodland.

Hypothesis

The oak woodland has a more varied leaf litter composition than the conifer plantation, so will support a wider variety of invertebrate species.

The **null hypothesis** is that there is no difference between the diversity of invertebrate species in oak woodland and coniferous plantation litter.

Oak woodland

Conifer plantation

Sampling programme

The student designed a sampling programme to test the prediction that there would be a greater diversity of invertebrates in the leaf litter of oak woodlands than in coniferous plantation.

Equipment and procedure

Sites: For each of the two forest types, an area 20 x 8 m was chosen and marked out in 2 x 2 m grids. Eight sampling sites were selected, evenly spaced along the grid as shown (right).

- The two general sampling areas for the study (oak and conifer) were **randomly selected**.
- Eight sites were chosen as the largest number feasible to collect and analyse in the time available.
- The two areas were sampled on sequential days.

Capture of invertebrates: At each site, a 0.4 x 0.4 m quadrat was placed on the forest floor and the leaf litter within the quadrat was collected. Leaf litter invertebrates were captured using a simple gauze lined funnel containing the leaf litter from within the quadrat. A lamp was positioned over each funnel for two hours and the invertebrates in the litter moved down and were trapped in the collecting jar.

- After two hours, each jar was labelled with the site number and returned to the lab for analysis.
- The litter in each funnel was bagged, labeled with the site number and returned to the lab for weighing.
- The number of each invertebrate species at each site was recorded.
- After counting and analysis of the samples, all the collected invertebrates were returned to the sites.

Assumptions

- The areas chosen in each forest were representative in terms of invertebrate abundance.
- Eight sites were sufficient to adequately sample the invertebrate populations in each forest.
- A quadrat size of 0.4 x 0.4 m contained enough leaf litter to adequately sample the invertebrates at each sample site.
- The invertebrates did not prey on each other once captured in the collecting jar.
- All the invertebrates within the quadrat were captured.
- Invertebrates moving away from the light are effectively captured by the funnel apparatus and cannot escape.
- Two hours was long enough for the invertebrates to move down through the litter and fall into the trap.

Note that these last two assumptions could be tested by examining the bagged leaf litter for invertebrates after returning to the lab.

Oak woodland or coniferous plantation

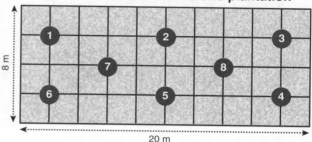

1 Sampling sites numbered 1-8 at evenly spaced intervals on a 2 x 2 m grid within an area of 20 m x 8 m.

Sampling equipment: leaf litter light trap

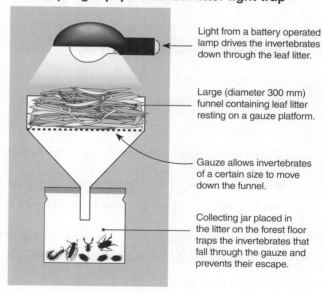

Light from a battery operated lamp drives the invertebrates down through the leaf litter.

Large (diameter 300 mm) funnel containing leaf litter resting on a gauze platform.

Gauze allows invertebrates of a certain size to move down the funnel.

Collecting jar placed in the litter on the forest floor traps the invertebrates that fall through the gauze and prevents their escape.

The importance of sample size

In any field study, two of the most important considerations are the **sample size** (the number of samples you will take) and the size of the **sampling unit** (e.g. quadrat size). An appropriate choice will enable you to collect sufficient, unbiased data to confidently test your hypothesis. The number of samples you take will be determined largely by the resources and time that you have available to collect and analyse your data (your **sampling effort**).

LINK **199** LINK **197** LINK **5** **DATA**

Results

The results from the student's study are presented in the tables and images below. The invertebrates are not drawn to scale.

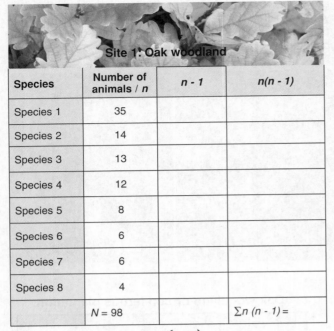

Site 1: Oak woodland

Species	Number of animals / n	n - 1	n(n - 1)
Species 1	35		
Species 2	14		
Species 3	13		
Species 4	12		
Species 5	8		
Species 6	6		
Species 7	6		
Species 8	4		
	N = 98		$\Sigma n(n-1) =$

Site 2: Conifer plantation

Species	Number of animals / n	n - 1	n(n - 1)
Species 1	74		
Species 2	16		
Species 3	4		
Species 4	2		
Species 5	2		
Species 6	1		
Species 7	0		
Species 8	1		
	N = 100		$\Sigma n(n-1) =$

Species 1 Mite | Species 2 Ant | Species 3 Earwig | Species 4 Woodlice | Species 5 Centipede | Species 6 Longhorn beetle | Species 7 Small beetle | Species 8 Pseudoscorpion

1. What type of sampling design is used in this study? _____

2. Explain the importance of each of the following in field studies:

   (a) Appropriately sized sampling unit: _____
   _____

   (b) Recognising any assumptions that you are making: _____
   _____

   (c) Appropriate consideration of the environment: _____
   _____

   (d) Return of organisms to the same place after removal: _____
   _____

   (e) Appropriate size of total sampling area within which the sites are located: _____
   _____

3. (a) Complete the two tables above to calculate the values for n(n-1) for the student's two sampling sites:

   (b) Calculate **d** for site 1: _____

   (c) Calculate **d** for site 2: _____

   (d) Compare the diversity of the two sites and suggest any reasons for it: _____
   _____
   _____
   _____

201 Agriculture and Biodiversity

Key Idea: Agricultural systems generally have lower biodiversity than natural ecosystems.

Throughout the world, the intensification of agriculture has been associated with a decline in biodiversity. After the native vegetation has been cleared, soil tillage and burning reduces microbial biomass in the soil, altering soil structure and processes such as decomposition and nutrient cycling. When habitats shrink, populations decline and small isolated populations may not be viable. Habitat fragmentation also disrupts the activity patterns of mobile species, especially those that will not move over open agricultural land. Modern farming practices, such as dependence on mechanisation and a move away from mixed farming operations, have greatly accelerated the decline in biodiversity. In the UK, steps to conserve the countryside, such as hedgerow legislation, policies to increase woodland cover, and schemes to promote environmentally sensitive farming practices are designed to reduce loss of biodiversity.

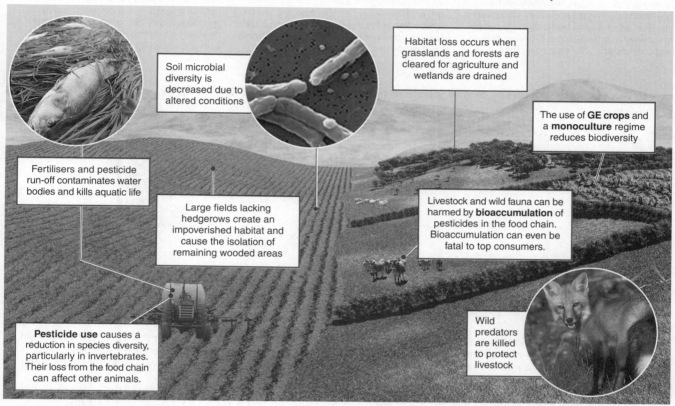

Soil microbial diversity is decreased due to altered conditions

Habitat loss occurs when grasslands and forests are cleared for agriculture and wetlands are drained

The use of **GE crops** and a **monoculture** regime reduces biodiversity

Fertilisers and pesticide run-off contaminates water bodies and kills aquatic life

Large fields lacking hedgerows create an impoverished habitat and cause the isolation of remaining wooded areas

Livestock and wild fauna can be harmed by **bioaccumulation** of pesticides in the food chain. Bioaccumulation can even be fatal to top consumers.

Pesticide use causes a reduction in species diversity, particularly in invertebrates. Their loss from the food chain can affect other animals.

Wild predators are killed to protect livestock

Natural grasslands are diverse and productive ecosystems. Ancient meadows may have contained 80-100 plant species, in contrast to currently cultivated grasslands, which may contain as few as three species. Unfortunately, many of the management practices that promote grassland species diversity conflict with modern farming methods. For example, the extensive use of fertilisers and selective herbicides on pastures favours aggressive species, such as nettles and docks, which out-compete ecologically important species such as orchids and cowslips. Appropriate management can help to conserve grassland ecosystems while maintaining their viability for agriculture.

Wildflower meadow in Britain

1. One solution to the conflicting needs of conserving biodiversity and productivity is to intensively farm designated areas, leaving other areas for conservation. From the farmer's perspective, outline two advantages of this approach:

   (a) _____

   _____

   (b) _____

   _____

   (c) Describe a disadvantage of this management approach: _____

   _____

   _____

LINK
202
WEB
201

KNOW

An increase in urban sprawl and the pressure on farmers to increase productivity are having a dramatic impact on the once common flowering plants of Britain's grasslands. Diversity can be maintained only through careful management and conservation of existing ecosystems.

Grassland conservation is not only important for maintaining plant diversity, many animals rely on these ecosystems for food and shelter. A reduction in the diversity of grassland plant species translates to a reduction in the diversity of other species.

This woodland in Yorkshire, England, is home to numerous species of organisms. Clearing land for agriculture reduces both biodiversity and the ability of the community to adapt to changing environmental conditions. Natural ecosystem stability is decreased as a result.

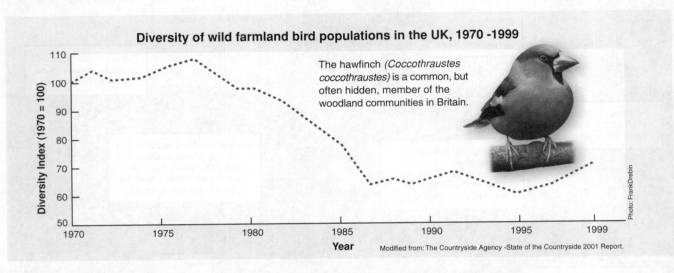

Diversity of wild farmland bird populations in the UK, 1970 -1999

The hawfinch (*Coccothraustes coccothraustes*) is a common, but often hidden, member of the woodland communities in Britain.

Y-axis: Diversity Index (1970 = 100), 50 to 110
X-axis: Year, 1970 to 1999

Photo: FrankDrebin

Modified from: The Countryside Agency -State of the Countryside 2001 Report.

2. Populations of wild farmland bird species, because of their wide distribution and position near the top of the food chain, provide good indicators of the state of other wildlife species and of environmental health in general. Over the last 25 years, there has been a marked net decline in the diversity of farmland bird populations (above). However, since 1986, diversity has ceased to decline further and, in recent years, has actually showed an increase.

Suggest two possible reasons for this decline in the diversity of farmland birds (also see the activity on hedgerows):

(a) _____

(b) _____

3. (a) Describe three initiatives local and national government have implemented in an attempt to reverse this decline:

_____

_____

_____

(b) Discuss the role of environmental impact assessments and biodiversity estimates when planning such initiatives:

_____

_____

_____

4. Provide an argument for retaining areas of uncultivated meadow alongside more intensively managed pasture:

_____

_____

_____

_____

202 Hedgerows

Key Idea: Hedgerows provide food, shelter and transport corridors for many species so are important for biodiversity. Since the 1940s, many thousands of kilometres of hedgerows have been removed from the British landscape each year as traditional mixed farms have been converted to farms with larger fields. In addition, neglect and improper management have been responsible for almost half of lost hedgerows every year. Hedgerows require maintenance and management in order to remain viable, yet hedge-laying and trimming skills are rapidly becoming lost. In 1997, legislation was introduced to control the destruction of hedgerows in rural settings. In England and Wales, landowners must apply to the local authority for permission to remove a hedgerow of greater than 20 metres in length, and this can be refused if the hedge is shown to be significant in terms of its age, environmental, or historical importance.

Hedgerows are important because...

▸ Hedges may support up to 80% of England's birds, 50% of its mammals, and 30% of its butterflies.

▸ The ditches and banks associated with hedgerows provide habitat for amphibians and reptiles.

▸ Hedges provide habitat, nesting material and food for birds and mammals.

▸ Some small mammals, e.g. dormice, once used hay ricks as overwintering habitat. With the loss of hay ricks, hedgerows are virtually their only alternative.

▸ They act as corridors, along which animals (e.g. pheasants) can safely move between areas of woodland.

▸ They provide overwintering habitat for predatory insects which move into crops to control pest insects in spring.

▸ Hedges provide shelter for stock and crops and reduce wind speed, which prevents erosion.

▸ Hedges act as barriers for windborne pests.

Photo courtesy, Kimberley Mallady

Bjorn Schulz

Hazel dormouse

Hedgerows commonly comprise hawthorn, blackthorn, field maple, hazel, and bramble. A hedgerow is essentially a linear wood and many of the associated plants are woodland species. At least 30 bird species nest in hedges. Hedgerows of different heights are preferred by different bird species, so management to provide a range of hedge heights and tree densities provides the best option for increasing diversity. For example, bullfinches prefer well-treed hedgerows over 4 m tall, whereas whitethroats, linnets, and yellowhammers favour shorter hedgerows (2-3 m) with fewer trees. The hedge base is important for ground-nesting species like the grey partridge. Hedgerows are important habitat for dormice and are used as dispersal corridors linking copses that are too small to support a viable populations on their own. Crucially they also support breeding populations independent of other habitats.

1. From an environmental perspective, describe three benefits of hedgerows to biodiversity:

   (a) _____

   (b) _____

   (c) _____

2. Explain why hedgerows might be regarded as undesirable from the perspective of a modern farmer: _____

   _____

   _____

   _____

3. Outline a brief argument to convince a farmer to retain and manage hedgerows, rather than remove them:

   _____

   _____

   _____

   _____

203 Quantifying Variation Using Student's *t* Test

Key Idea: Differences between two populations can be tested for significance using the Student's *t* test.

The Student's *t* test is commonly used to compare two sample means, e.g. means for a treatment and a control in an experiment, or the means of some measured characteristic between two animal or two plant populations. It is a simple test and useful for distinguishing real but marginal differences between samples. Usefully, the test remains robust even when sample sizes are small. A simple example outlining the steps in the Student's *t* test is provided below. It compares data for a treatment and a control from a hypothetical experiment (the units are not relevant in this case, only the values).

Steps in performing a Student's *t* test

1 **Calculate summary statistics for the two data sets**

Control (A)	Treatment (B)
6.6	6.3
5.5	7.2
6.8	6.5
5.8	7.1
6.1	7.5
5.9	7.3

$n_A = 6$, $\bar{x}_A = 6.12$, $s_A = 0.496$

$n_B = 6$, $\bar{x}_B = 6.98$, $s_B = 0.475$

n_A and n_B are the number of values in the first and second data sets respectively (these do not need to be the same).

$\bar{x}$ is the mean.

s is the standard deviation (a measure of scatter in the data).

2 **Set up and state your null hypothesis (H_0)**

H_0: there is no treatment effect. The differences in the data sets are the result of chance and they are not really different. The alternative hypothesis is that there is a treatment effect and the two sets of data are truly different.

3 **Decide if your test is one or two tailed**

A one-tailed test looks for a difference only in one particular direction. A two-tailed test looks for any difference (+ or −). This tells you what section of the t table to consult. Most biological tests are two-tailed. Very few are one-tailed.

4 **Calculate the *t* statistic**

For our sample data above the calculated value of *t* is −3.09. The degrees of freedom (df) are $n_1 + n_2 - 2 = 10$.

Calculation of the *t* value uses the variance which is simply the square of the standard deviation (s^2). You may compute *t* using a spreadsheet but manual computation is not difficult (see opposite). It does not matter if the calculated *t* value is a positive or negative (the sign is irrelevant).

> The absolute value of the *t* statistic (3.09) well exceeds the critical value for $P = 0.05$ at 10 degrees of freedom.
>
> *We can reject H_0 and conclude that the means are different at the 5% level of significance.*
>
> If the calculated absolute value of *t* had been less than 2.23, we could not have rejected H_0.

1. (a) In an experiment, data values were obtained from four plants in experimental conditions and three plants in control conditions. The mean values for each data set (control and experimental conditions) were calculated. The *t* value was calculated to be 2.16. The null hypothesis was: "The plants in the control and experimental conditions are not different". State whether the calculated *t* value supports the null hypothesis or its alternative (consult *t* table below):

_____

_____

(b) The experiment was repeated, but this time using 6 control and 6 "experimental" plants. The new *t* value was 2.54. State whether the calculated *t* value supports the null hypothesis or its alternative now:

_____

_____

2. Explain what you understand by statistical significance:

_____

_____

_____

_____

_____

Table of critical values of *t* at different levels of *P*.

Degrees of freedom	Level of Probability		
	0.05	0.01	0.001
1	12.71	63.66	636.6
2	4.303	9.925	31.60
3	3.182	5.841	12.92
4	2.776	4.604	8.610
5	2.571	4.032	6.869
6	2.447	3.707	5.959
7	2.365	3.499	5.408
8	2.306	3.355	5.041
9	2.262	3.250	4.781
10	2.228	3.169	4.587
15	2.131	2.947	4.073
16	2.120	2.921	4.015
17	2.110	2.898	3.965
18	2.101	2.878	3.922
19	2.093	2.861	3.883
20	2.086	2.845	3.850
25	2.060	2.787	3.725
30	2.042	2.750	3.646
40	2.021	2.704	3.551
50	2.009	2.678	3.496
60	2.000	2.660	3.460
100	1.984	2.626	3.390

© 2015 **BIOZONE** International
ISBN: 978-1-927309-19-3
Photocopying Prohibited

DATA

3. The table below presents data for heart rate (beats per minute) in samples of ten males and females from a population.
(a) Complete the calculations to perform the *t* test for these two samples. The steps are outlined in the right hand column.

X (bpm)		$x - \bar{x}$ (deviation from the mean)		$(x - \bar{x})^2$ (deviation from mean)²	
Male	Female	Male	Female	Male	Female
70	69	-2.3	1	5.29	1
74	62	1.7	-6	2.89	36
80	75				
73	66				
75	68				
82	57				
62	61				
69	84				
70	61				
68	77				

$n_A = 10$ $n_B = 10$

The number of samples in each data set

The sum of each column is called the sum of squares

$\Sigma (x - \bar{x})^2$ $\Sigma (x - \bar{x})^2$

(b) The variance for males: $s^2_A =$

The variance for females: $s^2_B =$

(c) The difference between the means for males and females

$(\bar{x}_A - \bar{x}_B) =$

(d) t (calculated) =

(e) Determine the degrees of freedom (d.f.)

d.f. $(n_A + n_B - 2) =$

(f) $P =$

t (critical value) =

(g) Your decision is: _____
_____
_____
_____
_____
_____

Step 1: Summary statistics

Tabulate the data as shown in the first 2 columns of the table (left). Calculate the mean and give the n value for each data set. Compute the standard deviation if you wish.

Males $\bar{x}_A = 72.3$ Females $\bar{x}_B = 68.0$
$n_A = 10$ $n_B = 10$
$s_A = 5.87$ $s_B = 8.47$

Step 2: State your null hypothesis

Step 3: Test is one tailed / two tailed (delete one)

Step 4: Calculating *t*

4a: Calculate sums of squares
Complete the computations outlined in the table left. The sum of each of the final two columns (left) is called the sum of squares.

4b: Calculate the variances
Calculate the variance (s^2) for each data set. This is the sum of squares ÷ by $n - 1$ (number of samples in each data set − 1). In this case the n values are the same, but they need not be.

$$s^2_A = \frac{\Sigma(x - \bar{x})^2}{n_A - 1}_{(A)} \qquad s^2_B = \frac{\Sigma(x - \bar{x})^2}{n_B - 1}_{(B)}$$

4c: Differences between the means
Calculate the difference between the means

$$(\bar{x}_A - \bar{x}_B)$$

4d: Calculate *t*

$$t = \frac{(\bar{x}_A - \bar{x}_B)}{\sqrt{\dfrac{s^2_A}{n_A} + \dfrac{s^2_B}{n_B}}}$$

4e: Determine the degrees of freedom
Degrees of freedom (d.f.) = $n_A + n_B - 2$ where n_A and n_B are the number of counts in each of populations A and B.

Step 5: Consult the *t* table

Consult the *t*-tables (opposite) for the critical *t* value at the appropriate degrees of freedom and the acceptable probability level (e.g. P = 0.05).

5a: Make your decision

Make your decision whether or not to reject H_0. If t_{calc} is large enough you may be able to reject H_0 at a lower P value (e.g. 0.001), increasing confidence in the alternative hypothesis.

204 Quantitative Investigation of Variation

Key Idea: The Student's *t* test can be used to test the significance of differences between populations for a variable phenotypic character.

White clover (*Trifolium repens*) is a common pasture plant. It has white flowers and distinctive leaves with three (or occasionally four) leaflets. The leaves are held on petioles that can be 150 mm or more long if left undisturbed. In pasture that is regularly grazed petiole length can be shorter.

Two paddocks containing white clover were grazed by cattle under different regimes during the peak growing season (late winter to early summer). Paddock A was grazed for one day every week whereas paddock B was grazed for one day every four weeks. At the end of the trial, quadrats were used to select random samples of clover and the lengths of the petioles were measured to evaluate the effect of grazing on morphology (in this case petiole length). The results are shown below. Use the Student's *t* test to determine the significance of the differences between the two populations (grazing regimes). The calculation steps are given in the blue boxes. Steps for calculating the summary statistics with a calculator are in the grey boxes.

Leaflets

Petiole

Clover leaf

x (length / mm)		x − x̄ (deviation from the mean)		(x − x̄)² (deviation from mean)²	
Paddock A	Paddock B	Paddock A	Paddock B	Paddock A	Paddock B
83	30	40.2	−77.5	1616.04	6006.25
70	87	27.2	−20.5	739.84	420.25
32	48				
61	92				
70	54				
45	33				
28	135				
34	60				
37	81				
20	139				
25	90				
30	78				
31	125				
35	174				
80	167				
22	184				
62	80				
35	125				
25	163				
44	197				
30	116				

The sum of each column is called the sum of squares

$\Sigma (x - \bar{x})^2$ $\Sigma (x - \bar{x})^2$

Step 1: Summary statistics

Tabulate the data as shown in the first 2 columns of the table (left). Calculate the mean and give the n value for each data set. Compute the standard deviation if you wish.

Popn A $\bar{x}_A =$ [   ]   Popn B $\bar{x}_B =$ [   ]
$n_A =$ [   ] $n_B =$ [   ]
$s_A{}^* =$ [   ] $s_B{}^* =$ [   ]

* These can be calculated using the variance equation or a standard scientific calculator (see below).

Step 2: State your null hypothesis

Step 3: Test is one tailed / two tailed (delete one)

Summary statistics on a calculator

Most standard scientific calculators will be able to provide you with the number of sample entrants (n), the mean (x̄) and the standard deviation (s) once you have entered the data. The procedure shown below is for a Casio fx-82 calculator, a standard classroom calculator. In most Casio models the procedure is similar. Consult the calculator's manual if necessary.

Input the data on a calculator

Step 1 Set the calculator to SD mode:

[MODE] [2]

Step 2 Clear the memory:

[SHIFT] [CLR] [1] [=]

Step 3 Enter the data for paddock A

83 [DT] 70 [DT] 32 [DT]

Repeat this procedure for paddock B after you have retrieved all the summary statistics and calculated the variance for paddock A (see next page).

© 2015 **BIOZONE** International
ISBN: 978-1-927309-19-3
Photocopying Prohibited

Step 4: Calculating t

4a: Calculate sums of squares

Complete the computations outlined in the table left. The sum of each of the final two columns (left) is called the sum of squares.

4b: Calculate the variances

Calculate the variance (s^2) for each data set. This is the sum of squares ÷ by $n - 1$ (number of samples in each data set − 1). In this case the n values are the same, but they need not be.

$$s^2_A = \frac{\sum(x - \bar{x})^2}{n_A - 1} \text{(A)} \qquad s^2_B = \frac{\sum(x - \bar{x})^2}{n_B - 1} \text{(B)}$$

4c: Differences between the means

Calculate the difference between the means

$$(\bar{x}_A - \bar{x}_B)$$

4d: Calculate t

$$t = \frac{(\bar{x}_A - \bar{x}_B)}{\sqrt{\dfrac{s^2_A}{n_A} + \dfrac{s^2_B}{n_B}}}$$

4e: Determine the degrees of freedom

Degrees of freedom (d.f.) = $n_A + n_B - 2$ where n_A and n_B are the number of counts in each of populations A and B.

Step 5: Consult the t table

Consult the t-tables in the previous activity for the critical t value at the appropriate degrees of freedom and probability level (e.g. P = 0.05).

5a: Make your decision

Make your decision whether or not to reject H_0. If t_{calc} is large enough you may be able to reject H_0 at a lower P value (e.g. 0.001), increasing confidence in the alternative hypothesis.

Retrieving the summary statistics

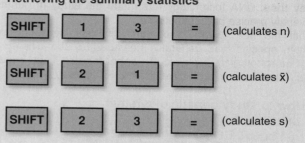

SHIFT 1 3 = (calculates n)

SHIFT 2 1 = (calculates $\bar{x}$)

SHIFT 2 3 = (calculates s)

Calculate the variance

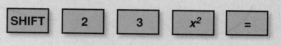

SHIFT 2 3 x^2 =

1. The variance for population A: s^2_A = _____

   The variance for population B: s^2_B = _____

2. The difference between the population means:

   $(\bar{x}_A - \bar{x}_B)$ = _____

3. (a) Calculate t:

   (b) $t_{(calculated)}$ = _____

4. Determine the degrees of freedom (d.f.)

   d.f. $(n_A + n_B - 2)$ = _____

   _____

5. P = _____

   $t_{(critical\ value)}$ = _____

6. Your decision is: _____

7. Write a conclusion for the investigation: _____

   _____

   _____

8. To further the investigation, it was decided to find out if the regular grazing affected the rate of dry matter increase in the clover. Suggest a way in which this could done:

   _____

   _____

   _____

205 Investigating Genetic Diversity

Key Idea: DNA technology has made the study of genetic diversity precise and quantifiable.

Until the late twentieth century diversity between and within species was generally measured by the difference in morphological (physical) appearance. This made the identification and classification of closely related or morphologically similar individuals difficult. However with the rapid advancement in DNA technology this can be done more easily and with greater precision. The ability to read DNA sequences down to individual base pairs allows different species and individual groups within species and populations and their genetic relationships to be identified.

How to study genetic diversity:

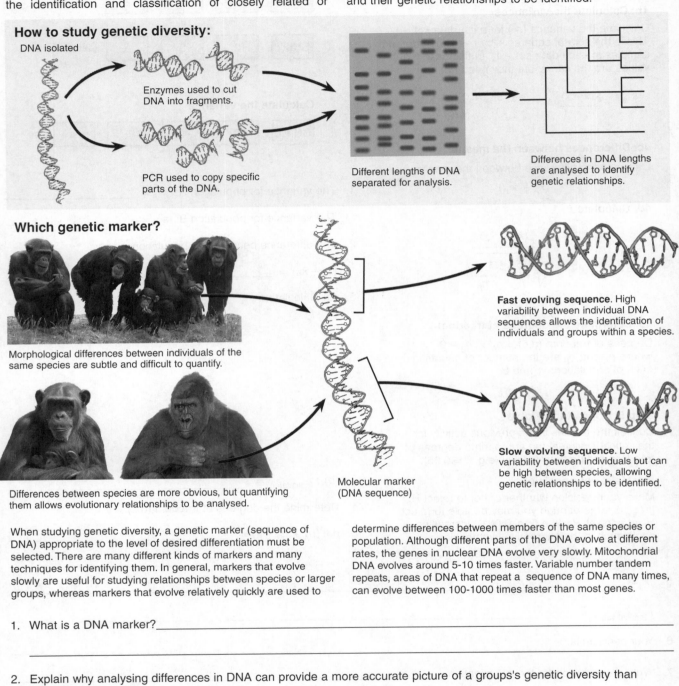

DNA isolated

Enzymes used to cut DNA into fragments.

PCR used to copy specific parts of the DNA.

Different lengths of DNA separated for analysis.

Differences in DNA lengths are analysed to identify genetic relationships.

Which genetic marker?

Morphological differences between individuals of the same species are subtle and difficult to quantify.

Differences between species are more obvious, but quantifying them allows evolutionary relationships to be analysed.

Molecular marker (DNA sequence)

Fast evolving sequence. High variability between individual DNA sequences allows the identification of individuals and groups within a species.

Slow evolving sequence. Low variability between individuals but can be high between species, allowing genetic relationships to be identified.

When studying genetic diversity, a genetic marker (sequence of DNA) appropriate to the level of desired differentiation must be selected. There are many different kinds of markers and many techniques for identifying them. In general, markers that evolve slowly are useful for studying relationships between species or larger groups, whereas markers that evolve relatively quickly are used to determine differences between members of the same species or population. Although different parts of the DNA evolve at different rates, the genes in nuclear DNA evolve very slowly. Mitochondrial DNA evolves around 5-10 times faster. Variable number tandem repeats, areas of DNA that repeat a sequence of DNA many times, can evolve between 100-1000 times faster than most genes.

1. What is a DNA marker? _____

_____

2. Explain why analysing differences in DNA can provide a more accurate picture of a groups's genetic diversity than morphological studies:

_____

_____

_____

3. What type of DNA marker would be appropriate for:

(a) A study on the genetic diversity a population of polar bears living in the Arctic: _____

(b) Investigating the evolutionary relationships between the different orders of mammals: _____

LINK 206   LINK 207   LINK 208   LINK 209

KNOW

© 2015 **BIOZONE** International
ISBN: **978-1-927309-19-3**
Photocopying Prohibited

206 Homologous DNA Sequences

Key Idea: The variation and relationships between species can be determined from the differences in their DNA.

DNA-DNA hybridisation (below) provides a way to compare the genomes of different species by measuring the degree of genetic similarity between DNA sequences. More closely related species have fewer differences between their genomes than more distantly related species. This technique gives a measure of 'relatedness' and can be calibrated as a **molecular clock** against known fossil dates. It has been used to help determine the approximate date of human divergence from the apes, which has been estimated to be between 10 and 5 million years ago.

DNA hybridisation

1. DNA from the two species to be compared is extracted, purified and cut into short fragments (e.g. 600-800 base pairs).

2. The DNA of one species is mixed with the DNA of another.

3. The mixture is incubated to allow DNA strands to dissociate and reanneal, forming hybrid double-stranded DNA.

4. The hybridised sequences that are highly similar will bind more firmly. A measure of the heat energy required to separate the hybrid strands provides a measure of DNA relatedness.

DNA homologies today

DNA-DNA hybridisation has been criticised because duplicated sequences within a single genome make it unreliable comparing closely related species.

Today, DNA sequencing and computed comparisons are more widely used to compare genomes, although DNA-DNA hybridisation is still used to help identify bacteria.

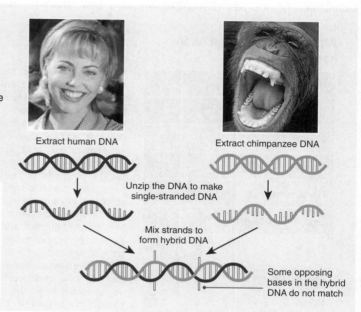

Extract human DNA   Extract chimpanzee DNA

Unzip the DNA to make single-stranded DNA

Mix strands to form hybrid DNA

Some opposing bases in the hybrid DNA do not match

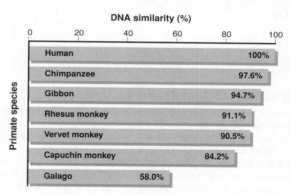

Flamingo   Ibis   Shoebill   Pelican   Stork   New World vulture

The relationships among the New World vultures and storks have been determined using DNA hybridisation. It has been possible to estimate how long ago various members of the group shared a common ancestor.

Similarity of human DNA to that of other primates

DNA similarity (%)

Primate species	
Human	100%
Chimpanzee	97.6%
Gibbon	94.7%
Rhesus monkey	91.1%
Vervet monkey	90.5%
Capuchin monkey	84.2%
Galago	58.0%

The genetic relationships among the primates has been investigated using DNA hybridisation. Human DNA was compared with that of the other primates. It largely confirmed what was suspected from anatomical evidence.

1. Explain how **DNA hybridisation** can give a measure of genetic relatedness between species:

_____

_____

_____

2. Study the graph showing the results of a DNA hybridisation between human DNA and that of other primates.

   (a) Which is the most closely related primate to humans? _____

   (b) Which is the most distantly related primate to humans? _____

3. State the DNA difference score for: (a) Shoebills and pelicans:_____   (b) Storks and flamingos: _____

4. On the basis of DNA hybridisation, state how long ago the ibises and New World vultures shared a common ancestor:

_____

207 Homologous Proteins

Key Idea: Proteins are the product of gene expression, so an analysis of the differences between the same protein in different taxa gives an indication of species relatedness. Traditionally, phylogenies were based largely on anatomical traits, and biologists attempted to determine the relationships between taxa based on similarity or by tracing the appearance of key characteristics. With the advent of new molecular techniques, homologies (similarities resulting from shared

ancestry) could be studied at the molecular level as well and the results compared to phylogenies established using other methods. Protein sequencing provides an excellent tool for establishing homologies. A protein has a specific number of amino acids arranged in a specific order. Any differences in the sequence reflect changes in the DNA sequence. Commonly studied proteins include blood proteins, such as haemoglobin, and the respiratory protein cytochrome c.

Amino acid differences in haemoglobin

Human beta chain	0
Chimpanzee	0
Gorilla	1
Gibbon	2
Rhesus monkey	8
Squirrel monkey	9
Dog	15
Horse, cow	25
Mouse	27
Grey kangaroo	38
Chicken	45
Frog	67

When the sequence of the **beta haemoglobin chain** (right), which is 146 amino acids long, is compared between humans, five other primates, and six other vertebrates, the results support the phylogenies established using other methods. The numbers in the table (left) represent the number of amino acid differences between the beta chain of humans and those of other species. In general, the number of amino acid differences between the haemoglobins of different vertebrates is inversely proportional to genetic relatedness.

Shading indicates (from top) primates, non-primate placental mammals, marsupials, and non-mammals.

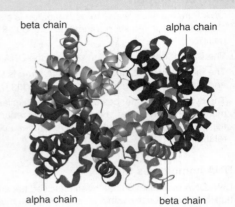

In most vertebrates, the oxygen-transporting blood protein haemoglobin is composed of four polypeptide chains, two alpha chains and two beta chains. Haemoglobin is derived from myoglobin, and ancestral species had just myoglobin for oxygen transport. When the amino acid sequences of myoglobin, the haemoglobin alpha chain, and the haemoglobin beta chain are compared, there are several amino acids that remain **conserved** between all three. These amino acid sequences must be essential for function because they have remained unchanged throughout evolution.

Using immunology to determine phylogeny

The immune system of one species will recognise the blood proteins of another species as foreign and form antibodies against them. This property can be used to determine the extent of relatedness between species. Blood proteins, such as albumins, are used to prepare **antiserum** in rabbits. The antiserum contains antibodies against the test blood proteins (e.g. human) and will react to those proteins in any blood sample they are mixed with. The extent of the reaction indicates how similar the proteins are; the greater the reaction, the more similar the proteins. This principle is illustrated (right) for antiserum produced to human blood and its reaction with the blood of other primates and a rat.

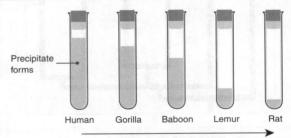

Decreasing recognition of the antibodies against human blood proteins

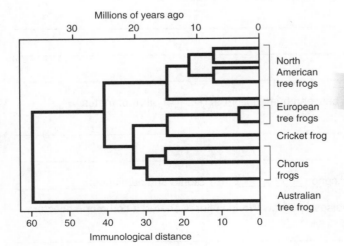

The relationships among tree frogs have been established by immunological studies based on blood proteins such as immunoglobulins and albumins. The **immunological distance** is a measure of the number of amino acid substitutions between two groups. This, in turn, has been calibrated to provide a time scale showing when the various related groups diverged.

WEB LINK

© 2015 **BIOZONE** International
ISBN: 978-1-927309-19-3
Photocopying Prohibited

Highly conserved proteins

Some proteins are common in many different species. These proteins are called **highly conserved proteins**, meaning they change (mutate) very little over time. This is because they have critical roles in the organism (e.g. in cellular respiration) and mutations are likely to prevent them from functioning correctly.

Evidence indicates that highly conserved proteins are homologous and have been derived from a common ancestor. Because they are highly conserved, changes in the amino acid sequence are likely to represent major divergences between groups during the course of evolution.

Cytochrome *c* (left) is a respiratory protein located in the electron transport chain in mitochondria.

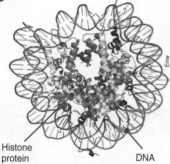

Histones (right) are a family of proteins that associate with DNA and organise it so that it can fit inside the cell nucleus.

Histone protein   DNA

The Pax-6 protein provides evidence for evolution

▶ The Pax-6 gene belongs to a family of genes that regulate the formation of a number of organs, including the eye, during embryonic development.

▶ The Pax-6 gene produces the Pax-6 protein, which acts as a transcription factor to control the expression of certain genes.

▶ Scientists know the role of Pax-6 in eye development because they created a knockout model in mice where the Pax-6 gene is not expressed. The knockout model is eyeless or has very underdeveloped eyes.

▶ The Pax-6 gene is so highly conserved that the gene from one species can be inserted into another species, and still produce a normal eye.

▶ This suggests the Pax-6 proteins are homologous, and the gene has been inherited from a common ancestor.

An experiment inserted mouse Pax-6 gene into fly DNA and turned it on in a fly's legs. The fly developed morphologically normal eyes on its legs!

1. Compare the differences in the haemoglobin sequence of humans, rhesus monkeys, and horses. What do these tell you about the relative relatedness of these organisms?

_____

_____

_____

2. (a) What is a highly conserved protein? _____

_____

(b) What type of proteins tend to be highly conserved? _____

_____

(c) Why are the proteins named in (b) highly conserved? _____

_____

(d) Why are highly conserved proteins good for constructing phylogenies? _____

_____

_____

3. (a) Describe the role of the Pax-6 gene: _____

_____

_____

(b) What evidence is there that the Pax-6 protein is highly conserved? _____

_____

_____

208 Genetic Diversity in Springtails

Key Idea: Genetic analysis of springtails in Taylor Valley has been able to separate morphologically cryptic species.

Genetic analysis is now widely used to investigate dispersal and divergence in all kinds of species. **Springtails** are tiny arthropods and have a limited capacity to move between locations. For this reason, they are good candidates for studying evolutionary phenomena. Researchers wanted to investigate the genetic relatedness of springtails in a Dry Valley in Antarctica. Results of a mtDNA study show two distinct genetic 'types' of springtail in Taylor Valley (see map, blue and white squares below). The two types have different DNA bases at a number of positions in a mitochondrial gene.

They also coexist in an area of **sympatry** in the middle of Taylor Valley. The results of the research are summarized on the following page. It shows an order of separation based on the genetic differences between the two types (TV1-14) compared with other populations of the same species (from Cape Evans, Cape Royds, and Beaufort Is). One other Antarctic species of springtail (*Biscoia sudpolaris*) is included on the diagram as an 'outgroup' (reference point). The genetic difference between populations is indicated by the distance to the 'branching point'. Groups that branch apart early in the tree are more different genetically than groups that branch later.

The springtail *Gomphiocephalus hodgsoni* (above) is a small arthropod, just over 1 mm long. It occupies the Dry Valleys region of Antarctica, particularly in Taylor Valley (below).

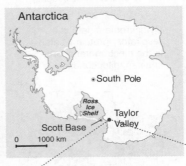

Sampling sites (below): A total of 14 sampling sites was used to build up a picture of the genetic diversity of springtails in an area of Taylor Valley. They were named TV1 through TV14 (TV = Taylor Valley). Bluesquares represent one genetic 'type' of springtail, while white squares represent another.

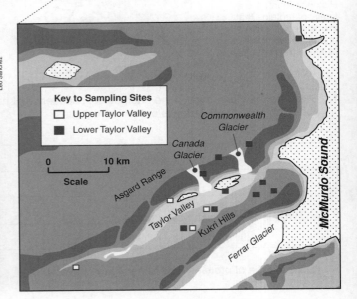

Taylor Valley (above) is one of the Dry Valleys in Antarctica, and is clear of snow virtually the whole year round. Any snow that falls in it soon melts as the dark rock surface heats up in the sun.

The process of DNA analysis of springtails:

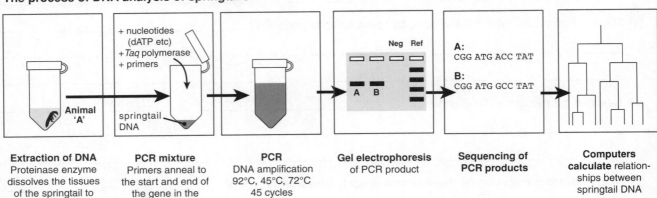

Extraction of DNA Proteinase enzyme dissolves the tissues of the springtail to release DNA

PCR mixture Primers anneal to the start and end of the gene in the mitochondrial DNA

PCR DNA amplification 92°C, 45°C, 72°C 45 cycles

Gel electrophoresis of PCR product

Sequencing of PCR products

Computers calculate relationships between springtail DNA

Source: Many thanks to **Liam Nolan**, teacher at Tauranga Girls' College, for supplying the information for these pages. Liam studied with the Centre for Biodiversity and Ecology Research (University of Waikato, Hamilton, New Zealand), whilst the recipient of a study award from the NZ Ministry of Education.

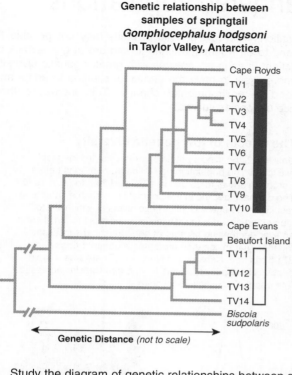

Genetic relationship between samples of springtail *Gomphiocephalus hodgsoni* in Taylor Valley, Antarctica

Cape Royds
TV1
TV2
TV3
TV4
TV5
TV6
TV7
TV8
TV9
TV10
Cape Evans
Beaufort Island
TV11
TV12
TV13
TV14
Biscoia sudpolaris

← **Genetic Distance** *(not to scale)* →

Mosses (right) are the tallest plants in Antarctica. They provide ideal habitats for springtails. Although springtails have antifreeze (glycerol) in their blood, they are still vulnerable to freezing. Antarctic springtails do not possess the proteins that some Antarctic fish have to help them avoid freezing.

This photo taken in **Taylor Valley** (left) shows an ephemeral stream (it dries up at certain times of the year) emerging from one of the many "hanging glaciers" that line the margins of the valley. Such streams provide the moisture essential for springtails to survive amongst rocks, moss, lichen, and algae.

1. Study the diagram of genetic relationships between samples of springtails (above). Describe what you notice about the branching point of the populations from the upper (TV11-14) and lower (TV1-10) Taylor Valley:

_____

_____

2. Studies of the enzymes from the two 'types' of springtails indicate that the springtails do not interbreed. Explain why this is significant:

_____

_____

_____

3. Springtails cannot fly and in Antarctica quickly dry out and die if they are blown by the wind. Discuss the significance of these two features for gene flow between populations:

_____

_____

_____

_____

4. Taylor Valley was once (thousands of years ago) covered in ice, with the only habitats available for springtails being the mountain tops lining both sides of the valley. Explain how this, together with low dispersal rates and small population size, could result in the formation of two species from one original species of springtail:

_____

_____

_____

_____

_____

_____

_____

209 Genetic Diversity in Endangered Populations

Key Idea: Genetic diversity can be measured by calculating the allele diversity in a population. Species with low genetic diversity may be at risk of extinction.

Genetic diversity refers to the variety of alleles and genotypes present in a population. Genetic diversity is important to the survival and adaptability of a species.

Populations with low genetic diversity may not be able to respond to environmental change and are at greater risk of extinction. In contrast, species with greater genetic diversity are more likely to have the genetic resources to adapt and respond to environmental change. This increases their chance of species survival.

Measuring genetic diversity

Measuring genetic diversity can help identify at-risk populations and prioritise conservation efforts for rare breeds or animals in captive breeding programmes. Pedigree animals may be tested for genetic diversity to assist in planning breeding programmes so that loss of genetic diversity is minimised. Eukaryotic chromosomes contain many genes and, in any one population, each gene may have a number of versions called alleles. The presence of more than one allele at a specific gene location (locus) is called polymorphism. When only one allele is present the locus is said to be monomorphic. One of the simplest measures of genetic diversity involves calculating the proportions polymorphic loci across a genome or a species. The following equation can be used:

$$\text{Proportion of polymorphic gene loci} = \frac{\text{number of polymorphic gene loci}}{\text{total number of loci}}$$

Measuring genetic diversity in African lions

Allele variation at 26 enzyme loci in an African lion population was studied (below). Twenty loci showed no variation (they were monomorphic) and six loci showed variation (they were polymorphic).

Enzyme locus	Allele		
	1	2	3
ADA	0.56	0.33	0.11
DIAB	0.61	0.39	
ESI	0.88	0.12	
GPI	0.85	0.15	
GPT	0.89	0.11	
MPI	0.92	0.08	
20 Monomorphic loci	1.00		

Data: Newman *et al.* 1985

1. What is genetic diversity? _____

_____

_____

_____

_____

_____

2. (a) For the lion data, identify the enzyme locus with the highest genetic diversity: _____

(b) Calculate the genetic diversity for the 26 loci studied above: _____

The effects of low genetic diversity

Until 1992, the Illinois prairie chicken was destined for extinction. The population had fallen from millions before European arrival to 25 000 in 1933 and then to 50 in 1992. The dramatic decline in the population in such a short time resulted in a huge loss of genetic diversity, which led to inbreeding and in turn resulted in a decrease in fertility and an ever-decreasing number of eggs hatching successfully. In 1992, a translocation programme began, bringing in 271 birds from Kansas and Nebraska. There was a rapid population response, as fertility and egg viability increased. The population is now recovering.

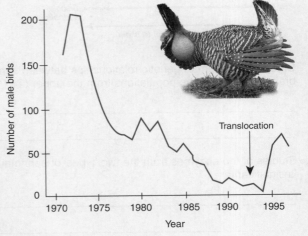

Photo: Dept. of Natural Resources, Illinois

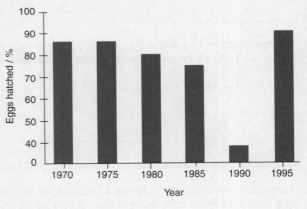

3. (a) Describe the factors contributing to the loss of diversity in the Illinois prairie chicken: _____

_____

_____

(b) Why did the translocation of 271 birds from outside Illinois into the Illinois population halt the population decline?

_____

LINK
205

© 2015 **BIOZONE** International
ISBN: 978-1-927309-19-3
Photocopying Prohibited

210 Chapter Review

Summarise what you know about this topic under the headings provided. You can draw diagrams or mind maps, or write short notes to organise your thoughts. Use the images and hints to help you and refer back to the introduction to check the points covered:

DNA, genes, and chromosomes:
HINT: Differences between eukaryotic and prokaryotic chromosomes. Genes and non-protein coding sequences.

DNA and protein synthesis:
HINT: Genes are transcribed and translated into proteins.

Genetic diversity
HINT: How does variation arise?

Genetic diversity and adaptation:
HINT: Describe the mechanism of natural selection.

REVISE

Species and taxonomy:
HINT: What are species and how do we classify them?

Community biodiversity:
HINT: Random sampling and the calculation and use of diversity indices.

Investigating diversity:
HINT: What methods can be used to investigate genetic diversity?

211 KEY TERMS: Did You Get It?

1. Test your vocabulary by matching each term to its correct definition, as identified by its preceding letter code.

adaptation

biodiversity

binomial nomenclature

exon (exonic DNA)

crossing over

homologous chromosomes

meiosis

mutation

natural selection

phylogeny

pre-mRNA

recombination

A Chromosome pairs, one paternal and one maternal, of the same length and centromere position, and with genes for the same characteristics at corresponding loci.

B The base sequences that are translated into proteins (expressed).

C The process of double nuclear division (reduction division) to produce four nuclei, each containing half the original number of chromosomes (haploid).

D Exchange of alleles between homologous chromosomes as a result of crossing over.

E A change in the base sequence of DNA.

F Event during meiosis where two homologous chromosomes exchange genetic material.

G A formal system of naming species of organisms by giving each a Latin name composed of two parts..

H Any heritable trait that equips an organism to its functional position in the environment.

I The evolutionary history or genealogy of a group of organisms. Often represented as a 'tree' showing descent of new species from the ancestral one.

J The process by which heritable traits in organisms become more or less common in a population as a function of their effect on fitness (differential reproductive success).

K The primary mRNA transcript which is edited before translation to remove the non-protein coding sequences.

L The sum total of the habitat, genetic, and species variation globally or regionally.

2. Describe the characteristics of each of the following types of natural selection, explain when each might operate, and give an example where it has been important in producing evolutionary change in a population:

(a) Directional selection: _____

_____

 Example: _____

(b) Stabilising selection: _____

_____

 Example: _____

3. Two populations of daisy were found growing in a small valley. One population was found on the south facing slope while the other was found on the north facing slope. Investigators measured the diameter of a sample of the daisy flowers from each population to determine if there was a difference between the two populations. The results are shown below:

Population	Flower diameter / cm										
A	1.3	1.2	1.4	1.5	1.2	1.1	1.0	1.4	1.3	1.3	1.2
B	1.1	1.3	1.1	0.9	0.9	1.3	1.4	0.8	1.3	1.1	1.0

(a) Calculate the mean flower size for population A: _____ Population B: _____

(b) Calculate the standard deviation for population A: _____ Population B: _____

(c) Determine the *t* value for the study: _____

(d) Use a *t*-table to determine if there is a significant difference in flower size between the populations: _____

_____

4. Put the following taxa groups in hierarchical order: *species, order, genus, kingdom, family, class, phylum*:

_____

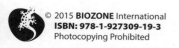

Image credits

The writing team would like to thank the following people and organisations who have kindly provided photographs or illustrations for this edition:

• PASCO for their photographs of probeware • Wadsworth Centre (NYSDH) for the photo of the cell undergoing cytokinesis • Louisa Howard and Chuck Daghlian, Dartmouth College for the freeze fracture image of the cell membrane • Dr. Raowf Guirguis. NCI for the image of the WBC attacking a cancerous cell • Louisa Howard, Katherine Connolly, Dartmouth College for the microvilli photo • Pennsylvania State University College of Medicine for the photo of the small intestine in cross section • Dan Butler for the photo of the cut finger • John Main • Waikato Hospital for the images of the karyographs • The late Stephen Moore for his photos of aquatic invertebrates • Kimberley Mallady for the hedgerow photo • Leo Sanchez for the Antarctic photo • Dept. of Natural Resources, Illinois, for the photograph of the threatened prairie chicken • Vernier for the image of the carbon dioxide sensor • Liam Nolan for his photographic and text contributions to the activity on the genetic biodiversity of Antarctic springtails.

We also acknowledge the photographers who have made images available through **Wikimedia Commons** under Creative Commons Licences 2.0, 2.5, or 3.0: • Rufino Uribe • J. Miquel, D. Vilavella, Z.widerski, V. V. Shimalov and J. Torres • Goran Ekstrom (PLoS) • CDC: Dr Lucille K. Georg • Jeffery M. Vinocur • Olaboy • JPbarrass • Emmanuelm • Zephyris • Volker Brinkmann • James Heilman, MD • G Beard • Nephron • Emmanueim • D_kuru • Kelvinsong • Alex Popovkin • BY-SA • alpsdake PD • Graham Colm • Dr. Hans-Heinrich Trepte • Laitche • JM Garg • Mbz1 • FrankDrebin • Bjorn Schulz • Burkhard Budel • C Johnson-Walker • and3K and caper437 • madprime

Contributors identified by coded credits:

BF: Brian Finerran (University of Canterbury), **BOB**: Barry O'Brien (University of Waikato), **CDC**: Centers for Disease Control and Prevention, Atlanta, USA, **DH**: Don Horne, **DW**: David Wells, **EII**: Education Interactive Imaging, **GW**: Graham Walker, **JDG**: John Green (University of Waikato), **KP**: Kent Pryor, **MPI**: Max Planck Institute for Developmental Biology, Germany **NASA**: National Aeronautics and Space Administration, **NIH**: National Institute of Health, **RA**: Richard Allan, **RCN**: Ralph Cocklin, **TG**: Tracey Greenwood, **WBS**: Warwick Silvester (University of Waikato), **WMU**: Waikato Microscope Unit.

Image libraries:

We also acknowledge our use of royalty-free images, purchased by BIOZONE International Ltd from the following sources: **Corel** Corporation from various titles in their Professional Photos CD-ROM collection; **Dollar Photo Club**, dollarphotoclub. com; **istock photos**, istockphoto.com; **IMSI** (International Microcomputer Software Inc.) images from IMSI's MasterClips® and MasterPhotosTM Collection, 1895 Francisco Blvd. East, San Rafael, CA 94901-5506, USA; ©1996 **Digital Stock**, Medicine and Health Care collection; ©**Hemera** Technologies Inc, 1997-2001; © 2005 JupiterImages Corporation www.clipart.com; ©1994., ©**Digital Vision**; Gazelle Technologies Inc.; ©1994-1996 **Education Interactive Imaging** (UK), **PhotoDisc**®, Inc. USA, www.photodisc.com. We also acknowledge the following clipart providers: TechPool Studios, for their clipart collection of human anatomy: Copyright ©1994, TechPool Studios Corp. USA (some of these images have been modified); Totem Graphics, for clipart; Corel Corporation, for vector art from the Corel MEGAGALLERY collection.

Index